Physiological Princip[illegible]

General Editors

Professor M. Hobsley
Department of Surgical Studies, The Middlesex Hospital and
The Middlesex Hospital Medical School, London.

Professor K.B. Saunders
Department of Medicine, St George's Hospital and St George's Hospital
Medical School, London

Dr J.T. Fitzsimons
Physiological Laboratory, Cambridge

Body Fluid and Kidney Physiology

Physiological Principles in Medicine

Books are published in linked pairs - the preclinical volume linked to its clinical counterpart as follows:

Endocrine Physiology by Richard N. Hardy
Clinical Endocrinology by Peter Daggett

Digestive System Physiology by Paul A. Sanford
Disorders of the Digestive System by Michael Hobsley

Respiratory Physiology by John Widdicombe and Andrew Davies
Respiratory Disorders by Ian R. Cameron and Nigel T. Bateman

Neurophysiology by R.H.S. Carpenter

Reproduction and the Fetus by Alan L.R. Findlay
Gynaecology, Obstetrics and the Neonate by S.J. Steele

Body Fluid and Kidney Physiology by S.B. Hladky and T.J. Rink

In preparation:

Disorders of the Kidney and Urinary Tract by F.D. Thompson and C.R.J. Woodhouse

Body Fluid and Kidney Physiology

S.B. Hladky

Lecturer in Pharmacology, University of Cambridge; Director of Studies in Medical Sciences, Jesus College, Cambridge, UK.

T.J. Rink

Vice-President Research, Smith, Kline and French Research Ltd., The Frythe, Welwyn, Herts., UK; Formerly Lecturer in Physiology, University of Cambridge; Fellow of King's College, Cambridge, UK.

First published in Great Britain 1986 by
Edward Arnold (Publishers) Ltd,
41 Bedford Square,
London WC1B 3DQ

Edward Arnold (Australia) Pty Ltd,
80 Waverley Road,
Caulfield East,
Victoria 3145,
Australia

British Library Cataloguing in Publication Data

Hladky, S.B.
Body fluid and kidney physiology. — (Physiological principles in medicine)
1. Kidneys
I. Title II. Rink, T.J. III. Series
612'.463 QP249

ISBN 0 7131 4411 4
ISSN 0260-2946

Text set in 10/11 pts Baskerville
by Colset Private Limited, Singapore
printed in Great Britain by Butler & Tanner Ltd
Frome and London

General preface to series

Student textbooks of medicine seek to present the subject of human diseases and their treatment in a manner that is not only informative, but interesting and readily assimilable. It is important, in a field where knowledge advances rapidly, that principles are emphasized rather than details, so that what is contained in the book remains valid for as long as possible.

These considerations favour an approach which concentrates on each disease as a disturbance of normal structure and function. Rational therapy follows logically from a knowledge of the disturbance, and it is in this field where some of the most rapid advances in Medicine have occurred.

A disturbance of normal structure without any disturbance of function may not be important to the patient except for cosmetic or psychological reasons. Therefore, it is disturbances in function that should be stressed. Preclinical students should aim at a comprehensive understanding of physiological principles so that when they arrive on the wards they will be able to appreciate the significance of disordered function in disease. Clinical students must be presented with descriptions of disease which stress the disturbances in normal physiological functions that are responsible for the symptoms and signs which they find in their patients. All students must be made aware of the growing points in physiology which, even though not immediately applicable to the practice of Medicine, will almost certainly become so during the course of their professional lives.

In this Series, the major physiological systems are each covered by a pair of books, one preclinical and the other clinical, in which the authors have attempted to meet the requirements discussed above. A particular feature is the provision of numerous cross-references between the two members of a pair of books to facilitate the blending of basic science and clinical expertise that is the goal of this Series. This coordination, which is initiated at the planning stage and continues throughout the writing of each pair of books, is achieved by frequent discussions between the preclinical and clinical authors concerned and between them and the editors of the Series.

MH
KBS
JTF

Preface

The rest of the body is affected only by the results of the kidneys' work, not by the renal mechanisms used to achieve them. Thus it is quite right that medical students and practising physicians should be interested first in what the kidneys do rather than how they do it. An introductory textbook should reflect this priority, and chapters 10 to 17 take this approach. It is, however, never completely satisfactory to treat a physiological system as a black box. If students are to comprehend the knowledge to be gained in the future, if they are to understand the rationale for treatments, or if they are simply curious, it is also necessary to study the mechanisms of kidney function.

The time is ripe for a new, introductory description of tubular mechanisms. Knowledge of kidney function has taken a tremendous jump forward since 1970 and rapid progress continues. These advances stem from substantial improvements in microelectrode techniques, from the introduction of new drugs which block specific molecular processes, and from the introduction of entirely new procedures. Notable among these procedures have been the dissection and study of individual tubule segments from the rabbit and the isolation of vesicles prepared from either apical or basolateral membranes of tubular cells. As a result of this progress, there is now a wide gulf between the mechanisms discussed in the journals and those presented in most textbooks.

Much of the material for this book has been drawn from the collections of reviews and books cited under General References. In addition we have benefited greatly from O'Connor's provocative account of renal function in conscious dogs and in man (O'Connor, W.J., 1982, *Normal Renal Function*, Croom Helm, London). Further information has been taken from major reviews published in the following: *Physiological Reviews; Annual Reviews of Physiology; Reviews of Physiology, Biochemistry and Pharmacology; International Review of Physiology* (series editor, A.C. Guyton, University Park Press, Baltimore) and also editorial reviews in the *American Journal of Physiology*. Many times we needed to go back to the original papers. The journals we consulted most frequently were, roughly in order: *American Journal of Physiology, Journal of Physiology, Journal of Clinical Investigation, Circulation Research, Kidney International* and *Clinical Science*.

We owe thanks to a large number of people who have in one way or another assisted us in preparing this book. J. Grantham helped introduce us to renal physiology and we have benefitted repeatedly from our discussions with him. Similarly G. Giebisch has been generous in providing information. The book would never have been started had not the late R.N. Hardy persuaded TJR that his lectures on renal physiology were a good basis for a textbook. Dick's sudden and untimely death has deprived us of valuable advice. Much encouragement has been given to us by members of the Physiology and Pharmacology Departments in Cambridge and, during SBH's sabbatical in 1982/83, by members of the Physiology Department at the University of Colorado Medical School. Of these and others we should thank individually: W.E. Balfour, C.J. Dickinson, J.C. Ellory, J.T. Fitzsimons, R. Hiley, C. Huang, S.R. Levinson and D. Thompson. The detailed criticism of the preliminary version of the entire manuscript by R. Green was particularly helpful. We owe a considerable debt to students who asked awkward questions, especially Kirsten McKennett for her critical approach to Chapter 8. Edward Arnold, our publishers, have helped greatly by their patient but persistent efforts to make us actually submit a manuscript!

The practical side of preparing the manuscript was assisted by Mary Whiting, Janet Eastwell, Mary Mayes, Kate de Courcy, and Nuala O'Connor. The unenviable task of preparing the index was undertaken by Hilary Hladky. We are grateful to all for their willing and competent help.

Inevitably defects and errors remain in this text, and these are of course our own responsibility. If you find a mistake, an important omission, or merely a point we have explained badly, please write and tell us.

1986

SBH
TJR

How to use this book

An introductory textbook is often the only supplement to lectures. While it must provide a clear, basic account, it should also contain adequate information on all aspects of the subject. We have tried to reconcile these requirements by careful organization of the text and by using two sizes of print. The small print sections are best skipped on first reading. On each topic the material in full print is intended as a text to be read in preparation for professional medical examinations. That in small print is intended to anticipate questions, to fill in more detailed information which may be part of some courses, and to provide evidence and arguments for the statements made in full print.

In the limited time available, few courses will cover all of the topics included in this book. To allow quick access to just those topics required, all section headings are included in the table of contents. Furthermore where a discussion depends upon information elsewhere in the book, cross references are given in the text. By using these and the table of contents, it should be possible to find and follow the main discussion of important points.

The processes occurring within the kidneys are described in Chapters 3 to 9. In these chapters those substances which are transported in a part of the nephron are considered together, because their transport mechanisms are interrelated. For instance, the mechanism by which active pumping of sodium leads to the reabsorption of sodium, bicarbonate, and organic solutes in the proximal tubule is considered in Chapter 6, while the different mechanism by which sodium pumping can lead to excretion of potassium and acid in the distal tubule is discussed in Chapter 7.

The changes in the body fluids produced by alterations in renal function and the changes in renal function produced by variations in the body fluids are described in Chapters 10 to 17. In these chapters all the factors affecting a regulated property, e.g. plasma potassium concentration (Chapter 12) or blood volume (Chapter 14), are collected together so that their net effect can be considered in one place.

The clinical aspects of renal physiology are considered in the companion volume: Thompson, F.D. and Woodhouse, C.R.J. *Disorders of the Kidney and Urinary Tract*, Edward Arnold, London. (In preparation).

General references

No attempt has been made to provide detailed citations within the text because these would have made the book longer, more expensive, and harder to read. Full references can be found in the books, reviews, and articles cited below and in the reference section at the end of each chapter.

There are several excellent collections of reviews:

Renal Physiology, Handbook of Physiology, Section 8. (1983). American Physiological Society, Bethesda. A valuable, but now ageing source of detailed information.

Brenner, B.M. and Rector, F.C. Jr. eds. (1981). *The Kidney*, 2nd ed, Saunders, Philadelphia. Comprehensive coverage of the highest standard.

Andreoli, T.E., Hoffman, J.F. and Fanestil, D.D. eds. (1978). *Physiology of Membrane Disorders*. Plenum, N.Y.

Giebisch, G. ed. (1979). *Membrane Transport in Biology, Vols, IVA* and *IVB, Transport Organs*. Springer-Verlag, Berlin.

Staub, N.C. and Taylor, A.E. (1984). *Edema*. Raven, N.Y.

The following textbooks and monographs provide detailed references to the original literature:

Wesson, L.G. Jr. (1969). *Physiology of the Human Kidney*, Grune & Stratton, N.Y. (A compendium of results obtained on humans.)

Pitts, R.F. (1974). *Physiology of the Kidney and Body Fluids, 3rd ed*, Yearbook Medical Publishers, Chicago. This is the classic textbook of the 1960s.

Valtin, H. (1983). *Renal Function, 2nd ed.*, Little, Brown & Co., Boston.

Valtin, H. (1979). *Renal Dysfunction*, Little, Brown & Co., Boston.

The relations between the body fluids and some aspects of the influence of these on kidney function have been discussed in detail by Guyton and his colleagues:

Guyton, A.C., Taylor, A.E. and Granger, H.J. (1975). *Circulatory Physiology II: Dynamics and Control of Body Fluids*. Saunders, Philadelphia.

Guyton, A.C. (1980). *Circulatory Physiology III. Arterial Pressure and Hypertension.* Saunders, Philadelphia.

Contents

Contents of Thompson and Woodhouse: Disorders of the Kidney and Urinary Tract

While reading this book you may find it helpful to refer to the companion volume, *Disorders of the Kidney and Urinary Tract*. The following list of contents will enable you to look up the clinical applications and relevance of the material contained in this book.

1

The body fluids

Our survival depends on control of the body fluids. The cells must regulate their own contents but they can do so only if the fluid which bathes them, the interstitial fluid, is properly maintained. This portion of the extracellular fluid is kept in good condition by perfusing the capillaries of each tissue with adequate amounts of 'good quality' arterial blood. It is the job of the cardiovascular system to get the right amount of blood flowing through each tissue. It is the job of other physiological systems including the kidneys, the lungs, and the liver to make sure that the quantity of blood and its composition in the arteries stay correct. Metabolic and respiratory control are considered in the books of Hardy and of Widdicombe and Davies in this series.

The body fluids can be regarded as being distributed into various compartments as indicated in Fig. 1.1. In order to understand the control of these fluids, it is essential to be familiar with this distribution, with the basic composition of the different fluids, and with the general principles governing transfer of water and solutes between the compartments.

Water

The main constituent of the body is water, about 42 litres in a 70 kg man or about 60 per cent of body weight. As shown in Fig. 1.1 the water is divided in a ratio of about 2:1 between that inside the cells, the intracellular fluid, and that which is outside the cells, the extracellular fluid. The major components of the extracellular fluid are the plasma and the interstitial fluid, separated by the capillary wall. There is additionally a small volume of transcellular fluid which is defined as that separated from the plasma by a layer of cells, i.e. by an epithelium. The most important components of transcellular fluid are the cerebrospinal fluid and the fluids inside the eyes, which amount to about 150 ml. There is also a very variable amount of transcellular fluid inside the gastrointestinal tract. The interstitial fluid can be further sub-divided, into the major part which is rapidly exchangeable with plasma and about 2 litres of much more slowly exchangeable fluid inside bone and dense connective tissue such as tendons and cartilage. There are about 5 litres of blood; 2 litres of red cells in addition to the 3 litres of plasma.

Approximately 40 per cent of the body weight is not water and is divided

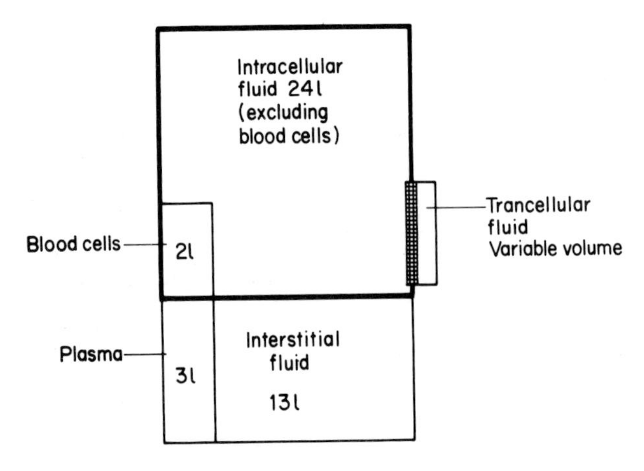

Fig. 1.1. The distribution of body water.

mainly between cellular protein, the matrix of bone, and fat. The amount of fat, of course, varies between individuals, typically accounting for *c* 10 per cent of the body weight in males and *c* 20 per cent in females. Other compenents of the 'dry weight' include extracellular proteins, the ground substance of the interstitial spaces, and the ionic and organic solutes of the body fluids. The body composition of infants and children differs from that of adults, but throughout this book, except where explicitly stated, we will discuss the body fluids of a 70 kg adult male.

Solutes

Extracellular

The concentrations of the major solutes of plasma are given in Table 1.1. The major components are sodium, chloride, and bicarbonate which together account for more than 90 per cent of the total solutes. The composition of interstitial fluid is closely similar to that of plasma since water and solutes other than large proteins freely permeate in capillaries of nearly all the tissues. The plasma does contain markedly more protein than the interstitial fluid, typically 70 g/litre compared with 20 g/litre, though the amount of protein in the interstitium can vary markedly from tissue to tissue.

Because the protein concentrations are different in plasma and samples of interstitial fluid and because the proteins bear a negative charge, the ion concentrations are also not identical, a phenomenon known as the Donnan effect (see p. 10). There is a slightly higher concentration of cations in the plasma and a slightly higher concentration of anions in the interstitial fluid, the difference being about 4 per cent for monovalent ions.

Table 1.1 Ionic composition of plasma

ion	Na^+	Cl^-	HCO_3^-	K^+	Ca^{2+}	Mg^{2+}	H^+	OH^-
concentration/mM	140	110	24	4	1.1	0.5	4×10^{-5}	2.5×10^{-4}

ion	phosphate	sulphate	organic anions	proteins
concentration/mM	1	0.5	*c* 12	1.5

The values for Ca^{2+} and Mg^{2+} are the concentrations of the free ions; the total amounts present are about twice as large since there is significant binding to plasma proteins. The organic anions include lactate and pyruvate. The protein concentration is often stated as 70 g/litre which in older literature is often referred to as 7 gms/100 ml or 7 per cent. About 93 per cent of the plasma volume is occupied by water, thus concentrations is mmol/(litre water) are about 1.08 times larger than those in the table.

Intracellular

Intracellular fluid varies from tissue to tissue but it always differs markedly from extracellular fluid. Potassium at approximately 140 mmol/(litre cell water), is the principal cation and there is much more magnesium, approximately 10–20 mmol/(litre cell water). Intracellular sodium concentration is typically 10 mmol/(litre cell water). Chloride is largely replaced by polyvalent anions such as DNA, RNA, many proteins, and organic phosphate compounds. Chloride concentrations are highly variable between different types of cells. For instances, values in mmol/(litre cell water) might be; 2 in muscle, 20 in various epithelial cells, 40 in lymphocytes, and 90 in red blood cells. Intracellular pH is typically 7.0–7.1. Intracellular bicarbonate is therefore approximately 12 mmol/(litre cell water)(see chapter 16). The solids inside cells, primarily macromolecules, occupy typically 25–30 per cent of the total cell volume.

Measuring the volume of fluid compartments

The principle of the measurement is to inject a known amount, Q, of a marker substance into the compartment in question. After it spreads evenly throughout the compartment a sample of a fluid is taken and a concentration, c, of the substance is determined. The volume, v, is given by $v = Q/c$. Since one can inject into, and sample from, only plasma, the compartments available for direct measurement are those of which plasma forms a part, i.e. the plasma itself, the extracellular fluid and the total body water. Interstitial fluid can be estimated from extracellular fluid vloume minus plasma volume, and the volume of cell water from the volume of body water minus extracellular fluid volume. A marker substance should be non-toxic and not metabolised, and all of it should be confined to the compartment in question until it is freely distributed. As discussed below, these criteria are particularly difficult to meet for extracellular fluid. In practice, useful marker substances include albumin labelled with radioactive iodine for plasma volume, inulin and radiolabelled sodium for extracellular volume and isotopic water for total body water. Clinical procedures are considered in Chapter 1 of *Disorders of the Kidney and Urinary Tract.*

Total body water

Injected tritiated or deuterated water (^3H_2O or D_2O) will take some hours to equilibrate fully with all the body water. This is because water in the transcellular fluid and in dense connective tissue may not rapidly equilibrate with plasma. However, loss of water from the body will rarely exceed 1 per cent of the total over the period needed for equilibration and can therefore be neglected or corrected for. Incorporation of injected radiolabel into components of the body other than water is a theoretical problem, but appears to be quantitatively negligible.

Plasma volume

Injected albumin mixes within a few minutes with the albumin in plasma, and loss of label across the capillary walls has a half time of many hours so that errors are rather small.

Extracellular fluid volume

Measurement of extracellular fluid volume is difficult for two main reasons.

1. It is difficult to be sure just what should be measured. Is it just plasma and interstitial fluid or transcellular fluid as well? There is also the problem of slowly exchangeable fluid in dense connective tissues.

2. It is difficult to find a market that distributes freely throughout the plasma and interstitial fluid without either entering into cells or being excreted at a significant rate by the kidneys. Substances like inulin, mannitol and ^{51}Cr EDTA do not enter the cells, but roughly 50 per cent of the injected compound is excreted in the first hour. Since mixing throughout the extracellular fluid takes at least tens of minutes, these markers are clearly not restricted to the compartment in question until mixing is complete. Markers like ^{24}Na and ^{82}Br are excreted slowly, but enter cells. Perhaps the best compromise is to use $^{35}SO_4$.

It is often taught than an extrapolation procedure can be used with markers like inulin or ^{51}Cr EDTA to correct for the effects of excretion. The marker is injected and, after a delay to allow mixing, a series of blood samples is taken from a peripheral vein. The logarithm of the marker concentrations in each sample is plotted against the time after injection, and a straight line is fitted to the points. This line is extrapolated backwards to the time of injection, and the volume of distribution is then estimated as dose/(extrapolated concentration). This procedure ignores several substantial complications.

1. Extrapolation underestimates excretion in the initial period after the injection because the plasma concentrations are then greater than the extrapolated values.
2. There is a gradient of marker concentration between the interstitial fluid and plasma during the measurements.
3. The marker may not reach all of the extracellular fluid during the measurements, e.g. it may not reach connective tissue and oedema fluid.
4. The marker concentration in plasma from a peripheral vein differs from that in the plasma of mixed venous blood.

Fortunately the 'errors' partly cancel. The extrapolation procedure remains in clinical use because for both the physician and the patient it is much simpler than the alternatives and in the absence of oedema the overall errors, e.g. *c* 20 per cent for ^{51}Cr EDTA, are not much bigger than the ambiguities in the volume to be measured.

Data free from the complications listed above can be obtained in experimental animals using a constant infusion method. The infusion is continued until the plasma and interstitial fluid concentrations of a marker like inulin are constant and the rate of excretion comes to equal the rate of infusion. The concentration at this time is measured and the infusion stopped. Urine formed after this time is collected via catheters in the ureters until essentially all the marker has been excreted and the amount of marker is determined. The steady-state volume of distribution of marker is then calculated as the total amount which was in the body divided by the plasma concentration just before the infusion was stopped. The steady-state volume of distribution of inulin is thought to represent the extracellular fluid volume excluding transcellular fluids and some fluid in dense connective tissues.

Reproducible estimates of changes in extracellular fluid volume can be obtained more easily using ^{24}Na. Although sodium slowly enters cells and slowly exchanges with sodium in bone, these disadvantages are acceptable because it is excreted sufficiently slowly that renal loss is not a problem. It is found that the errors introduced by uptake into cells, transcellular fluid and bone on the one hand and by incomplete equilibration on the other roughly cancel if the plasma concentration is measured one half hour after an injection. The substantially larger volume of distribution determined from the concentration after 24 hours is called the *sodium space*.

Further reading

Chantler, C., Garnett, E.S., Parsons, V. & Veall, N. (1969). Glomerular filtration rate measurement in man by the single injection method using ^{51}Cr-EDTA. *Clin. Sci.* **37**, 169–80.

More details, a comparison of markers, and discussion of the pitfalls are contained in Chantler, C, (1973). M.D. Dissertation, University of Cambridge.

Gaudino, N. & Levitt, M.F. (1949). Inulin space as a measure of extracellular fluid. *Am.J. Physiol.* **171**, 387–93.

Guyton, A.C. (1981). *Textbook of Medical Physiology*, 6th edn, Saunders, Philadelphia. Chapter 33, pp. 391–401. Partition of the body fluids: Osmotic equilibria between extracellular and intracellular fluids.

Hardy, R.N. (1981). *Endocrine Physiology*. Edward Arnold, London.

Maffly, R.H. (1981). The body fluids: Volume, composition, and physical chemistry. Chapter 2, pp. 76–115 in *The Kidney*, 2nd ed, Brenner, B.M. & Rector, F.C.Jr (eds), Saunders, Philadelphia.

Pitts, R.F. (1974). *Physiology of the Kidney and Body Fluids*, 3rd ed, Yearbook Medical Publishers, Chicago. Chapter 2, pp. 11–35.

Widdicombe, J. & Davies, A. (1983). *Respiratory Physiology*. Edward Arnold, London.

2

The relations between the body fluids and the mechanisms for the transfer of substances between them

The tissues of the body exchange materials with each other and with the outside world by way of the blood plasma. Therefore control of the composition and volume of plasma is central to body fluid regulation. However the objective of regulation is the proper functioning of the body as a whole. The relations between the other 39 litres of the body fluids and the 3 litres of plasma are the subject of this chapter. To understand these relations it is first necessary to consider the principles which govern the transport of substances in the body. Since the same types of transport occur within the kidneys, this chapter also lays the foundations for the discussion of renal mechanisms.

Concentrations, activities and osmolality

Molality and molarity

Concentrations can be expressed in several ways; those used commonly by biologists are

1. moles per litre of solution, molarity.
2. moles per kg of solvent, molality;
3. moles per litre of solvent.

A solution containing 1 mole of solute per litre of solution is often called a 1 molar solution, written as either 1 mole/l or 1 M. Similarly a solution containing 1 mmole of solute per kg of solvent is called 1 mmolal. As long as the solvent is water, for which the density is nearly 1 kg/l, molality and moles per litre of solvent are almost the same. Furthermore in relatively dilute, simple salt solutions molarity and molality are nearly the same. However, in plasma only about 93 per cent of the volume is water; the remaining 7 per cent is occupied by the plasma proteins. The *molal* concentration of, say sodium, in plasma is then about 8 per cent higher than the *molar* concentration. The difference is much larger inside cells where 25–30 per cent of the volume is occupied by the cell solids. Since the small solutes are dissolved in the water and not in the solids, it is misleading to use concentrations which very with the volume of the cell solids. Therefore intracellular concentrations are almost always given either as molalities or as moles per litre of cell water.

Free concentration

In complex solutions like plasma or intracellular fluid, solutes may be in free and bound forms usually at equilibrium with each other. That portion in free solution is able directly to enter into chemical reactions or participate in physical processes such as diffusion. The bound portion can be thought of as sequestered or temporarily 'out of action'. The 'total' concentration refers to the sum of free and bound forms. For monovalent ions such as sodium, potassium, and chloride which do not bind strongly to other ions, proteins, membranes, etc., the distinction between free and total concentration is of secondary importance. But for calcium and magnesium, for instance, a large proportion can be combined with other solutes. Similarly many molecules with hydrophobic portions bind strongly to plasma proteins.

Activity

The activity of a solute describes its chemical and biological effectiveness. In physiological fluids the activity is roughly proportional to the molality of the free form, i.e. the activity coefficient, equal to the ratio of activity to molality, is roughly constant. The distinction between free concentration and activity is important in quantitative treatments of chemical equilibria and in the Nernst equation (see below). However, we are usually concerned either with the ratios of concentrations in two solutions, e.g. between interstitial fluid and intracellular fluid, or with relative changes for any one solute. In either case the activity coefficients almost cancel and the use of free concentrations is usually adequate.

Osmolality

The osmolality of a solution is the total concentration of solute particles present adjusted to account for the extent to which they effectively dilute the water. The osmolality, or equivalently the total osmotic pressure of the solution (see below), is important since water moves from where its effective concentration is greater, i.e. a dilute solution with low osmolality, to where its effective concentration is less, i.e. a concentrated solution with high osmolality. The osmolality is roughly the sum of the molalities of all the solutes present. For example 150 mmolal sodium chloride has an osmolality of about 290 mosmol/kg water because both the sodium and chloride ions act to dilute the water. The osmolality is less than 300 (150 mmolal sodium plus 150 mmolal chloride) even though the sodium chloride is completely dissociated, because the ions still attract each other electrostatically and thus do not act independently.

As a measure of the dilution of the water, osmolality is greatly preferred to osmolarity. Consider a sample of normal plasma. Doubling the plasma protein concentration will increase the total volume by about 5 per cent. The sum of molarities will thus fall by about 5 per cent, while the sum of molalities, the osmolality, the osmotic pressure, and the effective dilution of the water are barely altered. This is not a trivial or insignificant point since a 1 per cent change in osmolality can have dramatic physiological effects (see chapter 13).

Tonicity

Osmolality denotes a precise physical property of the solution, often measured by the depression of its freezing-point. Tonicity, strictly, refers to the effect of solutions on cell volume; an isotonic solution causes no change in cell volume, a hypotonic solution swells cells and a hypertonic solution shrinks them. The difficulty with tonicity is that the effect on cell volume depends on the nature of the solutes and the permeability of the cell membrane. Different solutions of equal osmolalities can therefore have different tonicities, and one solution can be isotonic for one cell and hypotonic for another. For example, isosmotic saline made hyperosmolal by addition of urea would be isotonic for red blood cells, which are permeable to urea. A solution made hyperosmolal by addition of ethanol would be isotonic for all cells since all cell membranes are freely permeable to ethanol.

Mechanisms of transport of water and solutes

Bulk flow

In bulk flow everything tends to move together. When the flow is fast enough and the fluid travels through a sufficient distance, transfer against the stream can be completely ignored. The movements of blood along blood vessels and of tubular fluid along the nephrons occur by bulk flow. The flux of any substance, that is the number of moles which move per unit area of cross section per unit time, is then given by the product of the concentration and the average flow velocity. Bulk flow is particularly effective at transferring water since this is always present at high concentration (roughly 55 M). It is also the only practical method for transferring dissolved materials in the body over distances greater than about 0.1 mm.

Diffusion

Diffusion of molecules in a solution results from their random movements. The molecules are always moving about because of the kinetic energy they obtain from their surroundings. These random microscopic movements lead to net transfer whenever there is a concentration gradient. Molecules are more likely to be leaving a position where the concentration is relatively high, simply because there are more of them, than they are to be arriving from places where the concentration is relatively low. In a purely diffusive process the net transfer between two regions of different concentrations is proportional to the concentration difference. For water the concentration is always high (*c* 55 M) and the differences in concentration are small (e.g. 2 mM). Thus water transfer by diffusion is characterized by large fluxes in both directions, each proportional to the concentration, and a much smaller net flux proportional to the concentration difference.

Diffusion is rapid for transfer over very short distances but impossibly slow for long distances. The time taken for a particle to diffuse from one point to another is roughly proportional to the square of the distance. A useful practical estimate is that for small solutes like sodium and potassium ions, it takes 10 ms to go 10 μm. Thus it will take about 10 ms to cover a typical thickness of an epithelial cell layer in the kidney. To diffuse 1 cm, a length typical of tubule segments, would take 10 000s. Since fluid flow along a centimeter of tubule takes of the order of ten seconds, it is clear that diffusion can have time to produce significant transfer across the thickness of a tubule wall, but that it cannot account for any significant transfer along the tubule.

Movement of ions driven by electric fields

Charged particles can be persuaded to move by applying an electric field. This field can be regarded as changing the potential energy per charge, usually called just 'the potential' at any point. Positive charge is always pushed from high (i.e. more positive) to low potential, negative charge is pushed in the reverse direction. Potential differences between points more than a millimeter or so apart, as along the length of kidney tubules, have a negligible effect on transfer compared to bulk flow, but over short distances even just a few millivolts can be very important. An applied field, by pushing on the ions, makes it more likely that the otherwise random movements of the ions will occur more often in one direction than another. Thus a field can cause ions to move from a lower to a higher concentration. Conversely, given a concentration gradient, ions can be made to move from a lower to a higher electrical potential energy.

If ions are distributed between two compartments so that the tendency to move down their concentration gradient is balanced by the tendency to move in the opposite direction down their electrical potential energy gradient, no net movement occurs and the ions are said to be at *electrochemical equilibrium*. The relationship between the concentrations and the potential gradient at equilibrium is given by the Nernst equation. This well known relationship can be derived from a consideration of the work required to move the ions.

The work which must be done to move 1 mole of solute from a concentration C_1 to C_2 is given by $RT \ln C_2/C_1$, where R is the gas constant, T the absolute temperature, and ln is the natural logarithm. The work which must be done to move 1 mole of solute up a potential gradient from V_1 to V_2 is given by $zF(V_2 - V_1)$ where z is the valence and F Faraday's number. The sum of these works is called the *electrochemical potential difference (E)*. At equilibrium no work is being done on or by the system, i.e. the electrochemical potential difference is zero, and thus.

$$RT \ln C_2/C_1 + zF(V_2 - V_1) = 0$$

or more familiarly (recall in $(C_1/C_2) = -\ln(C_2/C_1)$)

$$V_2 - V_1 = E = (RT/zF) \ln C_1/C_2$$

which is about $60 \log_{10} C_1/C_2$ for a monovalent cation at 37°C, and $-60 \log_{10} C_1/C_2$ for a monovalent anion.

In the body electric fields and thus potential differences are created when positive and negative charges are separated from each other. Thus the inside of a cell becomes more negative with respect to the outside whenever positive ions are removed leaving negative ions behind. It is important to note that only a very small number of ions must be moved to produce a large change in potential. For a cubical cell with a typical volume at about 10^{-12} litres containing about 10^{11} potassium ions and surrounded by a smooth membrane with a capacitance of 1 $\mu F/cm^2$, removal of just 0.004 per cent of the potassium ions would change the potential difference by a hundred millivolts! Put another way, for all realistic potentials in the body there is very little separation of charge, i.e. if we take any volume of a body fluid greater than that of a small cell, the net charge in it will be so small that the number of positive and negative charges within the volume can be said to be approximately the same. The statement of this approximate equality is often called the *principle of electroneutrality*.

The Donnan potential

The macromolecules in the body fluids are usually negatively charged. Thus to preserve electroneutrality there are more small cations than small anions in the body fluids. There is a higher concentration of protein in plasma than in samples of interstitial fluid withdrawn for analysis and correspondingly more macromolecular negative charges. The concentration of small monovalent cations such as sodium is therefore about 5 per cent higher in plasma. Since as discussed below small ions can cross the capillary walls rapidly, those in plasma are virtually at equilibrium with those in the interstitial fluid. Thus from the Nernst equation the plasma must be about 1 mV negative with respect to the interstitial fluid, and the concentration of small monovalent anions will be about 5 per cent lower in plasma. These differences in the permeable ion concentrations are an example of the Donnan effect and the associated potential is called a Donnan potential.

Osmosis: Movement driven by osmotic pressure gradients

Osmosis is a term used to describe the tendency of water to move down its concentration gradient. The concentration of water is altered by varying the concentrations of solute in it. The larger the number of solute particles present the more dilute the water. Water therefore moves from regions of low total solute concentration or osmolality to regions of high solute concentration. The tendency for water to move is often stated as an osmotic pressure difference, which is defined as the hydrostatic pressure that must be applied to the solution with the higher osmolality to just prevent the net movement of water by osmosis. This notation is convenient in that it allows direct comparison of the effect of osmotic and hydrostatic pressure gradients.

The total osmotic pressure of a solution is a colligative property, depending (ideally) simply upon the number of dissolved particles per kg of water. It is directly proportional to the (adjusted) sum of the molalities of the solute particles, i.e. $OP = RT\text{x (osmolality)}$ where R is the gas constant and T is the absolute temperature.

Water movement driven by osmotic and hydrostatic pressure gradients

Pressure gradients can drive fluxes of water across a membrane by diffusion or bulk flow. If water crosses a membrane one molecule at a time by dissolving in the membrane material, then there is no possibility for the water molecules to nudge each other along, i.e. there is no bulk flow. A pressure gradient will, however, still produce a flux. In one view a higher hydrostatic pressure squeezes more water molecules into the membrane than does a lower pressure. Thus both hydrostatic and osmotic pressure differences between the solutions may produce a concentration gradient within the membrane and this causes the net flux. This kind of water flux across a membrane, or even a layer of cells, will display large fluxes in each direction. The small difference between these, the flow or net flux, will be proportional to the pressure difference. The water movements across most cell membranes are believed to occur primarily by such a diffusive process. Because the membranes are very thin and the surface area is large the movements in and out of cells are rapid even though water molecules are only slightly soluble in the membranes.

Even a few pores, i.e. water filled gaps in the hydrophobic barrier, can greatly increase the water permeability of a membrane. The increase is greater when the permeability is calculated from a net flux driven by pressure rather than from a one-way flux of tritiated water. In the pores any one water molecule is preceded and followed by others. In pressure driven movement each of these is more likely to be going down the gradient than up, which makes it easier for the others to do the same. By contrast in the oneway tracer flux experiments the total number of molecules going in each direction is the same. Thus in a pore whenever there is a net movement of the pore contents in one direction, a so-called volume flux, the net flux will be greater than expected from the one way, or tracer fluxes. Both hydrostatic and osmotic pressure gradients produce volume fluxes.

Transport by specific transporters

With the exception of neutral, lipid soluble substances such as O_2 and CO_2 most solutes cross cell membranes by means of specific transporters which can be thought of as enzymes catalyzing the transfer process. In addition, transport via some of these can be driven by energy obtained from the hydrolysis of ATP. The properties of several specific transporters are considered in Chapters 3, 7 and 8. The molecular mechanisms are still largely unknown.

Active transport

The definition of active transport is somewhat arbitrary. The conventions used in this book are the following:

1. transport of a substance is called active whenever the electrical and concentration gradients are such that work must be done on the substance for the transport to occur, i.e. the transport occurs against the electrochemical gradient. Such transport is often called 'uphill' since it occurs up the energy gradient;
2. transport via a mechanism which obtains energy directly from the hydrolysis of ATP is said to occur via a pump. When this transport is active it is referred to as *primary active transport*;
3. net transfer of one solute which is driven uphill by the downhill movements of another solute is referred to as *secondary active transport*. An example is the

active transport of glucose from the tubule lumen into proximal tubular cells via a sodium-glucose co-transporter.

The relation between plasma and interstitial fluid

The capillary wall and colloid osmotic pressure

The capillaries must be very permeable to small solutes in order to perform their basic function of supplying and removing substances in the tissues. In addition the fluid in the capillaries must be under pressure, since a pressure gradient is needed to drive the blood back to the heart. This pressure will tend to force the fluid through the permeable capillary walls into the interstitial spaces. Large scale loss of plasma and collapse of the blood vessels is prevented by an opposing gradient of osmotic pressure which results from the concentration difference of the large, very poorly permeant proteins, the colloids. Since the concentration of the colloids is low, the colloid osmotic pressure of plasma, *c* 28 mmHg, is much smaller than the total osmotic pressure, about 5000 mmHg. However, the colloid osmotic pressure is of critical importance because the smaller solutes rapidly equilibrate with the interstitial fluid and thus create no *gradient* of osmotic pressure. The colloid osmotic pressure is sometimes called *oncotic pressure*.

Any net movement of fluid which does occur across the capillary wall is driven by the balance between the colloid osmotic and hydrostatic pressures, π and P, of the fluids on either side. Thus

$$\text{net filtration} = K\,[P_{\text{plasma}} - P_{\text{interstitium}} + \pi_{\text{interstitium}} - \pi_{\text{plasma}}]$$

where K is the filtration coefficient. This determination of the size and direction of net fluid flow by the balance of hydrostatic and colloid osmotic pressures is called the Starling mechanism. Normally the pressures are close to balance, but there is a slight net movement of fluid from the capillaries to the tissues, amounting to about 2 ml/min for the whole body. This fluid is returned to the circulation via the lymphatics. The lymph flow is tiny compared to cardiac output, 5000 ml/min, but nevertheless it can amount to more than the entire volume of plasma in 24 hours.

The movements of molecules and ions across the capillary walls between plasma and interstitium occur by mechanisms which are very much more like diffusion than like bulk flow. For all small solutes and water there are large fluxes in each direction. For those solutes whose concentration differences across the wall are a large fraction of their concentrations, the net fluxes are relatively large. Oxygen and glucose for example diffuse out of the capillaries in muscle, while carbon dioxide and lactate can diffuse in. The net fluxes of sodium chloride and water, and thus the net flow of fluid, are small relative to their fluxes in each direction because the gradients driving the net fluxes are small. For water the ratio of the net flux to the 'unidirectional' fluxes is of the order of 1 part in 10^4 to 10^5 (see p. 8).

For any solute such as glucose, which has a large concentration gradient the effect of its own gradient on the net flux completely overshadows the effect of the hydrostatic and colloid osmotic pressures. However, for sodium chloride and water there is a difference between the movements in the two directions only when there is a gradient in these pressures. It is for this reason that the filtration equation given above, which is usually thought of in terms of bulk flow, can be used to describe a net flow which actually occurs by a primarily diffusive process.

It is now established that solutes which are not lipid soluble cross primarily by way of aqueous pathways, probably the narrow slits between the cells, and that the fluxes are not purely diffusive. For instance the probability for solute movement in the direction of the net flux of water through the slits is increased and that for movement in the opposite direction is reduced relative to pure diffusion since there is a tendency for the neighbouring water molecules to be moving in the direction of the net flow. These small fractional changes in the large fluxes in each direction can combine to produce a significant contribution to the net flux for solutes with small concentration gradients. This effect is sometimes called 'solvent drag' or *convective transport*. For small concentration gradients of the solute and small net fluxes of water, the net solute transfer is the sum of the fluxes which would be produced by the gradient alone, often called the *diffusive flux*, and by the solvent drag. Further interpretation has been difficult for several reasons including the following:

1. there is a range of sizes of aqueous pathways between the cells:
2. water crosses the capillary wall both through the cells and through the slits, and
3. the movement of water produces local changes in the concentrations of solutes near the wall which alter their rates of transfer.

There is good evidence from electron microscopy of capillary walls that macromolecules can cross the wall by vesicular transport through the cells. They enter the cells by endocytosis on one side and leave it by exocytosis on the other. The fraction of the transport of macromolecules which occurs by this mechanism is unknown, but even the serum albumins probably cross primarily through the slits.

The sizes of the colloid and hydrostatic pressures

The colloid osmotic pressure of plasma

Plasma contains proteins at 70 g/litre which produce a colloid osmotic pressure of about 28 mmHg. This pressure normally does not change along the length of the capillaries since there is very little change in the concentration of the colloids. The amount of albumin in the plasma is somewhat less than the amount in the interstitial fluid (see p. 15), but the concentration is about 3.5 times greater.

Because the plasma proteins are negatively charged they tend to hold extra cations in the plasma and exclude somewhat fewer small anions (see p. 10). Measured colloid osmotic pressures include both the contribution of the protein molecules themselves and the contribution of the extra ions held in the solution by the electrostatic effect. The size of this Donnan effect increases with the concentration of the colloid. Normally it accounts for 15 to 20 per cent of the measured colloid osmotic pressure of plasma.

Plasma colloid osmotic pressure is determined mainly by the albumin concentration. Albumin is synthesised in the liver and catabolized in tissues throughout the body giving a half-time of around 24 hours. Increased synthesis and release from the liver will elevate the plasma albumin concentration and colloid osmotic pressure; diminished release of albumin from the liver will lower colloid osmotic pressure. Liver disease is a well known cause of hypoalbuminaemia (too little albumin in the blood). Albumin synthesis and release is under feedback control from plasma colloid osmotic pressure, acting by as yet unknown mechanisms on the liver cells; decreased colloid osmotic pressure increases albumin release and increased colloid osmotic pressure reduces it.

Small changes in the plasma albumin concentration, e.g. 10–20 per cent, do not significantly affect the distribution of fluid between plasma and the interstitium (see p. 17), but they may change the fluid volumes by their effects on sodium excretion (see pp. 56, 74, and 163).

The hydrostatic pressure in the capillaries

The hydrostatic pressure tending to drive fluid into a tissue is the average pressure over the area of the capillaries and venules where filtration takes place. When the venous pressure is small (e.g. not in the feet when standing still), this pressure is typically measured to be between 15 and 20 mmHg.

Under certain circumstances the net flux of fluid can be out of the capillary at the arterial end and inwards in the venules. Similarly under some circumstances when the precapillary sphincter is closed, there can be net reabsorption along an entire capillary. These variations however, have negligible influence on the role of the capillaries in supplying nutrients and removing wastes. Furthermore it is only the overall net outword movement from the whole of the capillaries and venules into a tissue which is important for determining interstitial fluid pressure (discussed below) and lymph flow.

Interstitial fluid pressure

The interstitium contains a gel, not a liquid. This gel consists of a meshwork of hyaluronic acid fibres with the interstitial fluid occupying the spaces between. The gel somewhat resembles jelly or agar. It can be seen and handled in large amounts as Wharton's jelly of the umbilical cord. The gel allows almost unrestricted diffusion of solutes, including proteins, but it enormously reduces bulk flow. The meshwork tends to hold or imbibe the interstitial fluid somewhat analogously to the way a sponge holds water.

The tendency for the meshwork to hold fluid must be taken into account in the Starling mechanism. The value of the interstitial fluid pressure is therefore set equal to the pressure which would have to be exerted on free fluid for it to be at equilibrium with the fluid within the gel (see p. 16 for further discussion). For most tissues the total pressure on the gel, which is the average force acting per unit area on the surface of the gel, is either at or a few mmHg above atmospheric pressure. The interstitial fluid pressures are measured to be 5 to 6 mmHg less than the total tissue pressures. Thus in many tissues, especially subcutaneous tissue, the interstitial fluid pressure is slightly less than atmospheric. The difference between the total pressure and the fluid pressure is supported by the fibres in the interstitium which are therefore under slight compression (see Fig. 2.1).

Unlike many familiar gels such as agar and gelatin, the interstitial matrix of hyaluronic acid is not cross-linked. When the volume of fluid increases so that the interstitial fluid pressure is greater than the external pressure, the hyaluronic acid meshwork is no longer under compression, it disperses into solution, the interstitium becomes fluid, an it can be made to flow by applying pressure. These changes are the basis of the clinical sign of pitting in 'pitting oedema'.

As stated above the average hydrostatic and colloid osmotic pressures driving filtration almost balance. If free fluid is injected into a tissue, the interstitial fluid pressure is increased, the balance of pressures across the capillary walls favours reabsorption, and most of the excess fluid will be sucked into the blood vessels, in effect by the excess colloid osmotic pressure of the plasma.

Interstitial fluid colloid osmotic pressure

Interstitial fluid in many tissues, e.g. skin and muscle, contains about 20 g/litre

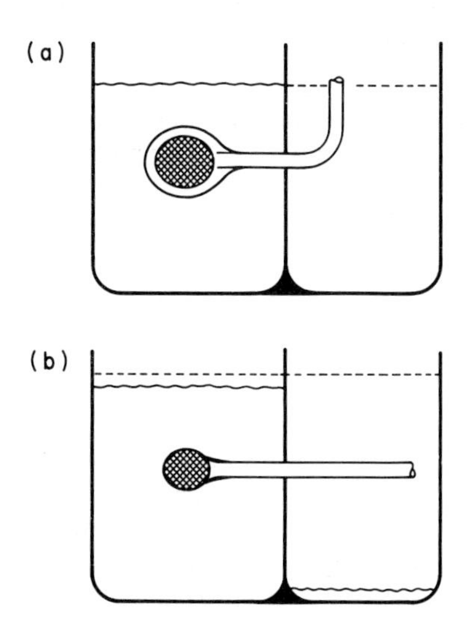

Fig. 2.1. A simple analogy for the difference between the external pressure on a tissue and the tissue fluid pressure. A floppy polythene bag containing a slightly smaller sponge is tied to a tube which passes through the wall of a beaker. The bag and beaker are filled with water as shown in (a). Initially the water levels are the same inside and outside the tube and the bag does not compress the sponge. The side tube is then bent horizontally so that the 'tissue fluid pressure', i.e. the pressure on the fluid in the side tube is less than the external pressure exerted by the fluid surrounding the bag. The difference in pressures squeezes the sponge into a smaller and smaller space until the inward and outward forces on the bag are again equal. Since the fluid pressure is less than the total pressure, relative to the total pressure the fluid pressure is negative. In the body, fluid enters and leaves 'the bag' through the capillary wall rather than a side tube. The tissue fluid pressure is then determined by the forces which tend to make water move, i.e. approximately by the difference, $P_{\text{plasma}} - \pi_{\text{plasma}} + \pi_{\text{interstitium}}$

of plasma proteins which exert a colloid osmotic pressure of about 7 mmHg. (Higher values are found in certain regions such as intestines, liver, and lung.) The total amount of plasma proteins in the interstitial fluid normally exceeds that in the plasma (see p. 13).

The gel matrix alters the relation between the molality of plasma proteins in the interstitium and the colloid osmotic pressure they exert. However, it has not been possible to separate this influence from the effect of the matrix on the interstitial fluid pressure. If the interstitial fluid pressure is assigned as described above (see p. 14), then the value of the 'interstitial colloid osmotic pressure' should be set equal to the colloid osmotic pressure of free fluid at equilibrium with the interstitium. If, in addition, the lymphatics do not selectively absorb or reject proteins (see below), this colloid osmotic pressure will be the same as in the lymph flowing from the tissue.

Maintenance of the colloid osmotic pressure gradient

Proteins permeate the walls of capillaries and venules very much less easily than do small solutes, but in most tissues there is a finite and significant leak, and over many hours plasma and interstitial concentrations would tend towards equilibrium. Therefore, some means must exist for removing proteins from the interstitium and adding them to the blood. This function is carried out efficiently by the lymphatics.

Capillaries can be made much less leaky to proteins like those in the brain (see below). However, some leak is required to allow entry into the blood of albumin and globulin from cells in the liver, entry of polypeptide hormones in secretory glands, and exit of these hormones throughout the body to allow them to reach their target cells. There are also functions for immunoglobulins and probably albumins in the interstitium and these too must be allowed to cross the wall.

The lymphatics do not preferentially extract proteins from the interstitium, they reabsorb tissue fluid. Furthermore in the steady state the rates at which lymph removes protein and fluid must be the same as the rates at which they cross the capillary walls. Thus the protein concentration in lymph, which closely reflects that in the interstitial fluid, must equal the rate of protein leak from the capillaries divided by the net filtration rate.

When water is filtered rapidly in comparison to the rate of protein transfer as in the glomerular capillaries (see Chapter 5) the filtrate is almost but not quite protein free, i.e. the protein concentration on the downstream side is very low. By contrast in the absence of net filtration, the protein concentration on the downstream side, i.e. in the interstitium, approaches that in plasma as protein diffuses down its concentration gradient. In most tissues even though water and the small solutes cross easily, the net filtration is driven by a very small net pressure gradient. The resulting filtration rate is sufficient, compared to the rate of protein leakage, to provide a filtrate (i.e. the interstitial fluid) with a protein concentration of about 20–50 per cent that in plasma.

Within limits, increasing the net filtration and lymph flow increases protein transfer by a smaller fraction, and therefore reduces the protein concentration of the filtrate. This effect, known as *protein washout*, lowers the interstitial colloid osmotic pressure and is an important part of the safety factor against oedema (see below).

The distribution of fluid between plasma and interstitium

Interstitial fluid volume is stable when net filtration from the blood vessels is precisely matched by lymph flow, i.e. when inflow matches outflow. If net filtration increases, then the volume of interstitial fluid will increase until the balance between the flows is restored. The increase in interstitial volume causes increased interstitial fluid pressure and, as discussed above, the increased filtration reduces interstitial colloid osmotic pressure. Both of these changes will limit the increase in filtration by reducing the net filtration pressure. Furthermore, the increase in interstitial fluid pressure causes increased lymph flow which comes to equal the increased filtration.

The relation between interstitial fluid pressure and lymph flow

Fluid apparently enters the ends of the lymphatics from the interstitium through regions where the cells of the lymphatic wall overlap forming a kind of flap valve. The gaps are open when the fluid pressure inside the lymphatic is less than outside, and they are closed when the pressure gradient is reversed. The average pressure inside is kept low, i.e. more negative than the interstitial fluid pressure, because fluid is moved along the lymphatic through additional one way valves whenever the ends are compressed by the surrounding tissues. Movement through the larger lymph vessels is propelled by contraction of the walls.

Lymph flow is a function of interstitial fluid pressure as indicated in Fig. 2.2. The less negative this pressure, the more easily fluid flows into the lymph vessels from the interstitial spaces. Over the normal range of pressures, the relation is steep. The importance of this relation is that an increasing input of fluid into the interstitium is normally readily met by a balancing increase in lymphatic drainage. Once the tissue becomes oedematous, lymphatic flow increases very little and continued filtration will result in progressive accumulation of fluid.

The relation between interstitial fluid pressure and volume

As long as interstitial fluid pressure is negative, the gel remains compact with no free fluid and as shown in Fig. 2.3 the volume changes very little with pressure. However, when the interstitial fluid pressure is positive, large changes in volume occur with small changes in pressure as free fluid forms and the tissue becomes oedematous.

Oedema

The term *oedema* comes from the Greek word for swelling. Tissues become oedematous when free fluid begins to accumulate, i.e. when interstitial fluid pressure exceeds the total pressure on the tissue. For an increase in capillary

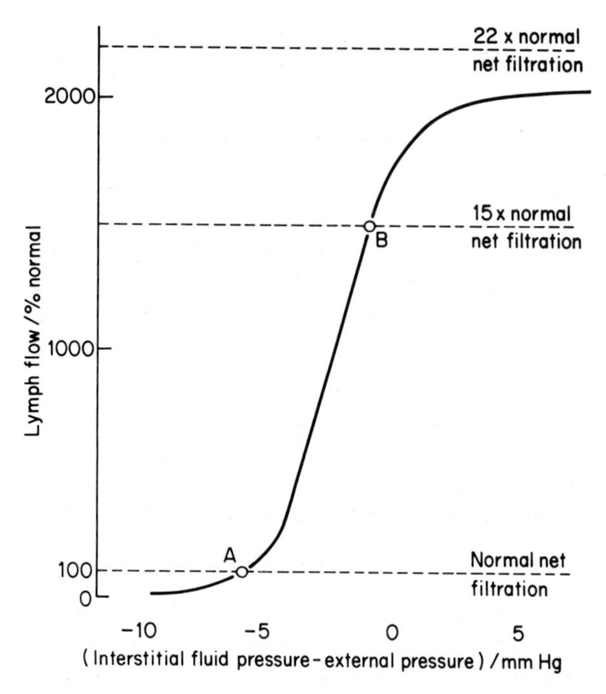

Fig. 2.2. Estimated relation between interstitial fluid pressure and lymph flow (see Guyton, 1975). As the pressure becomes less negative, it becomes easier for the terminal lymphatics to suck in fluid from the interstitium. Note that the lymphatic drainage can easily match the normal net filtration for a fluid pressure still less than the external pressure (point B) thus avoiding oedema formation. However, with the arrangement chosen for this diagram, lymph flow cannot rise to 22 times the basal value and with this increase in net filtration there would be progressive accumulation of oedema fluid.

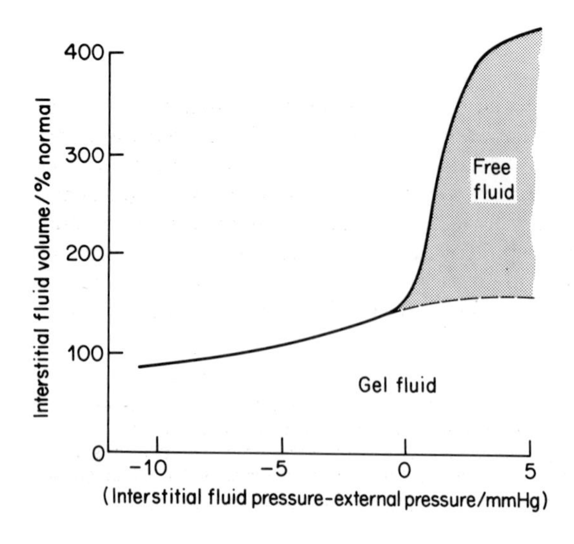

hydrostatic pressure or a decrease in plasma colloid osmotic pressure to produce this state the changes must be large. There are three main factors responsible for this 'safety margin' against oedema formation.

1. Increased filtration increases interstitial fluid volume which increases interstitial fluid pressure and opposes the filtration.
2. Increasing filtration washes protein out of the interstitium (see p. 16) which increases the colloid osmotic pressure gradient opposing filtration.
3. Increased lymphatic flow caused by elevated interstitial fluid pressure can balance net filtration produced by several mmHg excess net filtration pressure. Together these add up to a safety margin of 15–18 mmHg in most tissues.

The size of the safety margin has been assessed in two ways.

1. Reduced plasma protein concentration does not usually cause oedema until the colloid osmotic pressure is roughly halved, to 12–15 mmHg.
2. Negative pressures (less than atmospheric) applied to an area of skin produce oedema only when the pressures are more negative than about — 17 mmHg.

Oedema is much more serious in the lungs than in most other tissues and it is no surprise that there the safety margin is even larger, about 25 mmHg. The pulmonary capillary pressure is normally lower than for systemic tissues and the interstitial colloid osmotic pressure is larger. The net filtration pressure is not very different. Furthermore the lymphatic drainage is very efficient. Increases in filtration produced by increases in capillary hydrostatic pressure are smaller than in the systemic circulation because the enhanced lymph flow produces more protein washout and a smaller increase in interstitial fluid pressure is adequate to increase lymph flow. Over weeks and months even higher levels of net filtration pressure may not cause oedema, owing to the overgrowth and increased activity of the pulmonary lymphatic drainage vessels. For instance in patients with stenosis (narrowing) of the mitral valve, pulmonary capillary pressure can exceed 40 mmHg without causing pulmonary oedema.

Causes of oedema

Oedema may tend to be generalized throughout the body tissues or local to specific areas. It can result from a marked increase in net filtration pressure or from depressed lymphatic drainage. Increased net filtration pressure can result from elevated capillary pressure or a reduced colloid osmotic pressure gradient. Elevated capillary pressure can be produced by arteriolar dilatation, venous constriction or obstruction, increased circulating volume or any combination of these. A reduced colloid osmotic pressure gradient can be caused by decreased albumin production in liver disease, loss of albumin in the urine in nephrotic

Fig. 2.3. The relation between interstitial fluid pressure and interstitial fluid volume in subcutaneous tissue measured by the capsule technique. When the fluid pressure is less then the external pressure, small changes in volume produce large changes in fluid pressure; the compliance is low because the gel matrix resists compression. When the fluid pressure exceeds the external pressure, free fluid appears and the tissue becomes oedematous. Large amounts of fluid can accumulate with little further rise in interstitial fluid pressure.

syndrome, loss of the permeability barrier to protein leakage into tissues, depressed lymphatic function or internal bleeding.

Local changes can rapidly produce local oedema such as the swelling that is a 'cardinal sign' of inflammation. In a nettle sting for example, the swelling is produced by a combination of arteriolar dilatation and increased leakage of protein across the capillary walls. Generalized peripheral oedema of the sort seen in congestive heart failure or renal failure cannot be of rapid onset as there is not enough fluid in the plasma to increase sufficiently the interstitial fluid volume throughout the body. Interstitial fluid volume needs to be increased 50–100 per cent for oedema to occur and clearly 3 litres of plasma cannot provide even the 1–2 litres of excess interstitial fluid required to produce oedema in the legs. Generalized oedema is the result of a progressive accumulation of extracellular fluid resulting from continuing failure of salt and water excretion to match intake (see Chapter 14).

Pulmonary oedema results most commonly from cardiac failure with severely elevated left atrial pressure, and hence elevated pulmonary capillary pressure. The oedema can set in rapidly because there can easily be enough fluid in the circulation and systemic tissues to 'flood the lungs'.

The relation between intracellular and extracellular fluid

Cell membranes separate the extracellular fluid from the very different environment inside the cells. The basic structure of these membranes is a phospholipid bilayer with other types of molecules embedded in it. The hydrophobic core of membrane which is about 2.5 nm wide almost prevents transfer of most polar and charged solutes. Lipid soluble substances small enough to mix with the lipid hydrocarbon chains readily permeate the membrane. For instance the membrane is not a serious diffusion barrier to O_2, CO_2, NH_3, ethanol or steroid hormones. Water molecules, because they are so small, are also sufficiently soluble in the core to permeate, and water usually equilibrates between the interstitium and the cell interior within a few seconds.

The cell membrane is mechanically weak because it is so thin. By itself, it cannot support any more than a few mmHg hydrostatic pressure gradient and the total hydrostatic pressure inside animal cells is taken to be very close to that in the external medium. Because of the high water permeability of the membrane and the lack of hydrostatic pressure gradients, there can be no osmotic pressure gradient except during very rapid changes in cell volume, i.e. the total osmolality of intracellular fluid will be virtually the same as that of the extracellular fluid.

It is well known that bacteria, plant cells and fungal cells can maintain substantial osmotic pressure differences between inside and outside because they have polysaccharide walls outside the plasma membrane which are strong enough to support the requisite hydrostatic pressure gradient. It seems possible that such an effect can occur to a smaller extent in animals cells that form part of a compact tissue. The mechanical support for some degree of hydrostatic pressure difference between the intracellular fluid and the interstitium can come from the basement membrane and the network of connective tissue fibres. There is direct evidence that such an effect prevents the expected swelling of certain tissues, including kidney tubules, when they are exposed to hypo-osmolal solutions. Whether any cells in normal conditions have an intracellular pressure higher than that outside is not known. One point of interest in this context is that the tissue most susceptible to hypo-osmolality, the brain (see Chapter 13), lacks the extracellular fibrous network that supports most other tissues. (This is why brains are the least tough of all animal tissues to eat).

The cell contents

Cells can produce and maintain an intracellular medium whose composition of polar and changed solutes is quite different from that outside. They do so by two main means: the synthesis and breakdown of organic molecules, and the control of the transfer of solutes across the plasma membrane. Most of the organic solutes inside cells bear one or more negative charges and are effectively impermeant through the plasma membrane. They include the organic phosphates such as ATP and 2,3-diphosphoglycerate; carboxylic acids including the intermediates of the Krebs cycle; nucleic acids; and most proteins, which carry a net negative charge at physiological pH. Of the major intracellular macromolecules and organic solutes only the histones and a few polyamines carry a net positive charge. The organic ions are often collectively called the 'fixed anions' to emphasize the impermeability of the membrane to them.

The membrane potential

For most cells the electrical potential inside is several tens of millivolts negative with respect to the outside. This difference in potential is called a membrane potential since it occurs across the cell membrane. Typical resting values for nerve cells might be − 70 mV and for striated muscle − 90 mV. These negative values mean that there is a slight excess of negative charge within the cells, but as discussed on p. 10 the difference between the sum of the negative charges and the sum of the positive charges is very small.

The solute content of the cell will be stable when there is no net synthesis of macromolecules, the rate of net entry or exit of metabolized solutes matches their catabolism or synthesis, and the influx of non-metabolized solutes, e.g. Na, K, and C1, equals their efflux. For the latter group, the balance of influx and efflux can occur either when the solute is at electrochemical equilibrium or when the rate of active transport balances the net leakage. In many cells, chloride, which is the major extracellular anion, is not actively transported. Since most of the intracellular negative charges are carried by the 'fixed anions', intracellular chloride concentration must be low. For chloride to be at electrochemical equilibrium, the tendency for net entry down the concentration gradient must be balanced by net repulsion along the electrical gradient. In other words the membrane potential must be negative, which is of course what is observed. In striated muscle, which constitutes about half the cell volume of a lean individual, it is found that intracellular chloride activity is about 3 mmolal as predicted from a membrane potential about 90 mV and an extracellular chloride concentration of about 110 mmolal.

Given a negative membrane potential it can be seen that potassium ions are distributed much closer to electrochemical equilibrium than are sodium ions. For potassium the concentration gradient favours outward movement and the electrical gradient favours inward movement; for sodium both gradients favour inward movement. Despite this difference the leak rates must be very similar since these ions are pumped out of and into the cells by the sodium pump in the ratio three sodium to two potassium. This means that the potassium outward leak, which is equal to the rate of inward pumping, is just a little smaller than the inward leak of sodium, which is equal to the rate of outward pumping. In other words a small outward electrochemical gradient for potassium drives almost as many ions through the membrane as are driven by a large inward electrochemical gradient for sodium. The resting membrane must therefore be much more permeable to potassium than to sodium ions. This selective permeability results from the presence of special ion selective transporters. The hydrophobic core of most of the membrane is almost completely impermeable to both sodium and potassium.

The arrangement described above provides for a steady state of ionic cell contents and, since rapid water movement keeps the osmolality constant, the cell volume will be stabilized. The rate of sodium pumping increases rapidly for small increases in the intracellular sodium concentration so that moderate perturbations can be readily compensated. For instance, an increase in the influx of sodium will increase the internal concentration sufficiently to produce a balancing increased active efflux with only a minor increase in the cell solute content.

Stopping the sodium pump obviously leads to the replacement of cellular potassium with sodium. It also leads to depolarization of the membrane, i.e. the membrane potential becomes less negative, and to the accumulation of chloride along with more sodium. This increase in the solute content of the cells leads to entry of water and cell swelling and, in many types of cell, to a breakdown of the cell membrane and loss of cell contents, called lysis. The accumulation of chloride occurs primarily because the replacement of intracellular potassium by sodium depolarizes the cell as it reduces the concentration gradient for potassium. The membrane is selectively permeable for potassium and the electrochemical gradient for potassium is therefore always small, i.e. any decrease in the potassium gradient must be accompanied by a loss of membrane potential. (In fact it is the loss of potential, caused by stopping the pump and sodium entry, which drives potassium out.) Because the membrane potential is becoming less negative there is now an electrochemical gradient driving chloride entry into the cell. The net result of these factors is that the cell gains sodium partly in exchange for potassium, which does not add to the solutes, and partly along with chloride, which does.

The presence of a membrane potential and a large inward gradient of sodium is normally put to good use by the cells. The special role of membrane potential in the function of nerve and muscle and many other excitable cells is very well known and comprises a large and important part of physiology. Of more immediate relevance is the use made of the potential energy stored in the electrochemical gradient of sodium ions to drive secondary active transport of solutes across the plasma membrane. In principle the 'downhill' transfer of sodium into the cell could be made to drive the uphill net transfer of any solute either in or out of the cell rather as winding a spring can provide power for any type of machine. As we shall see in subsequent chapters, a large number of sodium-linked special transporting systems achieve just this. It seems likely that much of the influx of sodium into cells in fact represents such linked transport of substrates into the cell.

The blood-brain barrier

In most tissues of the body the great permeability of the capillary walls allows very rapid exchange of small solutes between plasma and interstitium. The capillaries of the central nervous system are different. They are not freely permeable to small solutes and are impermeable to proteins. The composition of interstitial fluid of the brain is therefore not determined directly by the composition of the plasma, but is a specially controlled, privileged environment for the neurons. In fact the capillary walls in the central nervous system have properties more akin to those of cell membranes. They allow ready passage of water and of lipophilic solutes such as O_2, CO_2 and ethanol. However, polar solutes, even those with low molecular weight, like sodium, potassium and amino acids do not cross the capillary walls rapidly unless special transporters are provided. The structural basis for this special feature of brain capillaries appears to be the tight apposition of the junction of the endothelial cells, which eliminates the slit-like aqueous pathways between the cells which occur in the capillary walls of other tissues. Brain cells rely on glucose from the circulation for their energy supply, and the capillaries have specific transporters for glucose.

Cerebro-spinal fluid

Proper anatomic descriptions of the circulation of CSF can be found in texts on the central nervous system. A brief outline will serve here. The brain and spinal cord are suspended in CSF which occupies the space between their outer surface and the bone of the skull and spinal cord. Also the brain is hollow, containing four interconnecting cerebral ventricles into which CSF is secreted and from which it circulates to the entire surface of the brain. The fluid has a vital mechanical role, supporting and cushioning the brain within the skull.

CSF is actively secreted across the epithelium of highly vascular structures in the lateral ventricles, the choroid plexuses. The inorganic composition of the fluid is determined primarily by the transport processes of the secretory epithelium. There are also striking differences in the organic solutes of CSF and plasma. CSF is almost free of protein and many other organic constituents of plasma including many hormones and most amino acids. The latter is exceedingly important as several amino acids serve as neurotransmitters, which is possible only if the basal concentration in brain interstitium is kept low.

The ionic composition of CSF is broadly similar to that of plasma, mainly sodium with chloride and bicarbonate. The potassium concentration is lower in CSF near 3.0 mM compared to about 4.5 mM in plasma. The chloride concentration is higher in CSF, as expected from the absence of most of the organic anions. There are small differences for other ions, but more important is the stability of the composition of CSF and presumably brain interstitium in the face of changing plasma levels. This is particularly well documented for potassium. The concentration in CSF may change only one tenth as much as that in plasma. The CSF concentrations of free calcium and magnesium are also stabilized. These ions, especially calcium and potassium, have profound effects on nerve function, so the ability to hold their concentrations within very narrow limits is of obvious value. The total osmotic pressure of CSF and brain tissue, however, rapidly follows that of plasma, since water rapidly equilibrates across the blood-brain barrier.

Brain interstitial fluid

All brain cells are within 100 μm of a capillary, but most are not close to free flowing CSF. Thus the interstitial concentrations near the cells of substances which can rapidly cross the blood-brain barrier, notably oxygen, carbon dioxide and glucose, are determined by exchanges with plasma and the cells. By contrast, the interstitial concentrations of most substances are determined by diffusional exchange with CSF since they cross the blood-brain barrier very slowly. Of the common ions, only bicarbonate appears to have a transporter for its movement across the blood-brain barrier. The available evidence suggests that, for bicarbonate, interstitial concentrations are affected by acid production by the cells and exchanges with both plasma and CSF.

Special regions

There are specific regions of the brain which lack a blood-brain barrier, that is they have highly permeable capillaries. These regions are mostly near the hypothalamus and appear to serve two main functions. First, since the interstitial fluid in these regions can reflect the composition of plasma, the cells in them can 'sample' the composition of plasma and monitor levels of hormones and metabolites from which the rest of the brain is protected. Second, substances secreted by cells in these regions, e.g. the posterior pituitary, can find their way into the blood stream and act as hormones.

The effects of additions or losses of water and salt

The two guiding principles are:

1. that water distributes rapidly to equalize osmotic pressure through all the compartments;
2. that sodium salts are confined to the extracellular compartment by virtue of the low sodium permeability of cell membranes and the presence of sodium pumps. Both water and salt, of course, readily equilibrate between the plasma and interstitial fluids (see p. 15).

Based on these principles, it is possible to make a simple analysis of the immediate effects of certain specific additions and losses. These analyses are necessarily over simplified and neglect many secondary effects such as renal excretion during fluid redistribution. They nonetheless highlight the important points and offer a valuable framework for understanding the physiology and clinical implications of disturbances and alterations in body fluids.

1. Distribution of fluid between the intracellular fluid and extracellular fluid.

(a) Addition of water

If a 70 kg man drank and rapidly absorbed 1 litre of water this would distribute through all the body increasing the water content and reducing the osmotic pressure of each compartment by approximately 2.5 per cent. Because about two-thirds of the body water is in the cells, about two-thirds of the extra water enters the cells.

(b) Loss of water

The loss of, for example, 2 litres of water would reduce the water content and elevate the osmotic pressure of all compartments by approximately 5 per cent.

(c) Addition of isosmotic saline

1 litre of isosmotic saline (e.g. $NaCl$ + $NaHCO_3$ to maintain pH) infused into a vein will distribute in the plasma and interstitial fluids. By definition the fluid has the same osmotic pressure as that of the body fluid so that it will not create a tendency for water to move in or out of the cells and the cell volume will be unchanged. The infused solute is confined to the extracellular fluid and no immediate change in the solute content of the cells occurs.

(d) Loss of isosmotic fluid

Loss of fluid that is isosmotic with plasma, e.g. loss of gut secretion in diarrhoea, is similarly confined to the extracellular fluid and both plasma and interstitial volume are decreased. Again there is no change in the osmotic pressure to move fluid across the cell membrane and no immediate change in cell volume.

(e) Addition of hyperosmotic salt solutions

This could happen if a person drank and absorbed sea water which has roughly 500 mM sodium chloride. Let us consider a hypothetical addition of 1 litre of such fluid to plasma. Imagine first the fluid initially distributed in the plasma and interstitial fluid, but with no movements across cell membranes. The extracellular fluid volume would be increased by 1 litre and the osmotic pressure of the extracellular fluid would be elevated by about 12 per cent. Now remove the artificial restriction on movements; the salt remains confined to the extracellular fluid but roughly 1.5 litres of water leaves the cells to equilibrate the intracellular and extracellular osmotic pressures. The net results are a markedly increased extracellular volume, a reduced intracellular volume and an osmotic pressure 4–5 per cent above normal throughout. In effect, the excess salt in the hyperosmotic fluid shifts water from the cells to the extracellular space.

(f) Loss of sodium salt

The body cannot directly lose just sodium salt but it can effectively suffer such loss by losing isosmotic fluid and replacing the lost volume with salt free solution. (This could happen to a patient losing gut secretions and being infused with isosmotic glucose solution). The effects are the converse of those seen with hyperosmotic addtion. The solute loss is confined to the extracellular space. Consider the loss of 220 mmol of sodium chloride. As the osmotic pressure of the extracellular fluid is reduced, water enters the cells to equalize the osmotic pressure of inter- and extracellular fluid. The net result is a reduced extracellular volume, increased intracellular volume, and reduced osmotic pressure of all the body fluids. It will be a helpful exercise to start with the body fluid distributions indicated in Fig. 1.1 and to calculate the approximate final water contents of intra- and extracellular fluid and the final osmotic pressure of the fluids following this loss of sodium chloride.

(g) Addition of a solute that permeates cell membranes

Some solutes, e.g. urea, are not excluded from the intracellular compartment, because they can permeate cell membranes. The initial effects of infusing solutions of urea are similar to those seen with saline. For instance, intravenous infusion of hyperosmotic urea will intially draw water from the cells to equalize intra- and extracellular osmotic pressures. Then over several minutes the urea distributes into the cells to equalize its concentrations. As the urea enters the cells, water follows it by osmosis. The net result is that the infused water and the urea both distribute throughout all of the body water. All compartments have an increased water content and an increased total osmotic pressure. These events are further discussed in Chapter 13. For these reasons, the great increase in urea concentration in renal failure does not itself disturb the distribution of body fluids.

2. Distribution of fluid between plasma and interstitium

The effects on plasma and interstitial fluid volume of addition or loss of an extracellular fluid are influenced by the nature and the amount of the fluid added or lost.

With loss or addition of isosmotic fluid lacking protein (i.e. with no colloid osmotic pressure) the change in volume is shared between the blood and interstitium; about one-third of the change occurs in the blood. The added fluid dilutes the plasma proteins and lowers the colloid osmotic pressure, as well as causing a slight elevation of capillary pressure. There is thus an increased filtration pressure and a transfer of fluid into the interstitium until the loss of fluid from the blood and gain by the interstitium restores a near balance of pressures across the capillary walls.

If very large amounts of fluid are infused or large amounts of water and salt are accumulated in the body, as in congestive cardiac failure, the interstitium becomes oedematous. At this point its compliance increases dramatically, as shown in Fig. 2.2. Now nearly all of the additional fluid passes into the interstitium. This effect protects the circulation against disastrous over-distension.

If plasma is lost or added, the bulk of the fluid stays in the circulation; there is no immediate change in the colloid osmotic pressure gradient across the capillaries. For this reason, transfusion with plasma or a solution of equivalent colloid osmotic pressure is more effective in increasing circulating volume than is transfusion with isosmotic saline.

Following loss of plasma or blood, both the direct reduction in capillary hydrostatic pressure and various circulatory reflex adjustments such as arteriolar constriction may result in significant transfer of fluid from interstitium to blood which may help to maintain the circulating volume. This effect is often smaller than might be expected because withdrawal of interstitial fluid rapidly makes the interstitial fluid pressure more negative. In normally hydrated dogs, for instance, it was found that after a 30–40 per cent blood loss, a volume equivalent to only 10 per cent of the original blood volume was transferred from interstitium to plasma.

Further reading

Aidley, D.J. (1978). *The Physiology of Excitable Cells*, 2nd edn, Cambridge University Press, Cambridge. Chapter 3, pp. 13-36 The resting cell membrane.

Aukland, K. & Nicolaysen, G. (1981). Interstitial fluid volume: Local regulatory mechanisms. *Physiol. Rev.* **61**, 556–643.

DeVoe, R.D. & Maloney, P.C. (1980). Principles of cell homeostasis. pp. 3–45 in *Medical Physiology*, 14th edn Vol. 1, Mountcastle, V.B. ed, Mosby, St. Louis.

Granger, H.J., Laine, G.A., Barnes, G.E. & Lewis, R.E. (1984). Dynamics and control of transmicrovascular fluid exchange. pp. 189–228 in *Edema*, Staub, N.C. & Taylor, A.E. eds, Raven, N.Y.

Guyton, A.C. (1981). *Textbook of Medical Physiology*, 6th edn, Saunders, Philadelphia. Chapter 31, pp. 370–382 The lymphatic system, interstitial fluid dynamics, edema and pulmonary fluid. Chapter 33, pp. 391–402 Partition of the body fluids: Osmotic equilibria between extracellular and intracellular fluids.

Guyton, A.C., Taylor, A.E. & Granger, H.J. (1975). *Circulatory Physiology II: Dynamics and Control of the Body Fluids*, Saunders, Philadelphia.

Hebert, S.C., Shafer, J.A. & Andreoli, T.E. (1981) Principles of membrane transport. Chapter 3 in *The Kidney*, 2nd edn, Brenner, B.M. & Rector, F.C. Jr., eds, Saunders, Philadelphia.

Hodgkin, A.L. (1958). Ionic movements and electical activity in giant nerve fibres. *Proc. Roy. Soc. Lond. B.* **148**, 1–37.

Katz, M.A. & Bresler, E.H. (1984). Osmosis, pp. 39–60 in *Edema*, Staub, N.C. & Taylor, A.E. eds, Raven, N.Y.

Kuffler, S., Nichols, J. & Martin, A.R. (1984). *From Neurone to Brain*, Sinauer,

Landis, E.M. & Pappenheimer, J.R. (1963). Exchange of substances through capillary walls. pp. 961–1034 in *Handbook of Physiology, Section 2: Circulation*, American Physiological Society, Washington, D.C. This is the standard reference for older work.

Manning, R.D. Jr.. & Guyton, A.C. (1982). Control of blood volume. *Rev. Physiol. Biochem. Pharmacol.* **93**, 69–114.

Maffly, R.H. (1981). The body fluids. Chapter 2 in *The Kidney, 2nd ed*, Brenner, B.M. & Rector, F.C. Jr., eds, Saunders, Philadelphia.

Pappenheimer, J.R. (1970). Osmotic reflection coefficients in capillary membranes, pp. 278–286 in *Capillary Permeability*, Crone, C. & Lassen, N.A. eds, Munksgaard. This paper and the discussion which follows it on pp. 293–299 raised the important issues of parallel pathways for water fluxes, unstirred layers, etc.

Renkin, E.M. & Curry, F.E. (1979). Transport of water and solutes across capillary endothelium. Chapter 1, pp. 1–45 in *Membrane Transport in Biology, Vols, IVA & IVB, Transport Organs*. Giebisch, G. ed. Springer-Verlag, Berlin.

3

Basic structure of the kidneys and mechanisms of urine production

Gross anatomy

In a normal sized adult male human each kidney weighs around 200 g and has a maximum dimension of about 11 cm. Blood is supplied via the paired renal arteries and drains through the renal veins into the inferior vena cava. The urine passes down the ureters into the base of the bladder. The kidneys are innervated chiefly by the sympathetic division of the autonomic system, the nerves distributing along the main arteries. There is also a visceral sensory supply and damage or swellings in the kidneys can be very painful. A distinct fibrous capsule surrounds the tissue. The total tissue pressure is several millimetres of mercury above atmospheric, i.e. there is a noticeable 'turgor' so that if the capsule is cut the underlying tissue bulges out slightly. Like other viscera, the kidneys have a well developed lymph drainage which doubtless serves the usual functions.

The cut surface of the kidney reveals to the naked eye several distinct regions. Fig. 3.1 shows a diagram of a rat kidney with the cortical region surrounding the medulla which is itself subdivided into inner and outer regions. The medulla ends in the papilla which opens into the renal pelvis, the funnel-like beginning of the ureter. The glomeruli are in the cortex.

The human kidney has a somewhat more complex arrangement being 'multilobed'. In effect there are several simple kidneys crammed together in one capsule with 12–18 papillae and an appropriately branched renal pelvis. The species difference probably relates to the much larger size of the human kidney and has no major functional correlate that we need to consider here. The disposition of the tubules and ducts (see below) in the cortex and medulla is essentially similar to the pattern found in simple unilobar kidneys. Details of the anatomy of the human kidney can be found in any anatomy text-book and features relevant to clinical problems are covered in *Disorders of the Kidney and Urinary Tract*.

Microstructure

A nephron is defined by anatomists to consist of a glomerulus, a proximal tubule, a thin segment and a distal tubule which can be divided into early and

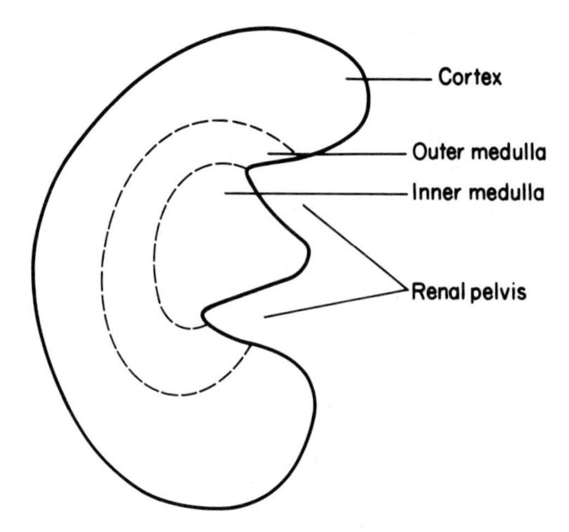

Fig. 3.1. Schematic coronal section through a rat kidney. Note that the volume of the cortex is very much greater than that of the inner medulla. The total number and cross-sectional area of the inner medullary collecting ducts (see Fig. 3.2) is only a few percent of the number and cross-sectional area of the proximal tubules. Many nephrons drain into one collecting duct.

late diluting segments. It empties into a cortical collecting tubule. These tubules and the medullary collecting ducts make up the collecting system which has an embryological origin different from that of the nephrons. However, because there is no other name, the term nephron is often used by physiologists to refer to all the structures leading from a glomerulus to the renal pelvis. The main parts of a nephron and the collecting system are shown in Fig. 3.2a and named in Fig. 3.3. The associated vasculature is shown in Fig. 3.2b. Each distal tubule returns to meet the arterioles of its own glomerulus. The structure at this point is termed the juxtaglomerular apparatus, a diagram of which is shown later in Fig. 9.1. As indicated in Fig. 3.2 not all nephrons have the same pattern. Two main classes have been distinguished, superficial and juxtamedullary nephrons. Superficial nephrons have glomeruli located towards the outer surface of the cortex and have short loops of Henle going no further down than to the outer medulla and with some not even leaving the cortex. Juxtamedullary nephrons have glomeruli located near the cortical-medullary boundary and have long loops of Henle.

The glomerulus comprises Malpighi's corpuscle encompassed by Bowman's capsule. Bowman's capsule is the cup-like beginning of the tubule, and Malpighi's corpuscle is a leash of capillary loops coming off an afferent arteriole. These capillaries differ from capillaries in muscle in that they rejoin and empty into an efferent arteriole rather than draining into venules. This high resistance postcapillary vessel makes the hydrostatic pressure in the glomerular capillaries much higher than in normal capillaries. In superficial nephrons the efferent arteriole gives rise to a network of peritubular capillaries which surround the cortical parts of the tubule and then drain into the interlobular vein. The juxtamedullary efferent arteriole not only supplies peritubular capillaries in the

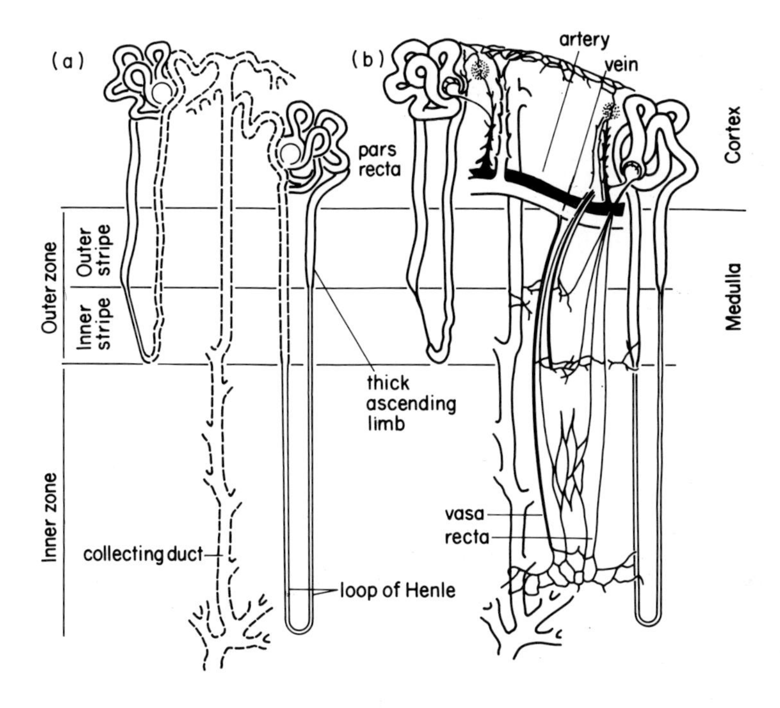

Fig. 3.2. Diagram of two nephrons. One nephron is more superficial with its loop of Henle reaching only into the outer medulla; the other, juxtamedullary nephron has a long loop of Henle. The main parts of the two nephrons and the collecting system are shown in (a). The arrangement of blood vessels is indicated in (b). (Reproduced from Gottschalk, 1964.)

cortex but also sends off vasa recta (straight vessels) which descend into the medulla and supply capillaries which rejoin to form the ascending vasa recta. The looped arrangement of both tubules and capillaries in the medulla is of great functional significance in the formation of concentrated urine and this will be taken up in Chapter 8.

The tubules comprise a single layer of epithelial cells and the different parts vary in outer diameter roughly as indicated in Fig. 3.2. In life a proximal tubule might have an outer diameter of 50 μm and a lumen of 30–40 μm so that the cells are 5–10 μm thick. The glomeruli are about 100–150 μm across. One thing which is difficult to convey in a diagram of the nephron is just how long and thin the tubules are. In the human kidney the average length may be 40 mm, so the tubule is approximately 1000 times longer than it is wide. The total length of the *c* 1 million tubules in a human kidney could be 40 kilometres.

The different parts of the tubule are specialized to perform different functions and accordingly have different fine structures as will be mentioned in the subsequent chapters.

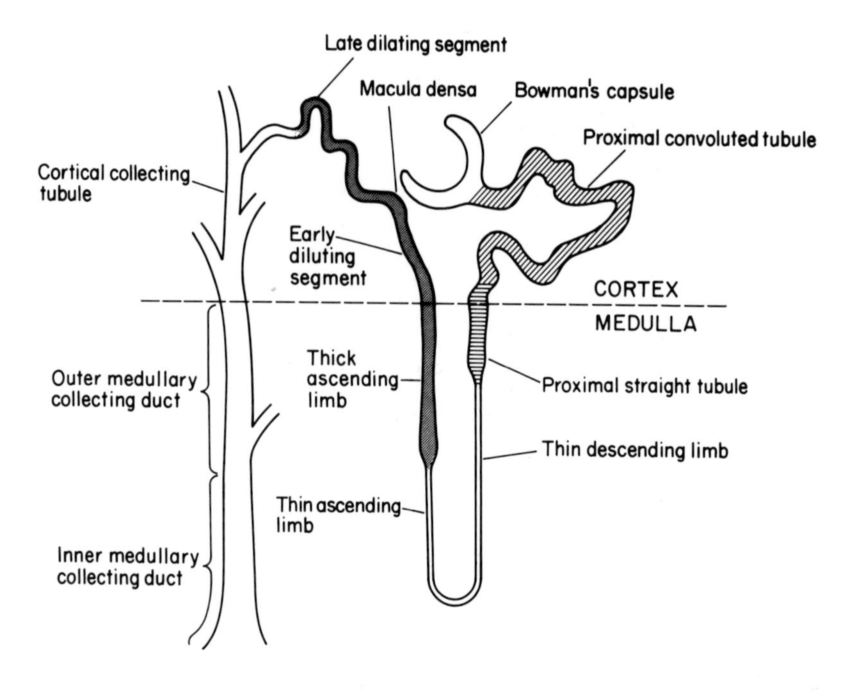

Fig. 3.3. The segments of the nephron and collecting system. The loop of Henle is usually defined to start at the beginning of the straight portion, the pars recta, of the proximal tubule and to end at the macula densa. The thick ascending limb is the part of the early diluting segment prior to the macula densa. The macula densa, a collection of modified tubular cells, is part of the juxtaglomerular apparatus (see Fig. 9.1).

Basic processes of urine production

The basic processes are indicated in Fig. 3.4. The initial step in urine production is the pressure filtration, or ultrafiltration, of plasma across the glomerular membrane into Bowman's capsule, to produce approximately 125 ml/min of almost protein-free fluid. As the fluid flows down the tubule, almost all of it is returned to the blood in the peritubular capillaries by a process called reabsorption. The few mls of urine left contain those things to be excreted. Additionally certain substances are secreted into the tubule from the peritubular blood.

Glomerular filtration is driven by the hydrostatic pressure of the blood in the glomerular capillaries, the energy coming from the contraction of the left ventricle. So far as the nephron is concerned this is a 'passive' process. The thin filtering membrane does not provide any energy for filtration. For small molecular weight substances, there is no selectivity in this membrane so that useful, waste and toxic substances all enter the tubule at near the free concentrations they had in the plasma water (actually at Donnan equilibrium with plasma).

The reabsorption of fluid from the tubules into the blood involves active transport processes requiring energy from the metabolism of the tubular cells.

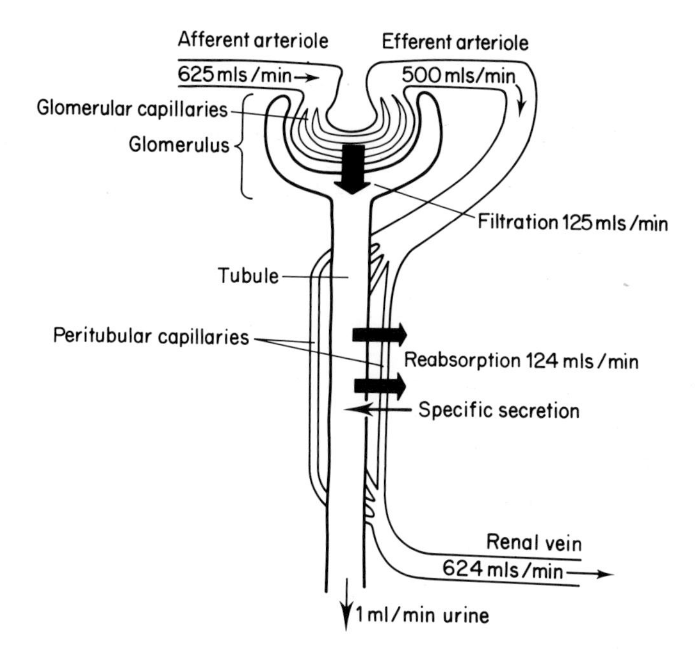

Fig. 3.4. The basic scheme of kidney function. About one fifth of the plasma flowing into the glomerular capillaries crosses the capillary walls into Bowman's space. As it flows along the tubule more than 99 per cent is reabsorbed. Much less material is secreted into the tubule than is reabsorbed.

These cells, except in the thin limbs of the loop of Henle, contain large numbers of mitochondria to provide this energy. This reabsorptive process is selective so that most useful substances are returned to the blood and the wastes and toxic substances can be left to be excreted in the urine. Tubular secretion also involves active transport.

Physiologists of the nineteenth century correctly deduced the main processes of urine production. Bowman and others concluded that production of a filtrate across the glomerulus was followed by tubular reabsorption by examining the fine structure of the kidney. It was then found experimentally that cooling the kidney or applying metabolic poisons could greatly increase the urine flow as expected if glomerular filtration is passive while reabsorption of tubular fluid requires energy consuming processes in the tubular cells.

Another experiment was to measure the pressure that developed following clamping of the ureters. The maximum pressure in the ureters never reached arterial blood pressure just as expected if production of tubular fluid requires pressure filtration across the glomerular membrane. By contrast the salivary gland (which is now known to produce its basic secretion by active transport across the acinar cells) could develop a salivary duct pressure substantially in excess of that in the arteries.

It was not until the twentieth century that Richards provided the final demonstration of glomerular ultrafiltration. He directly sampled fluid from Bowman's capsule and found that its composition was that of an ultrafiltrate.

It is difficult to over emphasize that the urine produced represents a very small difference between a large volume of fluid filtered and a large volume of fluid reabsorbed. Small proportional changes in either filtration or reabsorption can produce a very large change in the urine flow. This arrangement requires that glomerular filtration rate be relatively stable and that the amount of fluid reabsorbed be linked to the amount filtered so that spurious fluctuations in urine production can be avoided. However, mechanisms are also needed which can produce large changes in urine flow and composition when they are needed.

Why filter so much, reabsorb so much, and leave so little?

Before ending this general survey of renal function, we ought to ask why such an apparently strange way of producing urine has evolved. Would it not be better simply to secrete into a tubule the water and solutes that one does not want? There are perhaps two major advantages of the existing system.

1. Any polar substance that can be filtered can be excreted by the simple expedient of not providing a specific reabsorptive transport process. With the apparently simpler system of secreting all the urine, a transport system would have to be provided for each such compound that might require excretion.
2. Probably more important is the requirement that the same system is able at times to eliminate a very large volume of water while retaining solutes, but at other times to excrete waste solutes in a small volume of very concentrated urine. A filtration process followed by tubular reabsorption is ideal for excreting a lot of solute free water since the solute can be actively reabsorbed from a water impermeable part of the tubule. How to use the same tubular system to produce, when necessary, a highly concentrated urine is not quite so simple. The trick is to transport salt out of a large volume of fluid early in the tubule, concentrate it in a small region, then use it to extract water from a small volume of fluid in the collecting duct. This mechanism is described in Chapter 8.

What is urine?

Urine should consist of those things that must be eliminated to regulate the composition of the body fluids. The volume and solute content therefore depend on what you eat, drink and produce by metabolism, and on non-renal losses. Hence urine varies enormously under different circumstances. Nonetheless we can give a rough idea of what a 24 hour urine collection might typically be like. The volume would be 1 to 2 litres. It might contain around 100 mmol each of sodium and potassium with rather less than an equivalent amount of chloride. Other inorganic constituents could include about 50 mmol of phosphate, 25 mmol of sulphate, and 50 mmol of ammonium ions, with a few mmoles each of calcium and magnesium. Given an average Western diet urinary pH is on the acid side, pH 5 to 6 and there is almost no bicarbonate. There are, of course, numerous metabolic end products including a few hundred mmoles of urea, and a few mmoles of creatinine and uric acid. There should be almost no glucose and no protein, the readily detectable presence of either indicating definitive pathology. As described, the urine would be roughly isosmotic with plasma. The solutes can be excreted in much more water when water is taken in excess.

10 litres or more of very dilute urine can be produced per day. Alternatively, the solutes can be excreted in a smaller volume, to give a much more concentrated urine. It is generally accepted that the minimum, or obligatory, volume of urine when glomerular filtration is normal and as much as possible of the filtrate is reabsorbed is about 500 ml/day. The production of less urine than this signals the presence of some form of renal failure.

Further reading

Gottshalk, C. W. (1964). Osmotic concentration and dilution of the urine. *Am. J. Med.* **36**, 670–685.

Moffat, D.B. (1975). *The Mammalian Kidney*. Cambridge Univ. Pres, Cambridge.

Tisher, C.C. (1981). Anatomy of the kidney, chapter 1, pp. 3–75, *The Kidney, 2nd edn*, Brenner, B.M. & Rector, F.C.Jr., eds, Saunders, Philadelphia.

4

Methods for studying renal function

Measurement of plasma composition and urinary excretion

By far the commonest medical test for renal function is 'urea and electrolytes' where the laboratory typically gives values for urea, Na^+, K^+, Mg^{2+}, Ca^{2+}, Cl^-, HCO_3^-, phosphate and protein concentrations. If these are within normal limits then it is usually assumed that the kidneys are working adequately. These tests, however, fail to detect the complete absence of up to three-quarters of the nephrons provided the function of those remaining is disturbed only by the necessity of excreting the load normally handled by all of the nephrons. A more critical evaluation would include estimation of plasma creatinine (see p. 38). Abnormal plasma composition may be due to kidney malfunction, or to alterations in one or more of the other inputs and outputs to the ECF. Such alterations may be obvious, for instance, the patient may be persistently vomiting or have been inadvertently overtransfused with intravenous fluid. In any case the second obvious test, the measurement of urinary excretion, can show whether the urine is appropriate for correcting the observed disturbance in plasma or whether the urine is so inappropriate that kidney malfunction is likely to be the cause. Consider, for example, a patient with an abnormally high plasma sodium concentration. The appropriate kidney response is the production of a small volume of concentrated urine. Finding a large flow of dilute urine then indicates failure of renal concentrating ability.

Renal clearance

The rate of excretion of most solutes varies with their plasma concentration and thus a single value says little about kidney function. However, for many solutes the *ratio* of the excretion rate to the plasma concentration varies much less, and a single value is descriptive of the kidney mechanisms. This ratio is called the *clearance*.

$$\text{clearance (ml/min)} = \frac{\text{rate of excretion (mmoles/min)}}{\text{plasma concentration (mmoles/ml = moles/litre)}}$$

The name clearance arises because the ratio equals the (hypothetical) volume of plasma which would have to be completely 'cleared' of solute each minute to yield the amount excreted. Of course, in reality the kidney rarely completely clears a solute from any element of volume which passes through it.

Mathematically, renal clearance, C, is given by $C = (U \times V) / P$ where U = urine concentration, V is urine flow in ml/min, and P is plasma concentration. The clinical use of clearance measurements is discussed in Chapter 1 of *Disorders of the Kidney and Urinary Tract.*

Measurement of glomerular filtration rate (GFR)

For a substance that is freely filtered into the tubule, that stays there with no additions or losses, and that is therefore totally lost in the urine, the clearance equals the GFR. Here we really can think of the kidneys taking a volume of plasma equal to the amount filtered, totally stripping it of a solute, and excreting all of the solute in the urine.

One substance often used to measure GFR is the polysaccharide inulin, which is made and stored in dahlia roots. Inulin is almost ideal for the following reasons:

1. it is sufficiently small (molecular weight *c* 5200) to be freely filtered through the glomerular membrane;
2. it is not bound to plasma protein so that the plasma concentration will indeed equal that in the glomerular filtrate;
3. it is nontoxic and it is not metabolized;
4. it is easily measured at plasma concentrations for which, even after being concentrated in the tubule, it makes a negligible osmotic contribution to the osmolality of the tubular fluid;
5. it is unable to pass in or out of the tubule by active or passive transport.

Let us be quite sure we see why, with these properties, inulin clearance should give the GFR. Since it is freely filtered, its concentration in Bowman's capsule is the same as in plasma. The amount filtered per minute is therefore given by GFR $\times$ P (plasma concentration). But since inulin is neither secreted nor reabsorbed across the tubule wall the amount filtered equals the amount excreted, which is $U \times V$. Thus GFR $\times P = U \times V$ or GFR $= (U/P) \times V = C_{inulin}$. The value usually assumed for GFR in a young adult is 125 ml/min. The values measured using inulin clearance show distinct differences between healthy subjects ranging from 100 to 160 ml/min, but, for any one person, the values are rather stable. Within the accuracy of the technique, *c* 10 per cent, it is difficult to show changes in GFR except in extreme conditions such as strenous exercise or serious haemorrhage. (GFR determined using inulin is necessarily a value averaged over the tens of minutes needed to collect enough urine. Brief changes in GFR, e.g. the reduction in GFR resulting from sympathetic nerve activity when an animal is startled as by slamming a door, have little effect on inulin clearance.)

Inulin was originally used in the 1930s since the available indirect evidence suggested that it met the five requirements listed above. More recent direct tests at the level of the single nephron have confirmed that inulin does indeed show the desired properties. With the advent of radioactive labels it became possible to use many other compounds, e.g. the ^{51}Cr–EDTA complex. Obviously neither inulin nor ^{51}Cr–EDTA are normally present in the extracellular fluid and they must therefore be provided during the experiments. The proper procedure is to infuse one of these substances into a vein at a steady rate until the plasma level reaches the balance point at which urinary excretion matches the infusion input. The clearance is then given by the excretion rate (= infusion rate) divided by the plasma concentration. There are two short-cuts for getting a measure of GFR adequate for clinical purposes.

1. Inject a single dose of say, ^{51}Cr–EDTA, wait for the initial rapid phase of mixing throughout the extracellular fluid to be complete, start a urine collection, and then measure the plasma concentration at the mid-point of the collection period. This plasma sample can give a reasonable average plasma concentration for the period of collection.
2. Simpler yet is to measure the clearance of creatinine. This naturally occurring waste product is continually 'infused' into the ECF from muscle cells. It is freely filtered and not reabsorbed, but there is some active secretion into the tubules so that rather more than the amount filtered is excreted in urine. However, the standard chemical analysis slightly over-estimates plasma creatinine so that when the clearance is calculated as the ratio the two errors tend to cancel and the value for creatinine clearance is usually remarkably close to that for inulin clearance. Even simpler is to estimate GFR from just the plasma creatinine level. This requires the assumption that the rate of creatinine production and hence excretion is normal. Once the value of $U \times V$ is assumed, GFR is obtained by dividing by the measured P.

Despite the obvious possible errors this can give surprisingly satisfactory results. The use of creatinine is thus highly convenient and often adequate in medical practice. More accurate determination using, say, inulin, or ^{51}Cr–EDTA is often required for research purposes.

Measurement of renal plasma flow

Renal plasma flow can be estimated from the clearance of a substance such as para-aminohippuric acid. PAH is excluded from the blood cells and avidly secreted into the tubules so that little remains in the plasma entering the renal vein. The amount of PAH getting into the tubule and into urine is thus given by RPF $\times$ P. Since the rate of excretion is $U \times V$ and all of the PAH which enters the tubule is excreted, RPF = $U \times V/P = C_{PAH}$.

We can look at this another way. The Fick relation for flow through an organ gives

$$\text{flow} = \frac{\text{amount of substance extracted per minute}}{\text{arterial concentration minus venous concentration}}$$

So for PAH excretion in the urine,

$$\text{RPF} = \frac{U \times V}{P_{\text{arterial}} - P_{\text{venous}}}$$

but P_{venous} is near zero for PAH, so

$$\text{RPF} = (U \times V) / P_{\text{arterial}} = C_{\text{PAH}}$$

A typical renal plasma flow for a young adult would be around 625 ml/min.

PAH clearance gives an estimate of renal plasma flow. Renal blood flow is given by RPF/(1 – haematocrit) where the haemotocrit is the fraction of the blood volume occupied by red blood cells. For a typical haematocrit of 0.4 and RPF = 625 ml renal blood flow would be just above 1 litre/min.

Measurement of renal plasma flow by PAH clearance requires an infusion of PAH to achieve a steady plasma level. The plasma concentration can be measured in a peripheral vein since this will be virtually the same as that in the renal artery.

Renal vein levels of PAH are not zero even at low arterial concentrations but actually about 10 per cent of those in arterial blood so that PAH clearance underestimates renal plasma flow by approximately 10 per cent. The flow calculated from the PAH clearance is called the effective renal plasma flow. This name was originally based on the idea that the PAH in the venous blood represents all of the PAH in 10 per cent of the plasma from which no secretion can occur. Furthermore it has been suggested that this flow might be through the medulla since the loops of Henle do not seem to secrete PAH. However, proximal straight tubules do secrete PAH and those of the juxtamedullary nephrons lie alongside the capillaries of the vasa recta in the medulla. The word effective should therefore be taken solely as a reminder that for some reason the true total renal plasma flow is somewhat greater than the clearance of PAH.

It is clear that PAH clearance estimates renal plasma flow only so long as virtually all the PAH can be secreted from the peritubular capillaries into the tubules. If too much PAH is presented to the tubules, i.e. the plasma concentration of PAH is too high, then some PAH escapes the secretion mechanism and returns to the renal venous blood. Less of the renal plasma is now cleared and PAH clearance becomes less than renal plasma flow.

Glucose clearance

Although glucose (and amino acids) are freely filtered, they are almost (but not quite) entirely reabsorbed, so that virtually none remains in the urine (i.e. less than the detection limits of standard clinical assays). Thus we say that the clearance of glucose is zero. However, if the glucose concentration in plasma is substantially elevated, the amount filtered, GFR $\times$ P, increases and the capacity of the tubules to reabsorb glucose can be exceeded. Now more glucose remains in the tubule and enough is excreted in the urine to be detected, so that we say that some plasma is cleared.

Transport maximum: T_m

Fig. 4.1 shows how the rates of excretion and clearance for PAH, inulin, and glucose vary with plasma concentration at constant GFR. For inulin, excretion, equal to GFR $\times$ P, increases linearly with plasma concentration and thus the clearance is a constant. For PAH at any low concentration the rate of excretion is much higher than for inulin since the PAH which escapes filtration is subsequently secreted into the tubule and the excretion equals RPF $\times$ P. However as plasma concentration rises, the rate of secretion reaches its maximum and further increases in excretion are provided only by the increased amounts

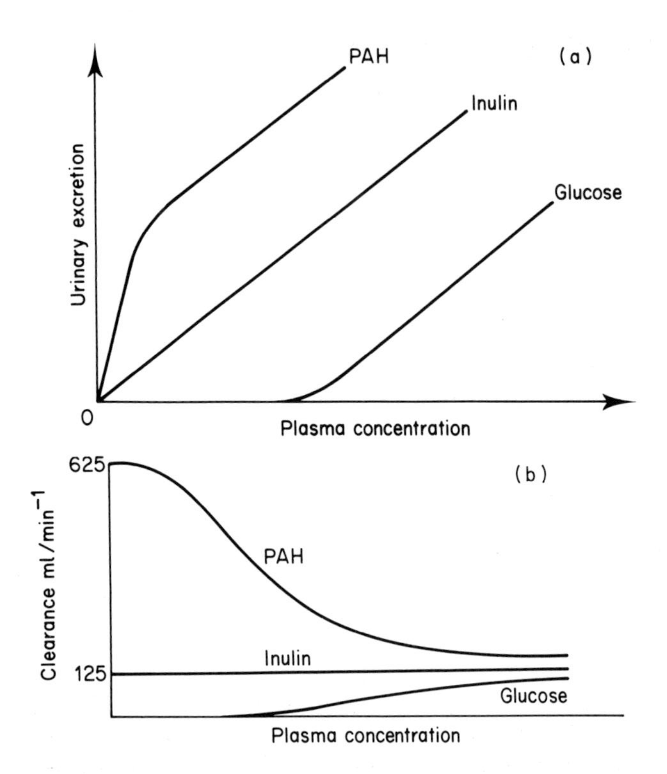

Fig. 4.1. Rates of excretion and clearances for inulin, PAH and glucose. In (a) these are presented as rate of excretion versus plasma concentration, while in (b) the same data are plotted as clearances.

filtered. The clearance therefore initially equals RPF but at high concentrations secretion contributes only a small proportion of the PAH excreted and the clearance approaches GFR. For glucose, at normal plasma concentrations, there is virtually no excretion but once the amount filtered exceeds the reabsorptive capacity of the tubules, the excess of the amount filtered over the amount which can be reabsorbed is left in the tubule and appears in the urine. The clearance is thus zero at low concentrations, but it approaches GFR at high concentrations.

Figure 4.1 shows strong evidence that inulin can be used to measure GFR. The clearance of any substance which is freely filtered must approach GFR as its concentration is increased provided the concentration can be raised high enough to saturate tubular transport mechanisms. These conditions will be satisfied for almost all polar solutes larger than the small inorganic ions. The clearance to which all these solutes converge is a good estimate of GFR. For inulin the clearance equals this value for all plasma concentrations.

From the data in Fig. 4.1 we can also plot the net tubular secretion for PAH and the reabsorption for glucose as a function of either the plasma concentration or the amount filtered. Fig. 4.2 shows these relations demonstrating a

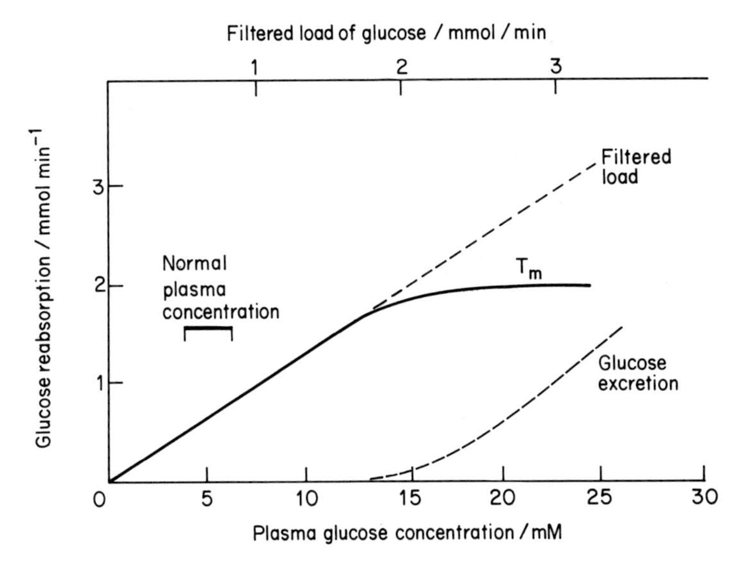

Fig. 4.2. Rate of filtration and rate of reabsorption for glucose calculated from the data in Fig. 4.1.

maximum amount that can be secreted or reabsorbed, the so called transport maximum or T_m for the solute. The T_m is different for different solutes and can be altered by physiological, pathological or pharmacological changes in tubular behaviour. The fact that the T_m for glucose is normally roughly twice the filtered load explains why the detection of glucose in urine usually indicates that the plasma glucose level is more than twice normal. The most common cause of glycosuria is *diabetes mellitus*.

Clearance ratios

The comparison of the clearance of any solute with that of inulin can tell you whether that solute is undergoing net tubular secretion or reabsorption. A clearance exceeding that of inulin shows that some of the solute excreted has come from the plasma in the peritubular capillaries as well as from the filtrate. For example, it was by finding a potassium clearance higher than that of inulin in potassium loaded rats that tubular secretion of potassium was first demonstrated. Conversely if a freely filtered substance has a clearance less than that of inulin then there is net reabsorption in the tubule. The clearance ratio for PAH i.e. C_{in}/C_{PAH} gives the filtration fraction, that is the fraction of the renal plasma flow that is filtered into the tubule. Normally this value is around $\frac{1}{5}$.

Note that we can obtain the clearance ratio by measuring just the concentrations of inulin and the solute in question in plasma and urine; we do not need to measure urine flow since

$$\begin{aligned} C_{solute}/C_{in} &= (U \times V/P)_{solute} / (U \times V/P)_{in} \\ &= (U/P)_{solute} / (U/P)_{in}. \end{aligned}$$

From this ratio for a reabsorbed solute one can easily calculate the proportion of the filtered load that is being reabsorbed, which is often a useful indicator of tubular function. It is often much more convenient to use creatinine instead of inulin and thus to measure $(U/P)_{solute}/(U/P)_{creatinine}$.

Osmolal clearance, free water clearance, and free water reabsorption.

As discussed later in Chapters 8, 13, and 14, control of sodium excretion determines extracellular fluid volume while control of water excretion controls the sodium concentration, and hence the osmolality of the body fluids. The rate of water excretion is almost the same as urine flow rate. However, urine flow is not itself a suitable measure for the rate at which the kidneys can change the extracellular sodium concentration and osmolality of the body fluids. Thus almost any flow of urine will fail to change plasma osmolality if it contains sodium chloride, at the same concentration as in extracellular fluid, together with an appropriate amount of urea.

A measure of the ability of the kidney to concentrate or dilute the body fluids is provided by either the osmolal or free water clearance. The osmolal clearance is 'the rate of excretion of osmoles' divided by the osmolality of plasma. Ignoring the distinction between osmolality and osmolarity in the urine, this becomes

$$C_{osm} = (\text{urine osmolality} \times V) / (\text{plasma osmolality})$$

where V equals urine flow rate. The osmolal clearance equals the flow rate of a hypothetical urine isosmotic with plasma which would be required to excrete the urinary solutes at the actual rate. It is thus a measure of how much water must be excreted to carry the solutes at the same osmolality as in plasma. The free water clearance is the difference between the actual rate of water excretion and this rate of excretion required to accompany the solutes.

$$C_{fw} = V - C_{osm}$$

The free water clearance equals the rate at which water must be added to the hypothetical isosmotic urine to make the real urine. When the osmolality of urine is less than that of plasma, the free water clearance is positive. Values up to 15 ml/min are observed with extensive water loading. When the urine is concentrated, the osmolality of the urine is greater than that of the plasma and the free water clearance is negative. It is common practice to refer to a negative free water clearance as a positive free water reabsorption since it is the amount of water which would have to be reabsorbed from a hypothetical isosmotic urine to make it as concentrated as the real urine. Urine osmolality can be much higher than that of plasma and even though urine flows are then typically only 1–2 ml/min, the free water reabsorption can be as large as 4 or 5 ml/min.

Methods for studying individual tubules

Measurements of plasma and urine reveal most of what we need to know concerning the functions of the kidney, but very limited information as to how these are carried out. Unravelling the mechanisms of the kidney has required the use of numerous histological, biochemical and physiological techniques. We shall outline below certain techniques that were developed for the study of the kidney.

It was emphasized by Homer Smith and more recently by O'Connor that clearance measurements can, in contrast to all the single tubule techniques, be used to study function in normal conscious unrestrained animals and people. All of the techniques for more detailed investigation require at least anaesthesia and exposure of the kidneys.

Micropuncture

The basic procedure of micropuncture is to insert a glass micropipette into a functioning tubule. Only those segments near the exposed surfaces are accessible which limits work to

1. the first two thirds of the proximial tubule of superficial nephrons;
2. a portion of the distal tubule and collecting system of superficial nephrons;
3. in some species a portion of the thin loop of Henle in the papillae.

In free flow micropuncture the pipette is used to take a small sample from the flowing fluid. This sample is then analysed for its composition. Alternatively it is possible to collect all of the fluid arriving at the pipette. Usually the animal receives an infusion of radio-labelled inulin. The single nephron glomerular filtration rate, SNGFR, is then calculated as the product of the volume of tubular fluid collected per minute, times the ratio of the inulin concentrations in the collected fluid and in plasma.

Split drop

The Gertz split drop technique is shown in Fig. 4.3. In its simplest form this technique is used to assess the rate of fluid reabsorption by monitoring the shrinkage of the drop of aqueous solution in the tubule. In a more elaborate form the aqueous drop is collected after a period of time and analyzed for its contents. Shrinking drop experiments are well suited to studies on proximal reabsorption of sodium chloride, sodium bicarbonate, and water since in this region water follows solute isosmotically and thus the change in volume accurately reflects solute transport.

Microperfusion

Microperfusion shown in Fig. 4.4 allows studies of transport with controlled, different luminal concentrations and flow rates. However, it is considerably more difficult experimentally than split drop experiments.

Double perfusion

In order to investigate the effects of plasma concentrations on tubular function, it is necessary to be able to change and control the plasma concentrations, i.e. the capillaries must be perfused. Capillary perfusion has been combined with both split drop and tubular perfusion protocols.

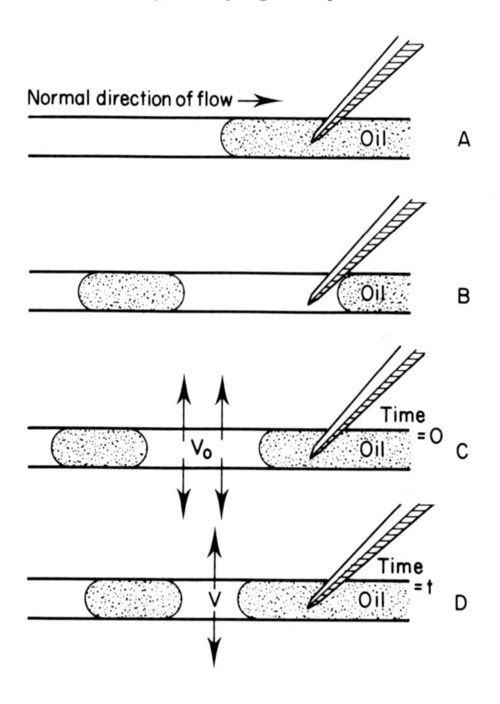

Fig. 4.3. The split drop technique. A drop of viscous oil, large enough to block flow, is injected into the tubule from one barrel of a double-barrelled micropipette, A. The drop is then split, B, by injecting the test solution through the other barrel and the drop is sealed off by injecting more oil, C. The proximal portion of the drop is small and moveable. Changes in the separation of the two parts of the oil drop then reveal the changes in the volume of the test solution within the lumen, D. (From Gertz et al)

Electrical recording

The electrical potentials of the lumen and of the cell interiors relative to that of the peritubular space are of considerable importance since the potential differences are a significant part of the driving force for passive movements of ions across the cell membrane and the tight junctions. The tubular lumen is large enough to be punctured using microelectrodes, but the measurements have been plagued by artifacts primarily because unusually accurate data are required. Thus in the proximal tubule, variations of less than 1 mV are functionally significant. Originally it was thought that the potential of rat proximal tubules was small and that like the much larger potentials in amphibia it was negative. More recently it has been concluded that when the potentials at the junctions between the electrodes and the fluids are properly taken into account, the actual potentials can be positive or negative depending on position. The potentials in the tubular cells are much more difficult to measure and most of the satisfactory data have been obtained using amphibian species with unusually large cells.

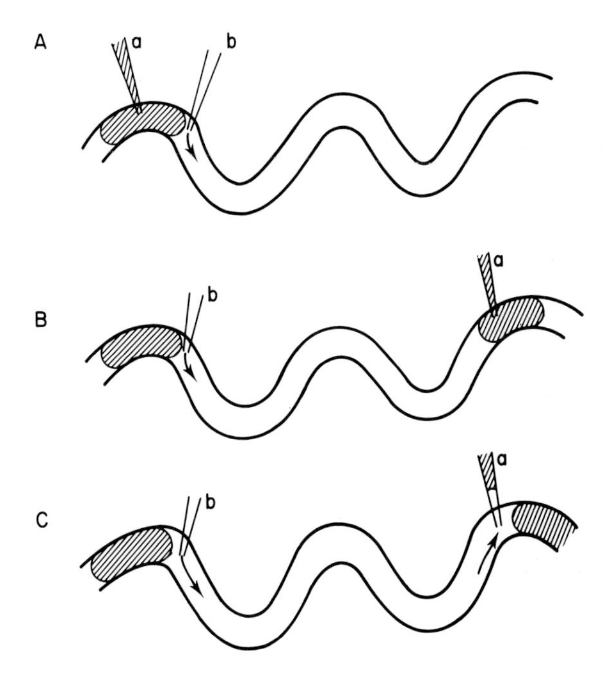

Fig. 4.4. A microperfusion technique. A drop of viscous oil is injected into the tubule from a micropipette, a. to provide a fixed plug. A second, perfusion pipette, b, is then inserted, A. After flow is started, the first pipette is removed and reinserted further along the tubule, B, and a second oil drop is injected which is carried just beyond the tip. Suction is then applied to pipette, a, such that all the fluid flowing along the tubule enters the pipette and the oil drop just beyond the region of interest remains stationary. It is standard to include a marker such as inulin in the perfusion fluid to allow measurement of fluid reabsorption independent of the difference between the injected and collected volumes. It is also possible to include markers in the blood to allow detection of accidental collection of peritubular fluid. (After Giebisch, Green, and colleagues)

In vitro perfusion

In this technique segments of tubules with their basement membrane intact are teased out of a kidney, cannulated at both ends, and maintained in an artificial bath. This preparation has allowed unprecedented control of the compositions of both luminal and peritubular solutions. Almost equally important, it allows access to single tubular segments from deep as well as superficial portions of the kidneys. However, the tubules are removed from contact with the peritubular capillaries which may alter their properties. Many of the differences between the account of tubular function given in this book and those to be found in earlier textbooks are a direct result of the detailed information uncovered since 1966 by this technique.

Unfortunately, the preparation of isolated tubules with intact basement membranes has so far been possible in only one species–the rabbit. Given this restriction, it is fortunate that the increasingly sophisticated micropuncture and electrical experiments in rodents and other animals have led to many of the same conclusions.

Membrane vesicles

Even the isolated tubule preparation is still complex. Thus any transport which occurs through the cell involves movement of solute across two membranes with the concentration and electrical potential in between unknown and changing with various manipulations. An extremely important new technique is the isolation of fragments of apical and basolateral membranes separate from each other. These fragments form vesicles with a single layer of membrane surrounding an aqueous interior. The composition of the interior can be set by preincubation, then the vesicle can be suspended in a medium of different composition. At intervals the vesicles are separated from the medium, usually by filtration, and their contents assayed. These measurements allow characterization of the types of transport available to the cells, but so far they have not been able to predict the rates of such transport. This technique will become much more useful if methods can be found to produce vesicles derived from different types of tubular cells, e.g. pure apical membrane from only proximal convoluted tubules.

Cultured cell lines

Several types of renal epithelial cells have now been cultured and they can be grown to form artificial transporting epithelia of large area composed of a single cell type. These epithelia can be investigated using many of the techniques developed for the study of natural epithelia, but free from many of the difficulties imposed by the very small size of the kidney tubules and the heterogeneity of the tubular cells. The cultured cells have little extracellular connective tissue and thus they should also be suitable for electrical recording. Furthermore they may be a good starting material for preparing membrane vesicles from a single source.

Further reading

Boulpaep, E. (1979). Electrophysiology of the kidney. Chapter 3. pp. 97–144 in *Membrane Transport in Biology, Vols. IVA & IVB, Transport Organs*. Giebisch, G. ed, Springer-Verlag, Berlin.

Burg, M.B. & Orloff, J. (1973). Perfusion of isolated tubules. Chapter 7, pp. 145–160 in *Handbook of Physiology, Section 8, Renal Physiology*, Orloff, J. & Berliner, R.W., eds, American Physiological Society, Washington, D.C.

Chantler, C., Garnett, E.S., Parsons, V. & Veall, N. (1969). Glomerular filtration rate measurement in man by the single injection method using ^{51}Cr–EDTA. *Clin. Sci.* **37**, 169–180.

Gaudino, M. & Levitt, M.F. (1949). Inulin space as a measure of extracellular fluid. *Am. J. Physiol.* **171**, 387–393.

Gertz, K.H., Mangos, J.A., Braun, G. & Pagel, H.D. (1965). On the glomerular tubular balance in the rat kidney. *Pflügers Archiv.* **285**, 360–372.

Green, R., Windhager, E.E. & Giebisch, G. (1974). Protein oncotic pressure effects on proximal tubular fluid movement in the rat. *Am. J. Physiol.* **226**, 265–276.

Gottschalk, C.W. & Lassiter, W.E. (1973). Micropuncture methodology. Chapter 6, pp. 129–144 in *Handbook of Physiology, Section 8, Renal Physiology*, Orloff, J. & Berliner, R.W., eds, American Physiological Society, Washington, D.C.

Handler, J.S., Perkins, F.M. & Johnson, J.P. (1980). Studies of renal cell function using cell culture techniques. *Am. J. Physiol.* **238**, F1–F9.

Kinne, R. & Schwartz, I.L. (1978). Isolated membrane vesicles in the evaluation of the nature, localization, and regulation of renal transport processes. *Kidney Int.* **14**, 547–556.

Levinsky, N.G. & Levy, M. (1973). Clearance techniques. Chapter 4, pp. 103–117 in *Handbook of Physiology, Section 8, Renal Physiology*, Orloff, J. & Berliner, R.W., eds, American Physiological Society, Washington, D.C.

Malvin, R.L. & Wilde, W.S. (1973). Stop-flow technique. Chapter 5, pp. 119–128 in *Handbook of Physiology, Section 8, Renal Physiology*, Orloff, J. & Berliner, R.W., eds, American Physiological Society, Washington, D.C.

Mudge, G.H. (1980). pp. 888–890 in *The Pharmacological Basis of Therapeutics*, 6th ed. Gilman, A.G., Goodman, L.S. & Gilman, A., eds, Macmillan, N.Y. (Free water and osmolal clearances.)

O'Connor, W.J. (1982). *Normal Renal Function*, Croom Helm, London. pp. 36–45. A critique of clearance measurements with emphasis on the inaccuracies.

Pitts, R.F. (1974). *Physiology of the Kidney and Body Fluids,* 3rd ed, Yearbook Medical Publishers, Chicago, Chapter 5, pp. 60–70 Clearance and rate of glomerular filtration.

5

Glomerular filtration

The Glomerulus

Blood enters the glomerulus via the afferent arteriole and traverses the glomerular capillaries where filtration occurs. The portion which is not filtered leaves via the efferent arteriole. Both the afferent and efferent arterioles have relatively thick muscle coats, that of the afferent being the more prominent. The glomerular tuft of capillaries is inserted into Bowman's space which is continuous with the lumen of the proximal tubule. The outside shell of the glomerulus is a sheet of cells, the parietal epithelium, which is continuous with the wall of the proximal tubule.

The filtered fluid must cross the capillary endothelium, the basement membrane, and the visceral epithelium of Bowman's capsule. The endothelial layer has gaps in it fenestrations, and is not a significant permeability barrier to molecules, only to blood cells. The major filtration barrier is the basement membrane. The visceral epithelial cells on the luminal side are not joined to form a simple sheet but instead are highly modified to form podocytes. Each podocyte, as shown in Fig. 5.1, has a compact cell body which stands away from the capillary and several long primary processes which are wrapped around the capillaries. The primary processes in turn have many branches called *pedicels* or foot processes. The pedicels from adjacent primary processes, which can belong to different cells, interdigitate to form a lattice of interleaved feet over the entire outer surface of the capillary. Filtration occurs through the basement membrane under the gaps between the feet (Fig. 5.2). This structure presents an area for transfer per unit area of wall which is much larger than is available in other capillaries. Presumably as a result of this larger fractional area for transfer, the filtration coefficient, i.e. the ratio of fluid flow per unit area to the net filtration pressure, is 50 to 100 times higher for glomerular capillaries than in any others.

There is an extensive literature on the site and nature of the permeability barrier between the capillaries and Bowman's space. The two principal properties which determine whether or not a molecule passes through are its size and charge. There is no selectivity among small molecules: all pass through so rapidly and/or are swept

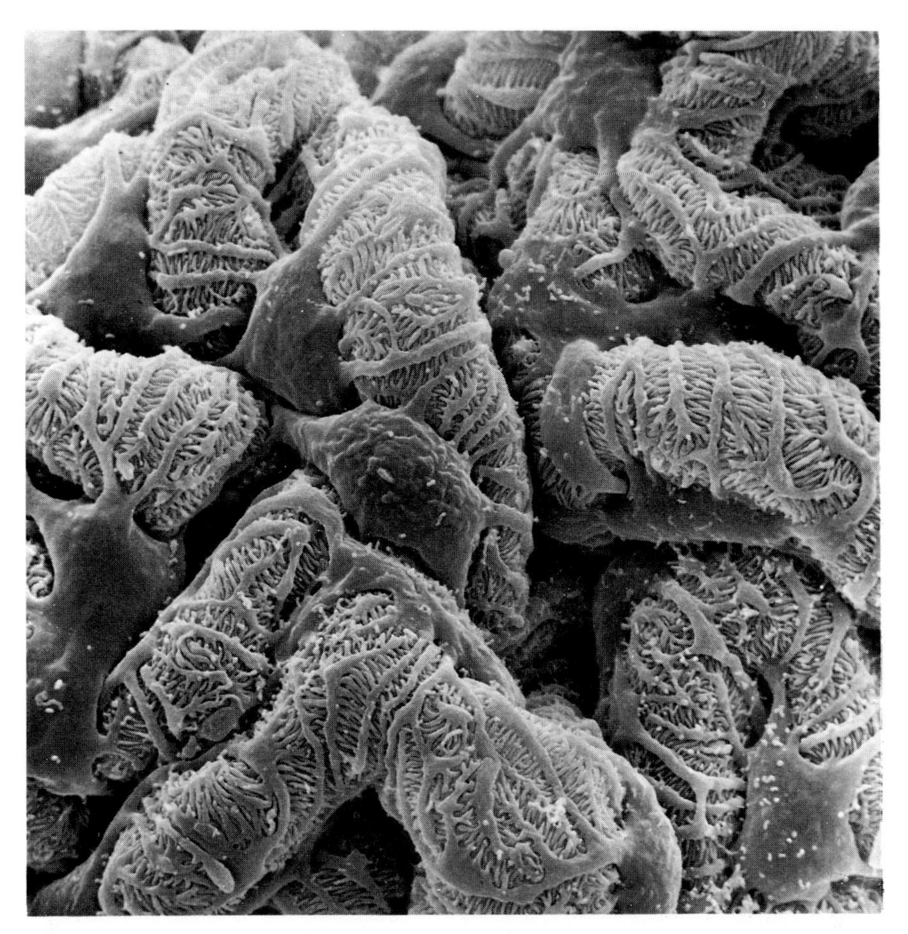

Fig. 5.1. Scanning electron micrograph of a glomerulus from a normal rat kidney. The processes of the podocytes are wrapped around the individual capillary loops. Adjacent processes can originate from different cells. Magnification 3300. (Reproduced from Tisher, C.C., 1981).

along by the water so readily that their concentrations in Bowman's space are at equilibrium with their concentrations in plasma. For larger neutral molecules the concentration in Bowman's space drops below equilibrium with plasma as the size increases. Inulin, molecular weight (MW) = 5200 and effective radius = 1.4 nm, passes freely, dextrans with radius about 3.0 nm are somewhat retarded, and dextrans with radius larger than about 4.0 nm hardly cross at all. For large molecules charge is also important. Serum albumins which carry a negative charge are hardly filtered, while positively charged markers such as a cationic DEAE dextran with the same effective radius cross into Bowman's space.

Most molecules which cannot permeate are not even able to enter the basement membrane. Some, particularly with positive charge, appear to enter the 'gel' which is continuous with the basement membrane and fills the gaps between the foot

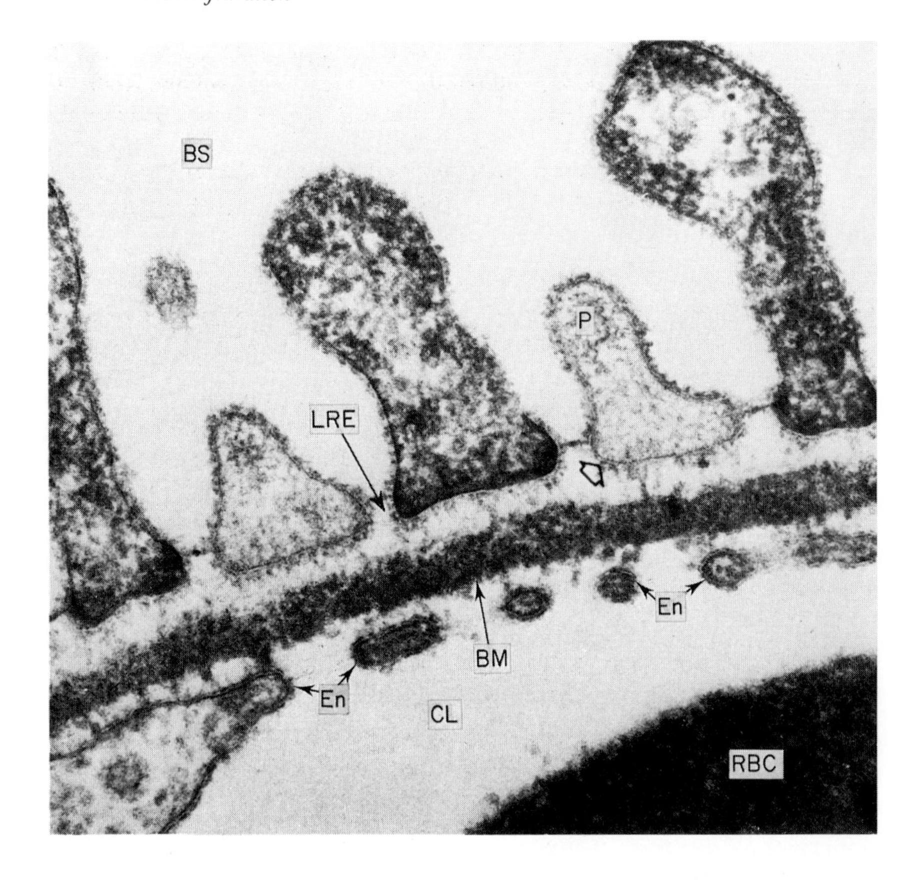

Fig. 5.2. Transverse section of the structures separating the blood from the glomerular filtrate. 'Reproduced with new labels from Tisher, C.C. (1981)'. BM Basement membrane, BS Bowman's space, CL capillary lumen, En capillary endothelium, LRE lamina rara externa, P pedicel, RBC red blood cell.

processes. There, however, they appear to stick to the gel. Molecules which pass the endothelial cell layer and then stick are eventually phagocytosed and removed. On the endothelial side of the basement membrane the cells responsible appear to be the mesangial cells.

The detailed properties of the permeability barrier are of some clinical interest since a break down of the selectivity of the barrier occurs in various disorders. For instance loss of fixed negative charge in the gel portion of the filtering membrane can reduce the permeability barrier to negatively charged macromolecules such as albumins. This seems often to be the basis of excessive filtration and urinary loss of albumin in nephrotic syndrome which is discussed in *Disorders of the Kidney and Urinary Tract*.

Factors determining GFR and filtration fraction

GFR, the sum of the filtration rates for all of the nephrons of both kidneys, is conventionally taken as 125 ml/min, and similarly renal plasma flow is 625 ml/min. Thus in the glomeruli one-fifth of the plasma volume is filtered across the capillary walls. Nearly all of this filtered fluid is reabsorbed into the peritubular capillaries as discussed on pp. 73ff.

The factors which affect filtration at any point along a glomerular capillary can be seen by inspection of the filtration equation.

$$J_v = k_f(\Delta P - \Delta\pi)$$

where J_v is the volume of fluid transferred per unit area of capillary wall, k_f is the filtration coefficient per unit area, ΔP is the difference in hydrostatic pressure across the capillary wall, and $\Delta\pi$ is the difference in colloid osmotic pressure. The colloid osmotic pressure in Bowman's space is negligible. The hydrostatic pressure there, determined by micropuncture, is about 10–15 mmHg. It varies with changes in GFR and hence tubular flow rate, because higher pressure is needed to drive faster flow, but the changes are usually small. Of more concern are the three remaining variables, the filtration coefficient and the hydrostatic and colloid osmotic pressures within the capillary.

Little is known about the control of the filtration coefficient in the intact animal. It can be altered by infusing acetylcholine, prostaglandins, bradykinin, and especially angiotensin II. Indeed except for acetylcholine the other agents may act by altering renin secretion and hence angiotensin II levels. The mesangial cells, which apparently are contractile, may be able to change the surface area available for filtration and are highly responsive to angiotensin.

The rate of glomerular filtration in a *single nephron* (SNGFR) is the aggregate of the filtration occurring at all points along the capillaries within its glomerular tuft and therefore it can be described by the following equation.

$$\text{SNGFR} = K_f(\overline{\Delta P} - \overline{\Delta\pi})$$

where K_f is the filtration coefficient for the glomerulus, $\overline{\Delta P}$ is the average difference in hydrostatic pressure across the capillary wall, and $\overline{\Delta\pi}$ is the average difference in colloid osmotic pressure. There is very little hydrostatic pressure drop along the glomerular capillaries, and ΔP can be taken as the same at all points, i.e. $\overline{\Delta P} = \Delta P$. However, the colloid osmotic pressure increases along each capillary as protein-free fluid is filtered. Thus the average difference in colloid osmotic pressure between glomerular capillary plasma and tubular fluid, $\overline{\Delta\pi}$, is larger than the arterial plasma colloid osmotic pressure.

The points discussed above can be indicated diagramatically as in Fig. 5.3. The upper panel shows what is thought to be the arrangement for the dog. In man values are less certain, but the capillary hydrostatic pressure may average about 60 mmHg. With a filtration fraction of $\frac{1}{5}$, the plasma colloid osmotic pressure rises from about 28 mmHg to somewhat more than 35 mmHg. (Colloid osmotic pressure rises more than proportionally with increasing plasma protein concentration.) The net filtration pressure thus falls by about one half by the end of the capillary.

Panel (b) to Fig. 5.3 indicates the arrangement found from direct measurements in the unusually accessible surface glomeruli of the Munich-Wistar strain of rats. In these glomeruli the capillary hydrostatic pressure is about 45 mmHg and the filtration coefficient several times larger than assumed for Fig. 5.3(a). Well before the

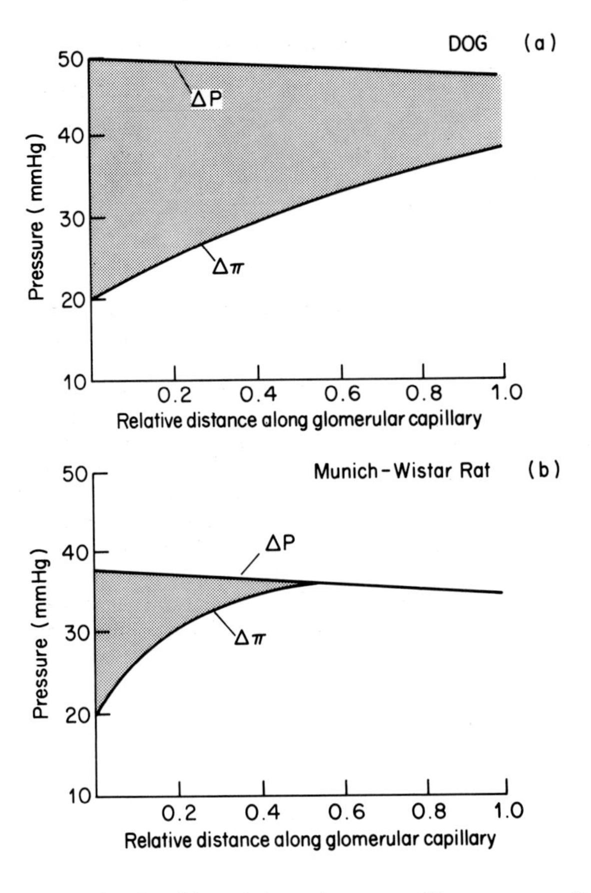

Fig. 5.3. Possible variations of pressure difference across the wall of a glomerular capillary. The height of shaded region gives the filtration pressure. $\Delta\pi$ rises as the plasma protein becomes concentrated by the filtration of almost protein-free fluid. Part (a) shows the arrangements through to operate in the dog kidney and in most other animals including man. Part (b) shows the arrangements found by direct measurement in the superficial glomeruli of a particular strain of rats. The arrangements in man are not known with certainty, but indirect evidence suggests that they are more like those in dogs than in Munich-Wistar rats. (Reproduced from Hall, J.E., 1982).

end of the capillary the increase in plasma colloid osmotic pressure reduces the net filtration to zero. No further filtration occurs along the remainder of the capillary. This condition is called *filtration equilibrium.*. The experimental evidence for filtration equilibrium in Munich-Wister rats is direct and convincing. However, data are available for more normal strains of rats and the evidence suggests that the arrangment in Fig. 5.3(a) applies. The evidence for dog, some types of monkey and man, though increasingly indirect, suggests that filtration equilibrium does not usually occur in those species.

Changes in the factors affecting GFR and filtration fraction

Table 5.1 summarizes the expected effects on glomerular filtration, renal blood flow, and filtration fraction produced by changes in any one of arterial blood pressure, arterial colloid osmotic pressure, afferent arteriolar resistance and efferent arteriolar resistance. Such independent changes are not seen *in vivo*, because changes in any one cause changes in the others. For instance increases in arterial pressure usually result in increases in afferent arteriolar resistance as discussed below.

For the glomerular conditions shown in Fig. 5.3(a) the changes in GFR can be predicted, approximately, from the changes produced in the hydrostatic and colloid osmotic pressures of plasma as it enters the glomerular capillaries. If instead the glomerular conditions are as shown in Fig. 5.3(b), i.e. filtration reaches equilibrium, then GFR also varies markedly with renal blood flow. Increases in renal blood flow tend to increase GFR even when the pressure at the beginning of the glomerular capillaries is constant. The cause of this effect can be understood by supposing that GFR remains constant when RBF is increased The filtration fraction would then fall and the colloid osmotic pressure would be less further along the capillary. As a consequence the driving force for filtration would be greater, and this would increase GFR. In fact GFR does increase and the filtration fraction decreases somewhat less than if GFR had been constant. This effect of RBF on GFR must occur when there is variation in the colloid osmotic pressure from one end of the capillary to the other. It is thus present in the conditions of Fig. 5.3(a) but very much more marked for those of Fig. 5.3(b).

Table 5.1

	GFR	RBF	F.F.
↑Arterial pressure	↑(↑↑#)	↑(↑)	→(↑)
↓Colloid osmotic pressure	↑*(↑*)	→(→)	↑(↑)
↑Afferent resistance	↓(↓↓#)	↓(↓)	↓(↓)
↑Efferent resistance	↑(→‡)	↓(↓)	↑(↑)
↑Total resistance	↘(↓)	↓(↓)	↑(→)

The expected effects of changes in arterial pressure, arterial colloid osmotic pressure, afferent resistance or efferent resistance while each of the others remains constant. Total resistance indicates an increase in both afferent and efferent resistances with their ratio held constant. For each entry the first arrows indicate the expectations based on Fig. 5.3(a), while the arrows within parentheses show the effects based on Fig. 5.3(b). ↑, increase, ↓, decrease; →, little change.

The double arrows indicate that GFR changes both as a result of the change in the initial glomerular hydrostatic capillary pressure (i.e. the pressure at the arterial end of the capillaries) and a change in renal blood flow.

‡ In the conditions of Fig. 5.3(b) when the efferent resistance is increased, the decreased RBF and increased initial glomerular capillary pressure have opposing effects on GFR.

* There is a suggestion that the filtration coefficient is decreased and that GFR remains almost constant.

Autoregulation and tubular-glomerular feedback

If GFR were allowed to vary greatly, it would be necessary to vary reabsorption over an equally wide range in order to avoid disastrous fluctuations in the excretion of water and solutes. In fact GFR is stabilized, and, in addition, reabsorption is adjusted in proportion to the filtered load. This adjustment, called glomerular-tubular balance is discussed in the next chapter. The stabilization of GFR is called autoregulation. When arterial blood pressure changes, GFR alters by much less than would occur if the other factors which control GFR remained constant. Autoregulation is observed in the intact animal and in isolated kidneys; it is a property of the kidney itself. Renal blood flow is also autoregulated over nearly the same range of pressures as shown in Fig. 5.4.

It is thought that over most of the range of arterial pressures, autoregulation is effected chiefly by control of muscle contraction in the afferent arterioles because like changes in arterial pressure changes in the afferent arteriolar resistance alter both blood flow and GFR in the same direction. Small changes in the efferent arteriolar resistance alter blood flow and GFR in opposite directions. There are two principal theories for how the changes in arteriolar resistances are brought about.

1. Increases in the pressure difference across the wall of the afferent arterioles are held to stimulate directly increased muscle contraction which reduces the diameter of the lumen (a 'myogenic' effect) and hence increases afferent arteriolar resistance to flow.

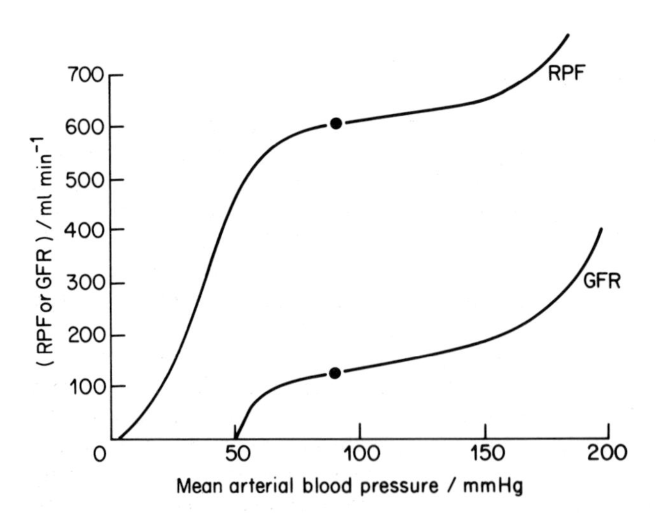

Fig. 5.4. Autoregulation of RPF and GFR in the face of changing arterial pressure. Filtration ceases at a pressure that still produces some blood flow, because no filtration is possible when glomerular capillary pressure falls below the sum of colloid osmotic pressure and tubular pressure. Note that the values shown here are merely illustrative. The actual, detailed changes in RPF and GFR following changes in blood pressure depend on the conditions in which the measurements are made and on the time elapsed after the change of pressure, usually 1 to 10 minutes.

2. Arteriolar contraction is influenced by delivery of fluid into the distal tubule which is thought to be monitored by the cells of the macula densa. Increases in the amount of sodium chloride reaching the macula densa lead to afferent arteriolar constriction. Decreases lead to afferent dilation and probably to efferent constriction. In this view the regulaton of blood flow and GFR is secondary to regulation of delivery of fluid for final processing by the distal tubule and collecting system.

It should be emphasized that the myogenic and tubular feedback theories are not mutually exclusive; probably both mechanisms operate. The experimental evidence for tubular-glomerular feedback is now compelling, but when tubular flow is blocked some autoregulation of blood flow is still observed.

The nature of the signal transmitted from the macula densa cells to the afferent arteriole is unknown, but prostaglandins are thought to play a part. Control of efferent constriction in response to changes at the macula densa may require release of renin and local formation of angiotensin. For further discussion see pp. 109–10.

There is evidence that the autoregulation of GFR takes precedence over that of RPF and that this precedence reflects tubular-glomerular feedback. For instance, tubular-glomerular feedback may explain the observation that when colloid osmotic pressure is increased (e.g. by infusion of albumin into the renal artery) GFR varies much less than renal plasma flow. The direct effects of increased colloid osmotic pressure are expected to be reduced GFR and increased peritubular reabsorption as described in the next chapter. These both reduce delivery of sodium chloride to the macula densa which stimulates afferent dilation. The net effect is that GFR is regulated back towards the normal value, while RPF is increased to above normal values.

Extrarenal factors which change GFR

Changes in glomerular filtration rate can be produced by a number of factors including changes in arterial blood pressure, colloid osmotic pressure, and increased activity in the renal nerves. However, the role of small changes in GFR in the physiological response to normal degrees of fluid excess or deficit is unknown. This is partly because measurements of GFR in humans are rarely sufficiently accurate to detect even 5–10 per cent changes in GFR which would have dramatic effects. With severe falls in arterial pressure both renal blood flow and glomerular filtration stop as indicated in Fig. 5.4.

Both sympathetic nerve activity, which releases noradrenaline, and circulating adrenaline produce afferent and efferent vasoconstriction. The efferent arteriole appears to be more responsive to adrenergic stimulation than the afferent. Moderate sympathetic activation can thus cause mainly efferent constriction and so maintain GFR while reducing blood flow, as is observed during sustained exercise. Strong sympathetic stimulaton can stop both blood flow and filtration, overriding the mechanisms normally responsible for autoregulation.

In dogs there are very large, up to two-fold, changes in GFR after a large meal. These are thought to be associated with the need to excrete nitrogenous waste products. The agents which produce the increase are unknown. The effects of eating on renal function in humans are not so dramatic, but changes in GFR have been reported. Their significance is presently obscure.

The detailed changes in GFR which follow changes in arterial colloid osmotic pressure in vivo are controversial as suggested in the legend to Table 5.1. The effects are apparently complicated by changes in filtration coefficient and in afferent and efferent arteriolar resistances (see p. 55). Yet a further factor is that a fall in colloid osmotic pressure produces swelling of the kidneys, just as of any other tissue (see Chapter 2) and the resulting increase in interstitial and tubular hydrostatic pressures may affect renal function (see pp. 74–75 & 110).

Redistribution of blood flow and GFR

The distribution of blood flow between superficial and juxtamedullary nephrons may be important in the control of sodium excretion. There are differences between nephrons with short or long loops of Henle. Thus even if GFR remains constant a shift of blood flow could divert glomerular filtration from nephrons with one reabsorptive capacity to those with another. However while redistribution appears to occur, there is little agreement on the physiological significance and in this book most emphasis has been put on factors which can affect filtration and reabsorption in a 'typical' nephron.

It is more likely that redistribution of blood flow may affect sodium excretion in another way. It has been proposed that raised arterial pressure or reduced plasma colloid osmotic pressure selectively increases medullary blood flow (see p. 102). This increased flow would lead to washout of sodium chloride and urea from the medullary core, and the decreased solute concentrations in the core would reduce sodium reabsorption in nephrons with long loops of Henle. In this proposal the selective decrease of sodium reabsorption in juxtamedullary nephrons (rather than the effects discussed on pp. 74ff) accounts for the observed natriuresis (see pp. 163–164).

Further reading

Brenner, B.M., Ichikawa, I. & Deen, W.M. (1981). Glomerular filtration. Chapter 6, pp. 289–327 in *The Kidney,* 2nd edn, Brenner, B.M. & Rector, F.C. Jr., eds, Saunders, Philadelphia.

Deen, W.M., Robertson, C.R. & Brenner, B.M. (1974). Glomerular ultrafiltration. *Fed. Proc.* **33**, 14–20.

Hall, J.E. (1982). Regulation of renal hemodynamics, pp. 243–321 in *Cardiovascular Physiology IV*, Guyton, A.C. & Hall, J.E.. eds, University Park Press, Baltimore.

Hollenberg, N.K. (1980). Angiotensin as a determinant of renal perfusion and function. Chapter 5, pp. 57–75 in *Captopril and Hypertension*, Case, D.B., Sonnenblick, E.H. & Laragh, J.H., eds, Plenum, N.Y.

Knox, F.G., Cuche, J.L., Ott, C.E., Diaz-Buxo, J.A. & Marchand, G. (1975). Regulation of glomerular filtration and proximal tubule reabsorption. *Circulation Res.* **36&37** (Sup. 1) 1–107 to 1–118.

Navar, L.G. (1978). The regulation of glomerular filtration rate in mammalian kidneys. Chapter 31, pp. 593–627 in *Physiology of Membrane Disorders*., Andreoli, T.E., Hoffman, J.F. & Fanestil, D.D., eds, Plenum, N.Y.

O'Connor, W.J. (1982). *Normal Renal Function*, Croom Helm, London, Chapter 2, pp. 13–45, Glomerular filtration rate.

Renkin, E.M. & Gilmore, J.P. (1973). Chapter 9, Glomerular filtration, pp. 185–248 in *Handbook of Physiology*, Section 8, Renal Physiology,

Orloff, J. & Berliner, R.W., eds. American Physiological Society, Washington, D.C.

Tisher, C.C. (1981). Anatomy of the Kidney, pp. 3–75 in *The Kidney*, 2nd ed. Brenner, B.M. & Rector, F.C. Jr. eds., Saunders, Philadelphia.

6

The transport functions of the proximal tubule

Structure

The proximal tubule is made up of flattened epithelial cells with a complex structure shown in Fig. 6.1. These are encased by a mechanically strong basement membrane which is in contact with the endothelial cells of the capillaries. The epithelial cells are joined to each other near the tubular lumen. This so called tight junction can be thought of as a collar which goes right round each cell, separating its plasma membrane into two distinct regions, the *luminal* (synonyms: apical or mucosal) membrane, and the *basolateral* (synonyms: serosal or peritubular) membrane. The luminal surface is highly folded into closely packed microvilli which together form a so-called brush border about 1 μm thick. The microvilli are so small and close together that they cannot be seen with a light microscope; the region appears as a blur. The serosal boundary

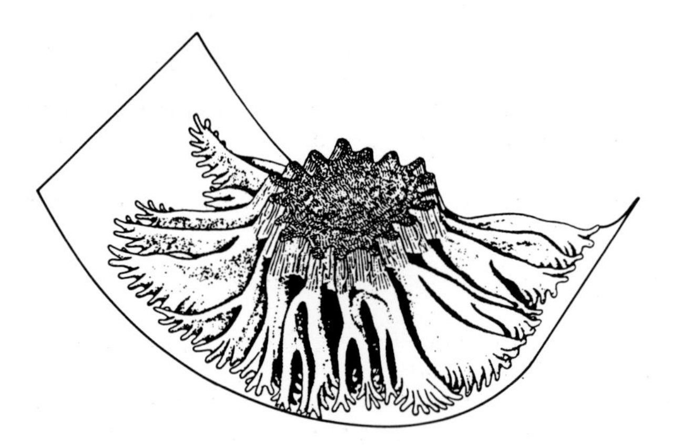

Fig. 6.1. The shape of a proximal tubular cell. Note the brush border on the luminal surface and the extensive folding of the lateral membranes. The distance between the luminal border and the base of the cell is about 6 microns. The lateral surfaces of other cells butt up against the lateral surface of the cell shown. The lateral space which remains between them is narrow, only about 100 mm wide, but it runs directly from the luminal to the basal surface. (Reproduced from Welling and Welling, 1976).

of each cell is also folded, but much less sharply curved. The resulting convolutions are, however, still very extensive (see Fig. 6.1) such that the total membrane areas of the two cell surfaces are similar. Each may be 10 times larger than the apparent area of the brush border seen in the light microscope. At the tight junctions the cell membranes of adjacent cells come into close contact to form a specialized structure. Over most of the remaining lateral surfaces the membranes remain separated by a distance of *c* 30 nm. However, even though the gap between the cells is quite narrow, the surfaces are so convuluted that the lateral spaces account for several percent of the volume of the cell layer. The large surface areas of the mucosal and serosal surfaces and the shape and size of the lateral spaces suggest that extensive transport occurs from the lumen into the cells and then into the lateral spaces.

The naming of tight junctions is unfortunate, for it is now clear that in epithelia which transport fluid isosmotically, such as those of the proximal tubule and the small intestine, the tight junctions are in fact leaky to small monovalent ions. In proximal tubules the evidence for this leakiness is largely electrical; the resistance between the lumen and the peritubular space is far lower than the resistance between the inside of the tubular cells and the outside. Thus current is able to cross the epithelium without going through the cells. The existence of this paracellular route has extremely important implications for the possible mechanisms of transport and this will be discussed below.

Basic scheme of transport

The overall function of the proximal tubule is indicated in Fig. 6.2. The glomerular filtrate is an isosmotic solution of sodium chloride and sodium bicarbonate which contains a large number of other solutes at low concentrations. Some of these solutes are valuable and need to be conserved, others are wastes to be excreted. As the filtrate passes along the proximal tubule roughly two-thirds of the sodium is reabsorbed with two-thirds of the chloride and bicarbonate (proportionately more bicarbonate than chloride). Since two-thirds of the water is also reabsorbed the total solute concentration remains nearly constant and the fluid remains isosmotic.

The reabsorption of sodium is primary and active. This is shown by a number of arguments.

1. Transport is abolished by cooling. In mammals even a drop from 37°C to 15°C stops reabsorption.
2. Replacement of sodium by any other cation, e.g. lithium, greatly reduces reabsorption of water and all other solutes.
3. Reabsorption continues at almost normal rates after substitution of chloride by various other anions; e.g. nitrate or perchlorate. Replacement of bicarbonate by other anions reduces reabsorption but by less than half.
4. When nontransported solutes, such as the monosaccharides mannitol and raffinose, are present in the lumen, the concentration of sodium chloride in the lumen beomes less than that in the plasma. By contrast the osmolality of luminal contents remains the same as that of the blood. Thus it follows that either sodium or chloride has been actively transported out of the lumen.

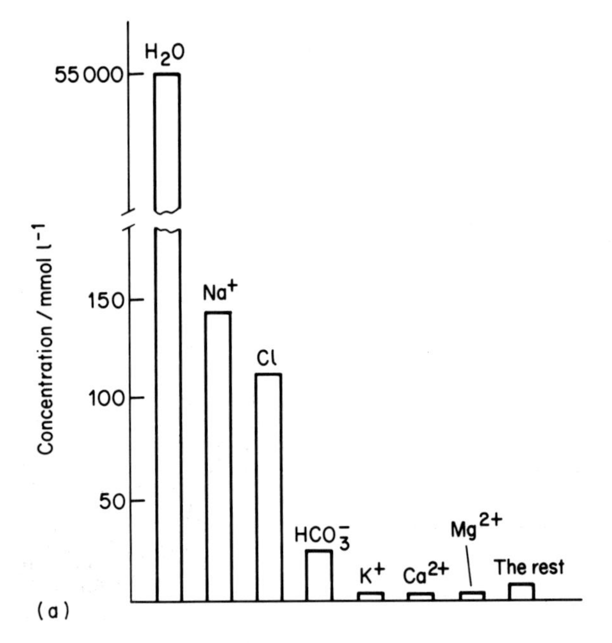

Concentration / mmol l⁻¹
55 000
150
100
50
H₂O
Na⁺
Cl
HCO₃⁻
K⁺
Ca²⁺
Mg²⁺
The rest
(a)

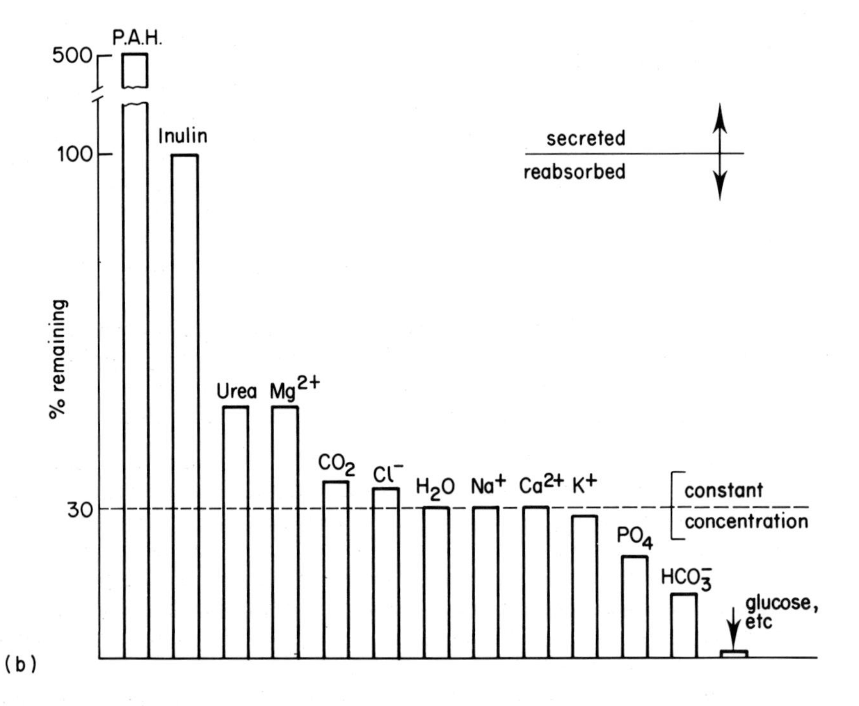

% remaining
500
100
30
P.A.H.
Inulin
Urea
Mg²⁺
CO₂
Cl⁻
H₂O
Na⁺
Ca²⁺
K⁺
PO₄
HCO₃⁻
glucose, etc
secreted
reabsorbed
constant concentration
(b)

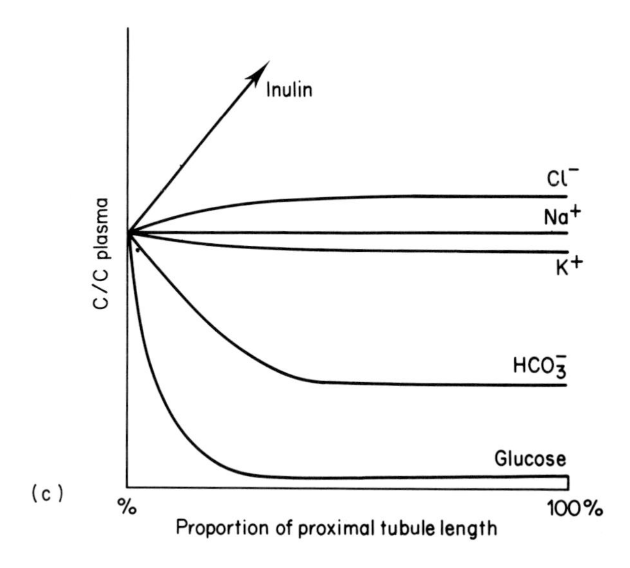

Fig. 6.2. The composition of proximal tubular fluid. In part (a) the load presented to the proximal tubule in the glomerular filtrate is indicated by the height of the vertical bars. Water is by far the most common substance. The three solutes, sodium, chloride and bicarbonate account for most of the osmolality. In part (b) the proportion of the amount filtered which remains in the tubular fluid at the end of the proximal tubule is indicated by the heights of the bars. These proportions are estimated for humans but based largely on animal data. Paraaminohippuric acid (PAH) and inulin are included, even though they are not normally present, as examples of substances which are actively secreted or not transported respectively. The variation of concentration with position along the tubule is shown for several substances in part (c). The concentration of sodium remains almost constant since sodium salts make up most of the osmolality of the fluid and water moves rapidly thus keeping the osmolality constant. The concentration of inulin rises since the amount of inulin is constant while the volume of fluid decreases. The concentrations of bicarbonate and glucose fall since these are avidly reabsorbed by specific transport mechanisms.

Water follows down whatever osmotic gradient is created by solute transport.

5. The epithelial cells have sodium pumps (the usual Na, K-ATPase) localized in the basolateral membranes. Inhibition of these sodium pumps by adding ouabain to or by deleting potassium from the peritubular medium greatly reduces reabsorption of sodium, water, and other substances.

The sodium pumps in the basolateral membranes use metabolic energy to keep the intracellular sodium concentration low. Sodium can thus enter the cells passively from the lumen. Most other active transport in the proximal tubule is now thought to be secondary to that of sodium. Thus glucose is transported uphill into the cell by a cotransporter which uses a sodium ion going downhill to provide the necessary energy. Similarly a large proportion of the secretion of hydrogen into the lumen occurs by tightly coupled sodium–hydrogen exchange across the luminal border.

All solutes which are lipid soluble and thus can easily penetrate lipid membranes will be reabsorbed in the same proportion as water. Their reabsorption occurs since the removal of fluid increases their concentration in the lumen, and the resulting concentration gradient drives their efflux. By contrast polar solutes larger than the common ions cannot readily cross the tubule wall unless there are special transport mechanisms. Glucose, amino acids and other desirable materials such as metabolic intermediates are strongly reabsorbed by specific transport processes and their concentrations in the tubular fluid are greatly reduced. Substances not reabsorbed, such as creatinine and inulin, become more concentrated.

The proximal tubule is also the site of secretion of many foreign and/or toxic compounds, particularly organic acids and bases. Provided these are not lipid soluble they are then trapped in the tubular fluid, concentrated along with other wastes, and excreted in the urine.

The proximal tubule determines the urine content of phosphate and sulphate. However, the excretion of water, potassium, calcium, magnesium and either acid or base is normally determined by how the distal tubule and collecting system handles the fluid delivered to it from the proximal tubule. The amount of sodium salts in the urine depends on the handling of the tubular fluid in all segments.

Transport of various substances

Glucose

The transport mechanism for glucose, the organic solute present at the highest concentration, is shown in Fig. 6.3. The glucose enters the cell via cotransport with sodium and leaves the cell across the serosal boundary using another specific transport system, which is not coupled to ion movement. Normally the sodium–glucose cotransport step is rate limiting. One sodium ion is transported for each glucose molecule and the net rate of glucose transport increases with the size of the inward gradient for sodium. For low concentrations of glucose the transport rate increases proportionally with glucose concentration, but at higher concentrations it approaches a limiting rate, i.e. the transport saturates.

The finding of a T_m for glucose (see Chapter 4) was the first evidence for the existence of a special glucose carrier. Later experiments have shown competition between sugars for transport which also presumably arises from competition for binding to the carriers. Thus a high concentration of either D-glucose or D-galactose reduces the transport of the other. By contrast L-glucose, fructose and mannose are not transported, and do not reduce the transport of D-glucose or D-galactose. Furthermore the transport of glucose can be specifically inhibited by phlorrhizin. Any remaining doubts that the glucose–sodium cotransporter exists have been eliminated by the successful reconstitution of sugar transport into lipid vesicles.

Amino acids and other valuable organic solutes

The mechanisms for transport of amino acids are similar to that for glucose. Entry of amino acids into the cell occurs by sodium linked cotransporters

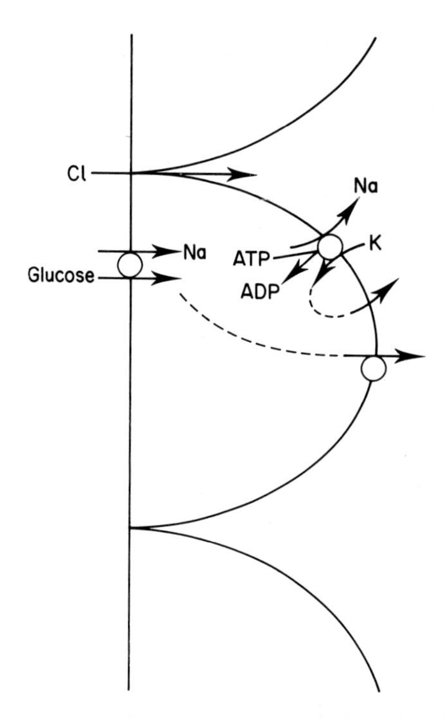

Fig. 6.3. The mechanism for glucose reabsorption in the proximal tubule. Glucose and sodium are both transported into the cell by a cotransporter present in the luminal membrane. Neither can enter via this transporter without the other. The sodium is pumped out of the cell on the basolateral side by the sodium pump. This keeps the intracellular sodium concentration low and the intracellular potential negative. Sodium entry on the luminal side is therefore down its electrochemical gradient. This downhill movement is used to drive the uphill movement of glucose into the cell. The glucose leaves the cell on the basolateral surface by a specific, but passive transport mechanism.

located in the mucosal membrane. Exit on the serosal side occurs by facilitated transport. There are several different carriers in the mucosal membrane, at the least, one for each of the following groups: neutral amino acids, e.g. phenylalanine and histidine; acidic amino acids, e.g. aspartic acid and glutamic acid; basic amino acids, e.g. lysine, ornithine, and arginine; imino acids and glycine.

Evidence for the existence of separate systems has been obtained from three sources.

1. The transport of an amino acid out of the lumen is reduced when another is added from the same group but not from a different group.
2. When one amino acid is present in the lumen at high concentration, the addition of a second produces further sodium transport and luminal potential changes if the second is from a different group, but not if it is from the same group.
3. There are genetic defects which affect one group and not the others (see *Disorders of the Kidney and Urinary Tract*)

Many other organic solutes, useful in the body, are also reabsorbed by sodium-coupled transport across the luminal membrane, e.g. pyruvate, lactate and many of the intermediates of the Kreb's cycle. As with glucose and the amino acids, the reabsorption of these substances occurs early in the proximal tubule. Under normal conditions the concentrations of these substances in the glomerular filtrate does not saturate the transport, but when plasma levels rise excessively reabsorption may not match the filtered load and some will be excreted in the urine. Important examples of such overflow are the excretion of lactate in lactic acidosis and of β-hydroxybutyrate in diabetic ketosis.

Proteins and polypeptides

Glomerular filtration produces an almost protein free tubular fluid, but even so more than 3 g/day of proteins and peptides enter the tubule. While this filtration is a significant route for eliminating biologically active (i.e. potentially toxic) materials from the blood (see Chapter 10), it also represents a large, undesirable loss of amino acids. The kidneys conserve the amino acids while eliminating the biological activity. Small peptides are apparently degraded to their constituent amino acids at the brush border and are then reabsorbed. Larger globular proteins are taken into the cells by endocytosis. Presumably there are binding sites on the cell surface which recognize that proteins are present and stimulate the formation of endocytotic vesicles. Once inside the cell the proteins are hydrolysed and the amino acids returned to the blood.

Secreted organic compounds

Organic acid secretion occurs primarily in the later, straight portions of the proximal tubule. The acids are transported into the cells actively from the interstitium and leave the cells into the lumen by facilitated transport.

The mechanism of the active transport step is still unclear. One possibility is co-transport with sodium. Another proposal is that the organic acids, which are very largely in the anionic form at plasma pH, are taken into the cell in exchange for chloride or bicarbonate. An ion exchanger with appropriate properties is known to exist in red blood cells. Like the organic acid secretion process, this exchanger (or possibly exchangers) transports acetate, lactate, ketomonocarboxylic acids, dicarboxylic acids, hippurate, and sulphonamides.

The secretion of organic bases has not been investigated in the same detail. It appears to occur primarily in the proximal convulated tubule and can handle various substances such as TEA (tetraethylammonium), methylguanidinium, morphine, and procaine.

The importance of these secretion processes in the elimination of toxic substances is discussed in Chapter 11. The thoroughness with which the proximal tubule secretes para-aminohippuric acid allows this substance to be used to measure renal blood flow as discussed in Chapter 4.

Uric acid

The urate anion is both secreted and reabsorbed and consequently its handling by the tubule is difficult to elucidate. Reabsorption is thought to occur both in the earliest and latest portions of the proximal tubule while secretion occurs in an intermediate zone. Secretion thus appears to occur in a different region of the tubule from the general acid secretion system, discussed above. The transporters involved in the movements of urate are unlikely to be highly selective since the transport can be altered by a large variety of substances which are transported by the epithelium, e.g. lactate and salicylate.

Under normal circumstances most of the urate filtered is reabsorbed, urate is added back to the tubular fluid further along and then a portion of that is reabsorbed. At low doses a number of substances, notably salicylate, inhibit the secretion without significantly affecting the reabsorption and thus they reduce urate excretion. At high doses, however, these substances appear to inhibit both secretion and reabsorption with the result that the filtered urate, which normally exceeds the amount secreted, is excreted. Thus the same inhibitor can produce opposite results on excretion at low and high doses. The renal handling of urate and its particular importance in humans is further discussed in Chapter 11.

Hydrogen and Bicarbonate

The kidneys are usually called upon to excrete an acidic urine and to adjust the amount of acid excreted in accordance with the amount produced in the body. The adjustment is best considered as a function of the distal tubule and collecting system. However, the hydrogen transport capacity of those regions would be swamped if the proximal tubule did not deliver a fluid from which most of the filtered bicarbonate had been removed. The consequence would be excretion of an alkaline urine rich in bicarbonate. Proximal reabsorption of most of the filtered bicarbonate is achieved by secretion of hydrogen ions as shown in Fig. 6.4.

Several experimental findings support hydrogen secretion as the mechanism of bicarbonate reabsorption:

1. Acid secretion adequate to account for bicarbonate reabsorption can be measured in proximal tubules perfused with bicarbonate-free phosphate buffered saline.
2. Proximal tubules reabsorb many other buffers with lipid soluble forms, some e.g. glycodiazine, as rapidly as they can reabsorb bicarbonate. The ability to reabsorb a variety of lipid soluble buffers, including bicarbonate (as carbon dioxide) is explained most simply by a hydrogen secretion mechanism.
3. In the presence of carbonic anhydrase inhibitors, the pH measured within the tubule during transport is more acid than that measured in the same fluid after it is withdrawn from the tubule. This so called disequilibrium pH is expected if hydrogen is then being secreted into the lumen more rapidly than the carbonic acid dissociates to CO_2 and H_2O.
4. Most of the H^+ secretion occurs by $Na^+ - H^+$ exchange. An exchange carrier with the appropriate properties has been studied in vesicles prepared from proximal tubule brush border. However, there is evidence that a portion, perhaps 20 per cent, of the hydrogen secretion occurs via a bicarbonate stimulated hydrogen pump, which is thought to be the main mechanism in the distal tubule (see Chapter 7).

Hydrogen ion secretion does not equal acid excretion

Most of the hydrogen secreted into the proximal tubule combines with bicar-

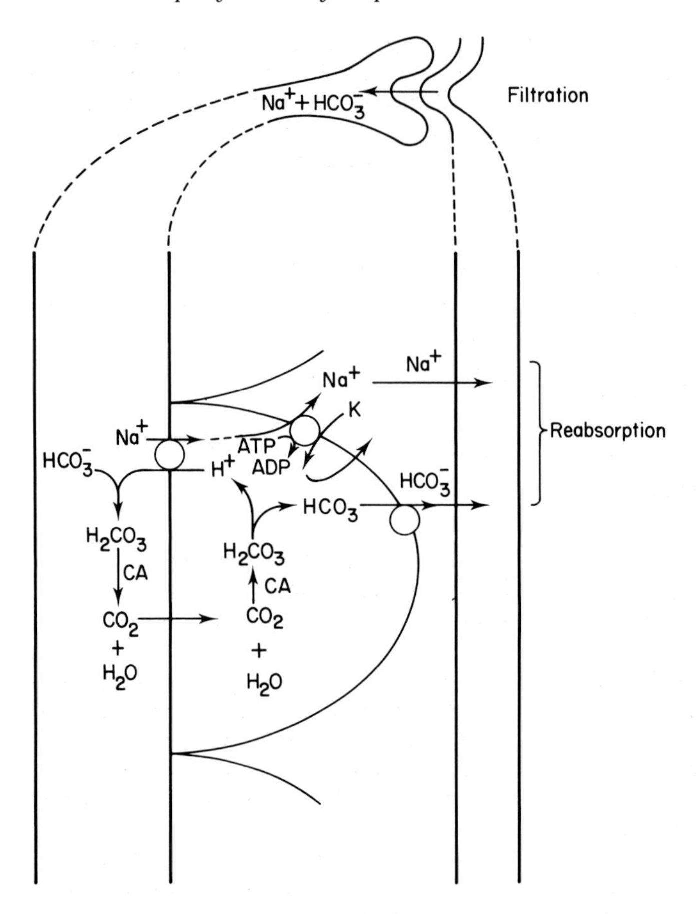

Fig. 6.4. The mechanism for bicarbonate reabsorption in the proximal tubule. Inside the cell the hydration of carbon dioxide to form carbonic acid is catalysed by intracellular carbonic anhydrase. The carbonic acid then dissociates to hydrogen ions and bicarbonate and the hydrogen is transported into the lumen by a sodium/hydrogen exchanger. Within the tubular lumen the hydrogen ions combine with bicarbonate to form carbonic acid which, catalysed by carbonic anhydrase at the mucosal membrane, dissociates to yield carbon dioxide and water. These can both diffuse across the cells to the blood. Bicarbonate generated within the cell leaves the cell via the basolateral membrane. The net result of all these steps is the reabsorption of sodium bicarbonate from the lumen. As expected from this scheme inhibition of carbonic anhydrase by acetazolamide greatly reduces the rate of bicarbonate reabsorption since the uncatalysed hydration of carbon dioxide to carbonic acid within the cell cannot keep pace with the normal rate of secretion of hydrogen.

bonate to form carbon dioxide which is reabsorbed. Thus these hydrogen ions serve merely to reabsorb the filtered bicarbonate from the lumen back into the blood. No net acid remains in the tubule for excretion as a result of this process! In the proximal tubule the bicarbonate concentration is reduced from about 25 to 10 mM while the volume of the fluid is reduced by about two-thirds. Thus only about 15 per cent of the filtered bicarbonate remains. By contrast a large amount of carbon dioxide has been formed within the tubule and thus its concentration has either risen or stayed the same. It follows that the fluid has become more acid (see Chapter 16). For this to have occurred a small proportion of the secreted hydrogen ions must have been used to titrate the other buffers in the fluid, mainly phosphate, from the initial pH of 7.4 to somewhat less than 7.1.

Factors that affect net proximal bicarbonate reabsorption

The principal factors currently thought to regulate net bicarbonate reabsorption are

1. the bicarbonate load in the tubule and hence luminal pH;
2. the pH in the peritubular blood.

In addition changes in

3. extracellular fluid volume;
4. plasma potassium concentration

can produce large changes in reabsorption. While changes in pCO_2 do change the rate of acid secretion and bicarbonate reabsorption, recent experiments have suggested that these effects are not direct, but rather are caused by changes in the pH of the blood and the filtered load of bicarbonate.

If the amount of bicarbonate entering the lumen is changed at constant peritubular pH, either by changing the plasma bicarbonate concentration or the glomerular filtration rate, tubular reabsorption changes in the same direction. Compared to a constant rate of reabsorption, this serves to stabilize the amount of bicarbonate delivered to the distal tubule. The fraction of filtered bicarbonate reabsorbed is increased as the peritubular pH is lowered and decreased by increasing peritubular pH. Bicarbonate reabsorption is virtually halted if, experimentally, this pH is raised to 8.2. For pH changes in the physiological range from roughly 7.2 to 7.6 these changes in reabsorption rates are smaller than those caused by variations in bicarbonate load.

The mechanisms by which the bicarbonate load and plasma pH influence hydrogen secretion are not certain. Increases in GFR presumably shift the decrease in luminal bicarbonate concentration farther along the tubule (see Fig. 6.2). Thus part of the explanation is that increases in load, whether caused by increased plasma concentration or increased GFR, raise the average bicarbonate concentration in the lumen and hence also luminal pH levels. These appear directly to increase the rate of sodium–hydrogen exchange by promoting the release of the hydrogen on the luminal side. Increased bicarbonate in the lumen will also reduce the net backfluxes of bicarbonate from the cells and through the tight junctions. Changes in peritubular pH presumably exert their effects by altering the pH inside the tubular cells.

In many older books (see e.g. Pitts, 1974) it is stated that there is an apparent T_m for bicarbonate, i.e. that increases in bicarbonate concentration do not increase bicarbonate reabsorption. Based upon this T_m it was concluded that the observed increase in bicarbonate reabsorption when plasma pCO_2, and hence also plasma bicarbonate concentration, are increased at constant pH must result from the increased pCO_2. However it is now known that, when plasma bicarbonate is raised at the expense of chloride by dialysis, no T_m is observed. Furthermore, in split drop and microperfusion experiments the reabsorption rate continues to increase as the bicarbonate concentration is raised from less than 10 mM to more than 50 mM. In peritubular capillary perfusion experiments where peritubular pH and pCO_2 can each be raised without changing tubular bicarbonate load, changes in pCO_2 at constant pH have virtually no effect on net proximal bicarbonate reabsorption. Thus at present there is little evidence for a direct effect of pCO_2.

Influences of extracellular fluid volume and plasma potassium concentration

Large increases (e.g. 30 per cent) in extracellular fluid (ECF) volume lead to markedly greater excretion of sodium bicarbonate. Large decreases (e.g. 15 per cent) in ECF volume completely stop its excretion. For ECF contraction less bicarbonate is filtered, since GFR is decreased, and a larger fraction of the filtered load is reabsorbed in the proximal tubule along with the increased fractional reabsorption of sodium (see pp. 72ff). Thus very little bicarbonate remains which can be excreted and the ability to excrete base is sacrificed in the face of the need to conserve sodium salts. The increase in the fraction of sodium reabsorbed in ECF contraction is considered briefly below. For ECF expansion it is widely believed, based largely on clearance data in dogs, that more bicarbonate is filtered and a smaller fraction is reabsorbed which leads to greatly enhanced delivery of sodium bicarbonate to the distal tubule and hence to bicarbonate excretion.

Increases in plasma potassium concentration lead to decreased bicarbonate reabsorption and vice versa. While the effect is clear and clinically important, the mechanism is not. It may reflect reciprocal changes in the intracellular content of potassium and buffered hydrogen ions.

Sodium and chloride

Sodium transport out of the proximal tubules is now thought to occur by four different types of mechanism.

1. Along with glucose, amino acids, and other substances, sodium can be transported electrogenically across the luminal membrane by specific cotransporters. While the entire proximal tubule is capable of this type of transport, the organic substances available for contransport are usually depleted in the first 5 to 10 per cent (1 to 2 mm) of its length. Sodium transport by this mechanism accounts for the negative potential of the early portion of the proximal tubule.
2. Sodium can enter the cells by neutral transport mechanisms which neither carry current across the apical membrane nor contribute directly to the potential of the lumen. One mechanism for electrically neutral transport of sodium across the luminal membrane is the sodium–hydrogen exchanger. It is unclear whether or not any others account for a significant proportion of sodium reabsorption.
3. In the proximal straight tubules of some nephrons, sodium appears to enter the cells alone. This mechanism removes positive charge from the lumen which tends to make it negative.

4. Sodium can move passively through the tight junctions and lateral spaces. In regions of the proximal tubule where the lumen has a positive potential (see below) this movement contributes to net sodium reabsorption.

Estimates of the proportion of proximal sodium reabsorption occurring by these mechanisms are roughly 10 per cent, 30–60 per cent, 5–10 per cent and 25–50 per cent respectively. Sodium which enters the cells by whatever means, is pumped out across the peritubular border by the sodium pump. This pump is the link between metabolic energy and the work of transport. Bicarbonate and chloride which have entered the cell leave it passively.

In most, probably all, mammalian species bicarbonate is reabsorbed proportionately faster than chloride and since water isosmotically follows solute, the chloride concentration in the lumen increases slightly while bicarbonate concentration falls. Typically the concentration of chloride rises from 115 mM to 132 mM and that for bicarbonate falls from 25 mM to 10 mM. The creation of concentration gradients of chloride and bicarbonate between lumen and blood has important consequences for sodium chloride reabsorption since chloride can now diffuse down its concentration gradient out of the lumen, through the tight junction, and into the peritubular space. This movement of negative charge out of the lumen leaves the lumen positive. This positive potential difference represents a driving force for the efflux of sodium through the tight junctions.

Reabsorption of sodium through the cells is inherently wasteful. The objective is to transfer sodium salts from one side of the epithelium to the other. Since there is little electrical or concentration gradient between the lumen and the blood, little energy should be needed for the transport provided a means can be found for it to occur. When sodium is reabsorbed through the cells, it enters them passively, a process which dissipates energy. Metabolic energy is then needed to pump it out on the basolateral side up steep concentration and potential gradients. This pumping is expensive in terms of ATP. Indeed the entire O_2 consumption of the kidneys would barely be adequate for the synthesis of enough ATP to pump all of the sodium reabsorbed in the proximal tubules alone. However, by reabsorbing sodium bicarbonate and then using the chloride and bicarbonate concentration gradients thus produced to transport sodium chloride, the sodium ions transported through the cell at full ATP cost are used to persuade others to cross for free via the tight junctions. The more salt which leaves the lumen via the tight junctions the less energy needed for the transport of salt and water. This reduction in energy cost may well be the reason why the tight junctions are leaky in epithelia which transport fluid isosmotically.

Water

Since the fluid reabsorbed in the proximal tubule has the same osmolality as plasma, it is widely accepted that the mechanism of water transport involves osmotic equilibration across the tubule. Solute transport produces a gradient of total solute concentration and thus a concentration gradient of water in the opposite direction. Water then moves passively down this gradient.

It is established beyond doubt that water movement in mammalian kidneys is passive and that its net transport is secondary to the active transport of sodium chloride, sodium bicarbonate and the cotransported organic substances. A convincing demonstration that water follows solute is seen when tubules are filled or perfused with fluids containing nontransported monosaccharides, e.g. mannitol or raffinose (see Fig. 6.5). With 50 mM mannitol and hence only about 125 mM sodium initially in the lumen, sodium salts are reabsorbed accompanied by water to maintain osmotic equilibrium. Since mannitol does not leave the tubule, its concentration rises while that of sodium falls. This fall increases the inward gradient for sodium and thus the leak of sodium into the lumen. The process continues until pumping and leak come into balance with a concentration difference across the tubular wall, in this example, of 45 mM. Note that with an impermeant solute to retain water in the lumen, reabsorption of both water and salt is greatly decreased. If isosmotic mannitol is placed in the lumen there is a net flux of sodium salts into the lumen until pump and leak balance when the sodium concentration reaches the same value as in the preceding example. The net inward movement of solutes is accompanied by a net inward movement of water. Thus water follows the solute, whichever way the solute moves.

Coupling of water to solute transport

The site and nature of the coupling between the solute and water flow have not been definitely identified and are still the subjects of much research. Three osmotic mechanisms have been proposed.

1. Removal of sodium salts actually does make the lumen slightly but adequately hypo-osmotic relative to the serosal medium and this hypo-osmolality drives water flow across the epithelium either via the cells or the tight junctions. Since the proximal tubule has a very high water permeability, a small osmotic difference would be adequate.
2. Water flow across the tight junctions is driven by an effective osmotic pressure difference resulting from the different compositions of the solutions on either side. The peritubular medium contains bicarbonate, chloride, and organic solutes at the concentrations in plasma. The concentrations of bicarbonate, glucose, amino acids, etc. in the tubules are reduced after the first few millimetres while that of chloride is higher. Since the tight junctions are more permeable to chloride than to these other solutes, chloride will be less effective osmotically in producing water flow via that route and the net effect will be a driving force for outward water flow.
3. Salt pumping from the lumen through the cells into the small volume of the lateral spaces makes these slightly hyperosmotic and this hyperosmolality drives water flow from the lumen into the lateral spaces via the cells and possibly the tight junctions. However, in this 'standing gradient hypothesis' the lateral spaces must be long enough to prevent the hyperosmolality being dissipated by diffusion. Because the proximal tubular epithelium is very thin, this standing gradient mechanism is unlikely to be operating.

The route that water takes through the tubule is still uncertain. The water permeability of the tight junctions calculated from the measured permeability to other small solutes is less than the measured permeability for the tubular wall. While this argument is by no means compelling, the result is consistent with the vastly greater area available for transfer of water across the apical membrane compared to the tight junctions, and suggests that much of the water passes through the cells.

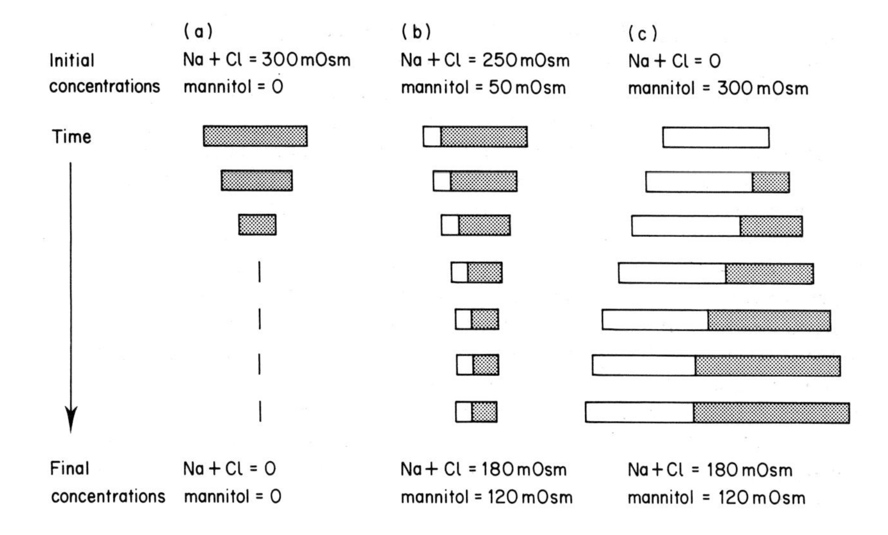

Fig. 6.5. The experimental demonstration using a split oil drop that sodium chloride transport is active and water transport passive in the proximal tubule. The total length of each bar is proportional to the length of the aqueous drop between two plugs of castor oil and hence to both the volume and total solute content of the drop. The contents are always isosmotic with plasma. The change in sodium chloride content and concentration for the same initial volume of various sodium chloride + mannitol solutions. The length of the shaded portion is proportional to the sodium chloride content, that of the plain portion to the mannitol content. In all columns with a patent lumen, the final sodium chloride concentration is $\frac{3}{5}$ that in plasma (150 mM) since at a concentration difference of about 60 mM the inward flux driven by the concentration gradient just balances the outward active transport. (a) Pure sodium chloride (150 mM, 300 mOsm) inside. There is no concentration difference for sodium chloride and so no backleak occurs. The pumping rate progressively reduces the amount of sodium chloride in the lumen and since water follows, the volume decreases proportionally and the concentration remains constant. The tubule eventually collapses, empty. (b) Sodium chloride initially 125 mM, mannitol 50 mM (300 mOsm total). There is now an inward gradient and passive flux so the net (active and passive) flux is smaller and the volume change is slower. Now as sodium chloride is pumped out, and water follows, the mannitol concentration increases and that of sodium chloride falls until the net flux of sodium chloride becomes zero. The sodium chloride content and volume are then stable. (c) Sodium chloride initially zero, and mannitol 300 mM. The passive influx of sodium chloride now exceeds the outward pumping rate, thus the drop expands. As it does so the sodium chloride concentration rises while that of mannitol falls. The final concentrations are the same as in (b), but the volume is greater in proportion to the increased amount of mannitol.

Potassium

The potassium concentration within the proximal tubule is normally slightly below that of plasma which is consistent with either active or passive transport. Normally about one-quarter of the filtered potassium is delivered to the distal tubule.

In split drop experiments with impermeant solutes (see e.g. Fig. 6.5) the tubule maintains lower concentrations of sodium, chloride, bicarbonate and potassium in the lumen than in plasma. Thus there appears to be a component of active potassium transport out of the tubule. Further evidence supporting the presence of some active reabsorption is that acetazolamide reduces the reabsorptions of sodium, bicarbonate, chloride and water but not that of potassium.

Phosphate

Phosphate is present in the tubule primarily in two forms: monohydrogen phosphate which carries two negative charges, and dihydrogen phosphate which carries one negative charge. These together are usually referred to as inorganic phosphate or often just as phosphate. Phosphate reabsorption occurs primarily in the proximal tubule and is active. It is thought to occur via sodium–phosphate cotransport across the brush border and facilitated passive transport of phosphate out of the cells into the capillaries. The transport system for phosphate normally operates near its maximum capacity. This is the basis of the overflow control of phosphate discussed in Chapter 12.

Parathyroid hormone lowers the transport capacity of proximal tubules for phosphate. The mechanism is unknown, but the effects are mediated by an increase in intracellular levels of c–AMP. In the early proximal tubule, parathyroid hormone acting via c–AMP depresses reabsorption of water and all solutes. The decrease in phosphate reabsorption in this region appears to be secondary to the decrease in net sodium and water transport since it also occurs in response to extracellular fluid expansion. However, in the later portions of the proximal tubule parathyroid hormone appears to have a specific effect, still via c–AMP, on phosphate transport.

Calcium and magnesium

In the proximal tubule calcium appears to be reabsorbed passively via the tight junctions. The proportion of filtered calcium reabsorbed thus varies together with the proportion of fluid reabsorbed. Because of this, the delivery of calcium to the distal nephron will change whenever the proximal reabsorption of sodium and fluid is altered. This finding largely explains the observation that calcium excretion can be increased by administering a sodium load.

It is not certain that all the calcium reabsorption is passive. Calcium in both the lumen and the peritubular fluid is partly free and partly complexed, e.g. with citrate. In plasma and in peritubular fluid some is also bound to macromolecules. Thus the electrochemical gradient for calcium cannot easily be calculated and it has not yet been measured. Any calcium which crosses the epithelium by entering the cells must be pumped out across the basolateral membrane.

The tight junctions appear to be poorly permeable to magnesium, and only a little is reabsorbed in the proximal tubule. Thus its concentration in the tubule increases by more than 50 per cent as fluid is reabsorbed. The magnesium transport that does occur is presumably by passive entry across the luminal membrane and active transport out of the cell into the peritubular space.

Urea

Renal handling of urea is discussed in Chapters 8 and 11. In the proximal convoluted tubule somewhat less than two-thirds of the quantity filtered is reabsorbed passively. In the proximal straight tubule and/or the thin descending loops of Henle from superficial nephrons, urea appears to be transported into the tubule, also passively. It has been suggested that the source of this urea is the capillary network emerging from the medulla.

Fluid absorption into the peritubular capillaries and lymphatics

The peritubular capillaries, like those in most other tissues, have a layer of endothelial cells jacketed by a thin basement membrane. Absorption of fluid into these capillaries is favoured by the large total surface area and a large net inward pressure gradient. While renal interstitial protein concentration and the peritubular capillary hydrostatic pressure are nearly normal, the protein concentration in the plasma leaving the glomeruli is about 20 per cent higher than that in arterial blood, because a virtually protein free fluid has been removed as the filtrate. Furthermore the interstitial fluid pressure is a few millimetres of mercury positive in contrast to the negative value in many other tissues (see p. 14). This positive pressure is generated by the active transport of fluid from the tubules into the interstitium. The kidneys do not blow up because they are enclosed in strong fibrous capsules. In life they are turgid, i.e. the total tissue pressure is also several millimetres of mercury positive.

Renal lymph flow is about 1 per cent of the rate of fluid reabsorption from the tubules. This lymph-flow is essential to remove plasma proteins from the interstitium as they leak out of the capillaries (see p. 16).

Factors influencing the amount of fluid reabsorbed

Altering extracellular fluid volume changes the excretion of sodium in an intact animal (see Chapter 14). The effects are indirect following changes in other factors such as arterial blood pressure, arterial colloid osmotic pressure, central venous pressure, activity in the renal nerves, and the levels of hormones such as aldosterone and angiotensin II. Aldosterone acts in the distal tubule. The other known factors can affect proximal sodium reabsorption.

Parathyroid hormone reduces sodium reabsorption (see p. 72), but this effect is unlikely to be part of normal control because its levels are determined largely by plasma calcium concentrations

Angiotensin

Small increases in angiotensin II concentration promote proximal sodium reabsorption. There appear to be two mechanisms. Firstly angiotensin constricts the afferent and efferent arterioles decreasing the renal plasma flow and increasing the filtration fraction. The increased filtration fraction is thought to increase reabsorption as considered in the next section. Secondly angiotensin appears to act directly on proximal tubule cells. The mechanism and importance of this direct effect are unknown. Higher levels of angiotensin constrict arterioles throughout the body and can increase arterial pressure to the point that the effects of the increased pressure overshadow the local actions of angiotensin and sodium excretion is increased (a pressure natriuresis).

Peritubular capillary colloid osmotic and hydrostatic pressures

Gradients of colloid osmotic pressure and hydrostatic pressure do not provide the driving force for reabsorption of fluid across the epithelial layer, but these pressures may nevertheless be important. Experimental changes in renal artery pressure and plasma protein concentration change the rate of fluid reabsorption and, in vivo, similar changes may be important in glomerular-tubular balance and in tubular responses to acute changes in extracellular fluid volume. The mechanisms have not been established. However, whenever the protein concentration in the capillaries is reduced or the capillary hydrostatic pressure is increased, fluid will accumulate in the interstitial spaces, interstitial hydrostatic pressure will increase, renal lymph flow will increase, and interstitial protein concentration and colloid osmotic pressure will decrease (see p. 16). It has been proposed that the increased interstitial volume and hydrostatic pressure make the tight junctions more leaky to solutes such as glucose and bicarbonate. Increased backleaks of these substances would dissipate their gradients and thus a part of the driving force for fluid reabsorption. In addition, though the mechanism is unknown, reabsorption of fluid by isolated perfused rabbit proximal tubules is suppressed by a decrease in the concentration of plasma proteins in the bathing medium.

The hypothesis that reabsorption from the lumen is driven by gradients of hydrostatic and colloid osmotic pressure is disproved experimentally by the observation that addition of enough colloid to the lumen to abolish any such driving force has virtually no effect on fluid reabsorption. Water movement across the tubule wall is driven by the gradients of all the solutes which are poorly permeant, not just the gradient of the colloid. If a gradient of colloid osmotic pressure or hydrostatic pressure is applied across the wall, water will initially flow, but this will rapidly dilute the small solutes at one surface of the membrane and concentrate those at the other. Since these solutes are present at high concentration, very little water flow is needed to induce an osmotic gradient sufficient to bring the water flow almost to a stop. Thus rapid flow of water and small solutes across the tubular epithelium cannot be driven by the Starling mechanism. Instead the solutes are transported first and the water follows. The means used have been discussed in the preceding sections.

By contrast to the tubular wall, the capillary wall is highly permeable to small solutes. Thus they can be transported into the capillaries with such small concentration gradients that they do not prevent fluid movement driven by the hydrostatic and colloid osmotic pressure differences.

To summarize, fluid movement from the interstitium into the capillaries is controlled by the differences across the capillary wall of the concentration of the colloids and the hydrostatic pressure. Fluid movement out of the lumen into the interstitium is driven by the differences across the tubule wall of the concentrations of all solutes, but the permeability and hence the rate of movement depend in some manner on the hydrostatic pressure and possibly the colloid osmotic pressure in the interstitial spaces. The interstitial pressures will come to values which make the two flows equal.

The account just given of the control of proximal sodium reabsorption is based on results from several independent laboratories. There are, however, other groups who have found from peritubular capillary perfusion experiments that changes in the colloid osmotic pressure of the perfusion fluid do not affect reabsorption from the tubules. The subject remains controversial (see p. 56).

Bicarbonate concentration

The passive reabsorption of sodium chloride depends on the size of the bicarbonate concentration gradient across the tubular wall. If the bicarbonate concentration in plasma is low, this gradient becomes smaller which reduces sodium chloride reabsorption. This inhibition will promote diuresis and natriuresis and hence extracellular fluid contraction as seen in both metabolic acidosis (i.e. when plasma pH and bicarbonate concentration are both low) and respiratory alkalosis (plasma pH high, plasma bicarbonate low).

Glomerular-tubular balance

Alterations in glomerular filtration rate change the amount of solutes and water presented for absorption per unit time in the proximal tubule. Furthermore, single nephron filtration rates vary widely between nephrons. For water and many solutes, e.g. glucose, phosphate, potassium, calcium, bicarbonate, chloride, and sodium, the rate of reabsorption in mammals is somehow altered in proportion to changes in GFR. As shown in Fig. 6.6 reabsorption of a constant proportion of the filtrate rather than a constant amount leads to smaller changes in the amount delivered to the distal tubule.

There are two types of mechanism which may contribute to glomerular-tubular balance. Firstly, either the increased rate of flow of tubular fluid or the increased delivery to the tubule of some substance caused by increased GFR may somehow increase reabsorption. Close balance might be achieved if proximal reabsorption were especially sensitive to the concentration within the tubule of some as yet unidentified filterable component of plasma or to a substance added to the filtrate in the glomerulus. This possibility is the most attractive explanation for some experimental observations. When part of the flowing tubular fluid is collected early in the proximal tubule using one micropipette and the rest collected more distally using another, the rate of reabsorption between the two pipettes increases with the fluid flow in that segment.

The second type of explanation holds that physiological glomerular-tubular balance is a consequence of changes occurring in the peritubular capillaries and interstitial spaces. Increases in GFR are often associated with increases in filtration fraction. An increase in filtration fraction implies an increased concentration of plasma protein in the peritubular capillaries, i.e. an increase in the colloid osmotic pressure. As noted earlier, an increase in plasma colloid osmotic pressure is thought to favour net movement of fluid out of the tubule which would contribute to glomerular-tubular balance.

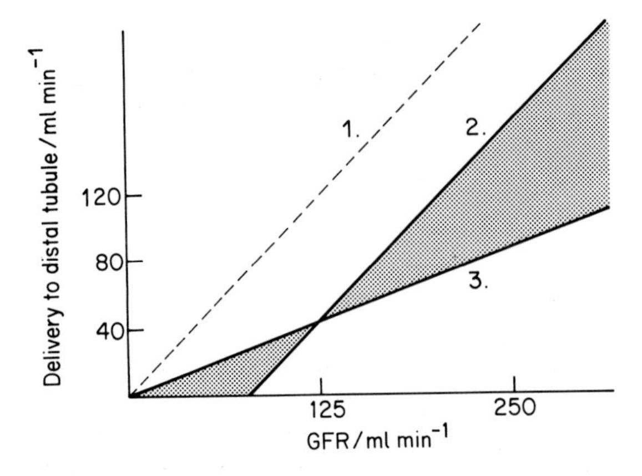

Fig. 6.6. Changes in delivery of fluid to the distal tubule assuming 1. no proximal reabsorption; 2. constant reabsorption of 80 ml/min in the proximal tubule; 3. proximal reabsorption proportional to GFR, i.e. with glomerular-tubular balance. For a change in GFR of 5 per cent from normal, distal delivery changes by 15 per cent for constant reabsorption, but by only 5 per cent for proportional reabsorption. Thus glomerular–tubular balance greatly reduces fluctuations in the delivery of sodium chloride and water to the distal tubule.

Further reading

Alpern, R.J., Cogan, M.G. & Rector, F.C. Jr. (1983). Effects of extracellular fluid volume and plasma bicarbonate concentration on proximal acidification in the rat. *J. Clin. Invest.* **71**, 736–746.

Andreoli, T.E. & Schafer, J.A. (1979). Effective luminal hypotonicity: the driving force for isotonic proximal tubular fluid absorption. *Am. J. Physiol.* **236**, F89–F96.

Bartoli, E., Conger, J.D. & Earley, L.E. (1973). Effect of intraluminal flow on proximal tubular reabsorption. *J. Clin. Invest.* **52**, 843–49.

Burg, M.B. (1981). Renal handling of sodium, chloride, water, amino acids and glucose. Chapter 7, pp. 328–370 in *The Kidney*, 2nd edn, Brenner, B.M. & Rector, F.C. Jr., eds, Saunders, Philadelphia. (An authoritative review which provides an excellent starting point for further reading.)

Chan, Y.L., Biagi, B. & Giebisch, G. (1984). Control mechanisms of bicarbonate transport across the rat proximal convoluted tubule. *Am. J. Physiol,* **242**, F532–F543.

Chonko, A.M. & Grantham, J.J. (1981). Disorders of urate metabolism and excretion. Chapter 20, pp. 1023–1055 in *The Kidney,* 2nd edn, Brenner, B.M. & Rector, F.C. Jr., eds, Saunders, Philadelphia.

DeWardener, H.E. (1978). The control of sodium excretion. *Am. J. Physiol.* **235**, F163–F173.

Frömter, E. (1979). Solute transport across epithelia: What can we learn from micropuncture studies on kidney tubules? *J. Physiol.* **288**, 1–31.

Giebisch, G. (1978). The proximal nephron. Chapter 32, pp. 629–660 in *Physiology of Membrane Disorders*, Andreoli, T.E., Hoffman, J.F. & Fanestil, D.D., eds, Plenum, N.Y.

Giebisch, G., Malnic, G. & Berliner, R.W. (1981). Renal transport and control of potassium excretion. Chapter 9, pp. 408–439 in *The Kidney*, 2nd ed, Brenner, B.M. & Rector, F.C. Jr., eds, Saunders, Philadelphia.

Hesse, I.F.A. & Johns, E.J. (1984). The subtype of α-adrenoceptor involved in the neural control of renal tubular sodium reabsorption in the rabbit. *J. Physiol.* **352**, 527–538.

Irish, J.M. III & Grantham, J.J. (1981). Renal handling of organic anions and cations. Chapter 13, pp. 619–649 in *The Kidney*, 2nd edn, Brenner, B.M. & Rector, F.C. Jr., eds, Saunders, Philadelphia.

Kinne, R. (1979). Metabolic correlates of tubular transport. Chapter 11, pp. 529–562 in *Membrane Transport in Biology Vols. IVA & IVB, Transport Organs*. Giebisch, G. ed, Springer-Verlag, Berlin.

Koeppen, B., Giebisch, G. & Malnic, G. (1985). Mechanism and regulation of renal tubular acidification pp. 1491–1525. In Chapter 65, *The Kidney. Physiology and Pathology*, Seldin, D.W. & Giebisch, G. eds, Raven, N.Y.

Malnic, G. & Giebisch, G. (1979). Cellular aspects of renal tubular acidification. Chapter 6, pp. 299–355 in *Membrane Transport in Biology, Vols, IVA & IVB, Transport Organs*. Giebisch, G. ed, Springer-Verlag, Berlin.

Rector, F.C. Jr. (1983). Sodium, bicarbonate, and chloride absorption by the proximal tubule. *Am. J. Physiol.* **244**, F461–F471. (This Homer Smith award lecture contains the opinion of one of the most influential investigators.)

Sasaki, S., Berry, C.A. & Rector, F.C. Jr. (1982). Effect of luminal and peritubular HCO_3^- concentrations and pCO_2 on HCO_3^- reabsorption in rabbit proximal convoluted tubules perfused in vitro. *J. Clin. Invest.* **70**, 639–649.

Silbernagl, S., Foulkes, E.C. & Deetjen, P. (1975). Renal transport of amino acids. *Rev. Physiol. Biochem, Pharmacol.* **74**, 105–167.

Stein, J.H., Lameire, N.H. & Earley, L.E. (1978). Renal hemodynamic factors and the regulation of sodium excretion. Chapter 36, pp. 739–772 in *Physiology of Membrane Disorders*., Andreoli, T.E., Hoffman, J.F. & Fanestil, D.D., eds. Plenum, N.Y.

Sutton, R.A.L. & Dirks, J.H. (1981). Renal handling of calcium, phosphate, and magnesium. Chapter 12, pp. 551–618 in *The Kidney*, 2nd ed, Brenner, B.M. & Rector, F.C. Jr., eds, Saunders, Philadelphia.

Ullrich, K.J. (1979). Renal transport of organic solutes. Chapter 8, pp. 413–448 in *Membrane Transport in Biology, Vols, IVA & IVB, Transport Organs*. Giebisch, G. ed, Springer-Verlag, Berlin.

Warnock, D.G. & Eveloff, J. (1982). NaCl entry mechanisms in the luminal membrane of the renal tubule. *Am. J. Physiol.* **242**, F561–F574.

Warnock, D.G. & Rector, F.C. Jr. (1981). Renal acidification mechanisms. Chapter 10, pp. 440–494 in *The Kidney*, 2nd ed, Brenner, B.M. & Rector, F.C. Jr., eds, Saunders, Philadelphia.

Welling, L.W. & Welling, D.J. (1976). Shape of epithelial cells and intercellular channels in the rabbit proximal nephron. *Kidney International* **9**, 385–394.

Windhager, E.E. & Giebisch, G. (1976). Proximal sodium and fluid transport, *Kidney International* **9**, 121–133.

7

The transport functions of the distal tubule and the collecting system

Structure

The distal tubule and the proximal tubule are connected together by the thin segment of the loop of Henle. For convenience the thin segment will be considered here together with the distal tubule. In cortical nephrons the thin segment is entirely descending, it joins to the thick ascending limb at, or just before, the hairpin turn (see Fig. 3.2). In juxtamedullary nephrons which have long loops of Henle, the thin segment has both descending and ascending portions. The cells of the thin segment are only 1 or 2 μm thick and have negligible brush borders and few mitochondria. The relatively simple structure of thin segment cells has led to the strong suspicion that they are not involved in active transepithelial transport. The transport which does occur is considered in Chapter 8.

The thick ascending limb and the distal convoluted tubule are joined at the macula densa. However, in both function and ultrastructure the thick ascending limb and the earliest portion of the distal convoluted tubule are very similar, and together they are now called the early diluting segment. The cells of this region are *c* 10 μm thick, and have extensive folding of the basolateral membrane, and contain numerous elongated mitochondria parallel to the basolateral membrane folds. The apical membranes are rather smooth in the medulla and covered with short microvilli in the cortex. The increase in apical membrane area in the cortex may reflect the increased transport capacity of the cortical region.

The next portion of the distal convoluted tubule, the pars convoluta of the anatomist, differs from the early portion in its structure and the mode of sodium transport, but it shares the relative impermeability to water and lack of sensitivity to ADH. It is therefore called the late diluting segment. The cells of this region are somewhat similar to those in the proximal tubule (see Fig. 6.1): they have well developed brush borders, extensive basolateral folding and interdigitation, and numerous mitochondria. This structure suggests that large quantities of solutes are transported through the cells in this region.

The collecting system can be subdivided into the cortical (or initial) collecting tubule and the cortical and medullary segments of the collecting duct.

The collecting system is not homogenous in structure and certainly possesses a number of cell types subserving different functions. The most common cell type, known as the light or agranular cell, contains few mitochondria. The dark, or granular cells which represent perhaps 40 per cent of the cells in the cortex and only 1 per cent in the medulla, contain many mitochondria, stain heavily for carbonic anhydrase and have short microvilli. The presence of the mitochondria suggests that these cells are responsible for some type of active transport.

There must also be differences between the cells to allow them to respond to different hormones. ADH increases c-AMP levels in some light cells, parathyroid hormone acts in some dark cells, and isoproterenol (a beta-adrenergic agonist) in some of each.

The early diluting segment

Normally a flow equal to about 25% of the GFR enters this segment. Rather more may flow into it in water diuresis and somewhat less in strong antidiuresis, owing to different extractions of water in the descending limb of the loop of Henle (see Chapter 8). The early diluting segment has a low water permeability but actively reabsorbs salt, hence its name. By the time the fluid has reached the cortical part of the segment it is always hypotonic to plasma, at least in those tubules accessible to micropuncture, even during an antidiuresis. Thus the concentration of sodium chloride can fall to less than 50 mM while the volume of tubular fluid is hardly changed.

Sodium and chloride

The probable mechanism for salt reabsorption in the early diluting segment is indicated in Fig. 7.1. It is thought that one sodium, two chlorides and possibly one potassium enter the cell together across the luminal membrane by a cotransport process. If potassium is required, it leaks back into the lumen. The net process moves negative charge from the lumen into the cells. The lumen becomes sufficiently positive to drive additional sodium out of the tubule via the tight junctions which are cation selective. The luminal potential may vary from about 5 mV when the sodium gradient is small and sodium is easily driven out to as much as 25 mV when the luminal sodium concentration has fallen to less than 50 mM. The sodium that enters the cells is pumped out of the cells across the basolateral membrane by the usual sodium pump; chloride presumably leaves the cells passively. Sodium chloride transport in this segment is inhibited by the so called loop diuretics, e.g. frusemide, bumetanide and ethacrynic acid, which apparently block the sodium–chloride cotransporter from the luminal side. They can be particularly effective because they are secreted into the proximal tubule so that their concentration in the early diluting segment can be much higher than the plasma concentration. These drugs greatly increase the salt load delivered to the rest of the distal tubule and collecting system.

The detailed mechanism of salt transport in this segment has been a matter of some controversy. Chloride is reabsorbed against electrical and concentration gradients and is, by definition, active, but this does not imply the existence of a primary chloride pump. Evidence in favour of the cotransport of sodium and chloride described here is convincing.

1. The outer medulla is exceedingly rich in Na, K, Mg–ATPase, the sodium pump, localized on the basolateral membranes of the cells of the thick ascending limbs.

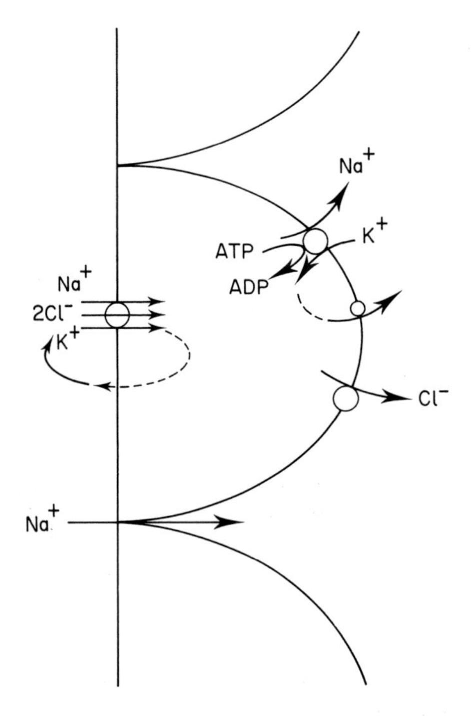

Fig. 7.1. The mechanism for sodium chloride reabsorption in the early diluting segment. Movement of sodium into the cell down electrical and chemical gradients is used to drive the reabsorption of 2 or more chloride ions. Removal of two chloride ions for each sodium ion leaves the lumen positive which drives more sodium out through the cation selective tight junctions. The evidence for cotransport of sodium and chloride is convincing. The indicated role of potassium is consistent with the available data.

Ouabain, which blocks the sodium pump, blocks sodium and chloride transport in the thick ascending limb.

2. In isolated perfused ascending limbs, either replacement of chloride by other small anions such as nitrate, or replacement of sodium by choline, virtually abolishes transport. Thus transport of neither sodium nor chloride can proceed without the other. Membrane vesicles displaying sodium and chloride co-transport have been isolated from cells in the thick ascending limb.

The much weaker evidence for the involvement of potassium is that the active transport of chloride is reduced when potassium is eliminated from the luminal fluid.

It is noteworthy that in the early diluting segment, as in the proximal tubule, the transport systems are arranged so that active transport of some of the sodium via the cells drives, at no further energy cost, reabsorption of additional sodium through the tight junctions.

Hydrogen

The early diluting segment can secrete hydrogen and the cells contain carbonic anhydrase so there can be some bicarbonate reabsorption. The extent to which the hydrogen secretion occurs by neutral sodium–hydrogen exchange, or by a hydrogen pump, is not clear.

Potassium

Potassium is strongly reabsorbed in the early diluting segment. Part of this reabsorption may be passive since the lumen is positive and the tight junctions are cation permeable. Under most circumstances almost all of the filtered potassium is reabsorbed before the tubular fluid enters the late diluting segment. Potassium reabsorption in the early diluting segment may also occur via the co-transporter thought to mediate sodium chloride transport across the luminal membrane.

Calcium and Magnesium

Calcium and magnesium are both strongly reabsorbed in the early diluting segment, though the pathways are uncertain. Any calcium or magnesium which passes through the cells must be transported out of the cells by some active process across the basolateral membrane. Calcium is relatively permeant across the tubule and transfer of calcium from lumen to peritubular fluid appears to occur only in the presence of favourable concentration or electrical gradients. The normally positive luminal potential provides an adequate driving force and it is therefore likely that calcium reabsorption is passive, through the tight junctions. The diluting segment is the major site of magnesium reabsorption in the kidney. Magnesium seems to be much less permeant than calcium through the intracellular junctions which suggests that transport occurs mainly through the cells. Magnesium reabsorption in this segment is augmented in magnesium deficiency and depressed by elevated plasma concentrations of magnesium. The detailed mechanisms of this control are unknown.

The late diluting segment, corticol collecting tubule, and collecting duct

It is convenient to take these segments together when considering ion transport. There are, however, important differences in the transport of water and urea. The late diluting segment is always relatively impermeable to both: the cortical collecting tubule and outer medullary collecting duct have an ADH-dependent water permeability but remain relatively impermeable to urea; and the permeability of the inner medullary collecting duct to both water and urea is greatly increased in the presence of high concentrations of ADH. The handling of urea is considered in Chapter 8. The electrical resistance varies, increasing towards the collecting duct, but is always much greater than in the proximal tubule. The tight junctions are much less permeable to small ions.

Sodium.

Sodium ions are thought to enter the cells passively across the luminal membranes without being directly coupled to any other ion movements. They are then pumped out of the cells into the peritubular medium by the Na, K, Mg–ATPase. The transport is presumed to occur primarily in the light principal cells since these are the most common, especially in the medulla. The net process removes positive charge from the lumen and thus will tend to make the potential negative. The electroneutrality of the lumen is maintained by

1. reabsorption of chloride into the cells probably driven passively by its concentration gradient (p. 83);
2. secretion of potassium from the cells, probably driven passively by the potential difference and the concentration gradient (pp. 83–84);
3. active secretion of hydrogen from the cells (p. 85ff). Each of these processes becomes faster as the lumen is made more negative, and conversely as these processes become faster the lumen becomes less negative. Thus via their effects on the potential of the lumen the transport of sodium, chloride, potassium and hydrogen are all linked to each other (see Fig. 7.2).

The rate of active sodium transport is limited by the rate of sodium entry into the cells. This rate increases with increasing luminal sodium concentration, and

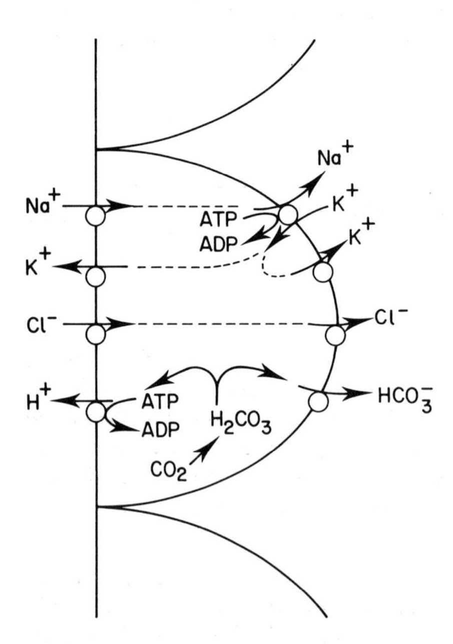

Fig. 7.2. Ion transport in the late diluting segment and collecting system. Movements of sodium, potassium, hydrogen and chloride across the luminal membrane can each vary independently of the others except for the restriction that the sum of all the movements must preserve electroneutrality. If, as indicated, the ion movements through the tight junctions are negligible, the net current through the cells must be zero. The actual transporters for sodium, potassium, chloride, and hydrogen have not been characterized.

is reduced as the lumen becomes more negative. The maximum concentration gradient for sodium between lumen and blood increases along the tubule, and a concentration of less than 1 mM can be achieved in the collecting duct during sodium deprivation.

During natriuresis, as follows extracellular fluid volume expansion or administration of diuretics like frusemide, delivery of both sodium and fluid to the distal nephron are high. The concentration of sodium in the lumen then remains high since even the relatively high rate of sodium reabsorption which occurs is given insufficient time to reduce the concentration as the fluid flows past. The distal tubule and collecting duct thus reabsorb some, but not all, of the extra delivered sodium.

The number of functional sodium transporters in the luminal membrane is increased by aldosterone especially in the cortical collecting tubule (see p. 93). The transporters can be blocked by potassium sparing diuretics such as amiloride but they are insensitive to loop diuretics, e.g. frusemide. Under normal conditions the lumen of the late diluting segment and the inner medullary collecting duct is negative, e.g. – 30 to – 40 mV, as a consequence of the active removal of sodium. In the cortical collecting tubule the potential is negative in the presence of aldosoterone, but in its absence the potential can be positive in some species, possibly including man. The positive potential may result from active hydrogen secretion.

It is by no means certain that all of the important factors which affect sodium reabsorption are known. This question is considered further in Chapters 10 and 14.

Chloride

The mechanisms of transport of chloride are still unknown. The reabsorption is thought to be driven primarily by the concentration gradient of chloride and the electrical potential difference.

Potassium

Potassium is secreted into the late diluting segment and the collecting system, probably from the light, principal cells. The final luminal concentration is highly variable but typically 80 mM, i.e. 20 times that in plasma. While the lumen is normally less negative than the cells, the potassium is at a higher concentration in the cells than in the lumen, and the concentration gradient is adequate to drive the efflux across the luminal membrane. The rate of secretion is affected by a number of factors.

1. Raised plasma potassium concentration markedly increases potassium secretion and similarly lowered concentration reduces it. Presumably changes in plasma concentration produce changes in the intracellular concentration, but the mechanism by which such small changes alter secretion is unknown.
2. Potassium secretion requires sodium reabsorption. Although there is no known direct link in the luminal membrane between sodium influx and potassium efflux, reducing sodium reabsorption decreases potassium secre-

tion because the lumen becomes positive and the cell potassium concentration falls as a consequence of the decreased rate of basolateral sodium–potassium exchange via the sodium pump. Sodium reabsorption can be reduced by administering a potassium sparing diuretic, e.g. amiloride, or by eliminating sodium from the lumen. Sodium is almost absent from the lumen in severe extracellular fluid concentration.

Greater sodium reabsorption increases potassium secretion because it makes the lumen more negative and raises intracellular potassium.

3. Potassium secretion is increased by saline diuresis and thus by any factor which increases glomerular filtration rate or decreases sodium and fluid reabsorption in the proximal tubule or the early diluting segment. In addition to the effect of increased sodium reabsorption there is an effect of fluid flow rate. The faster the flow, the lower the luminal concentration of potassium at any point along the late diluting segment and the collecting system, hence the faster the rate of net secretion at that point. Potassium secretion during water diuresis is modest because it is limited by the amount of sodium which can be reabsorbed.
4. Potassium secretion is increased during alkalosis and decreased during acidosis. The mechanism by which changes in plasma and hence presumably intracellular pH change potassium excretion is unknown. Increased luminal bicarbonate concentrations stimulate both hydrogen (see p. 87) and potassium secretion. Since the bicarbonate anion is less well reabsorbed than chloride, these effects of bicarbonate result at least partly from the increased luminal negativity caused by replacing chloride by a less permeant anion (see p. 82). This effect would increase potassium excretion in metabolic alkalosis.
5. Aldosterone stimulates potassium secretion by increasing the potassium permeability of the luminal membrane and by increasing sodium reabsorption. The effect on potassium permeability occurs rapidly, within minutes.

In severe potassium depletion the potassium permeability of the luminal membrane is reduced, perhaps mediated by a fall in aldosterone levels. This reduction blocks the secretion and unmasks a parallel, apparently independent, active reabsorption process. The mechanism of the active reabsorption is not known, but it is blocked by either peritubular ouabain or elimination of luminal sodium and thus it appears to be secondary active transport driven by sodium entry into the cell.

Calcium

Calcium enters the cells passively and is actively transported across the basolateral membrane into the peritubular space. It is not known whether this active transport is primary or secondary via exchange for peritubular sodium. Parathyroid hormone stimulates calcium reabsorption by stimulating production of c-AMP in the late diluting segment which in turn increases the calcium permeability of the luminal membrane.

Increased plasma calcium concentration leads to increased calcium delivery to the distal nephron and to decreased reabsorption largely as a consequence of the decreased level of parathyroid hormone. There is thus increased calcium excretion. Decreased plasma calcium concentration similarly leads to decreased excretion. Administration of parathyroid hormone, however, increases plasma calcium concentration largely via its effects on bone, and paradoxically, excretion can then be increased even though there is increased reabsorption.

Extracellular volume expansion or any factor increasing sodium delivery from the proximal tubule also increases calcium delivery and hence calcium excretion.

Parathyroid hormone increases in roughly the same proportion delivery of both sodium and calcium from the proximal tubule. However, its specific effect on calcium reabsorption in the distal tubule is the dominant effect for calcium. Thus for constant plasma concentrations of sodium and calcium parathyroid hormone increases sodium excretion and decreases calcium excretion. For the effects of parathyroid hormone on phosphate see p. 72.

Reabsorption and secretion of organic solutes

The specialized transporters for organic solutes occur primarily in the proximal tubule. In the distal nephron the fate of these solutes depends more on their physical properties as discussed further in Chapter 11. The effect of pH on the transfer of weak acids and bases is considered for ammonium on p. 89ff.

Hydrogen secretion, reabsorption of bicarbonate and acidification of urine

Hydrogen secretion and bicarbonate reabsorption occur in the distal tubule by mechanisms similar to those previously described for the proximal tubule, as indicated in Fig. 7.3. The secretion apparently occurs from the dark, intercalated cells since these stain heavily for carbonic anhydrase. Urinary pH can become as low as 4.5.

Reabsorption of bicarbonate: Hydrogen secretion does not equal acid excretion

It should be emphasized that even in the distal tubule the reabsorption of filtered bicarbonate requires most of the hydrogen secretion. This is true even when the amount of acid actually being excreted is high. Typically about 10 per cent of the filtered bicarbonate, about 450 mmol day is reabsorbed in the distal tubule and collecting system, more than 5 times the average daily net acid excretion. If the amount of bicarbonate delivered to the distal tubule and collecting system exceeds their capacity to secrete hydrogen ions then some bicarbonate will remain in the tubular fluid to be excreted in the urine which will then be neutral or alkaline. Such excretion of base occurs during alkalosis or extracellular fluid expansion. In the latter case, reabsorption of both sodium chloride and bicarbonate are reduced in the proximal tubule and a substantially increased bicarbonate load is delivered to the distal tubule. Other factors which may alter the ratio of hydrogen secretion to delivered bicarbonate are discussed in the following sections. It should be noted that hydrogen secretion must increase and

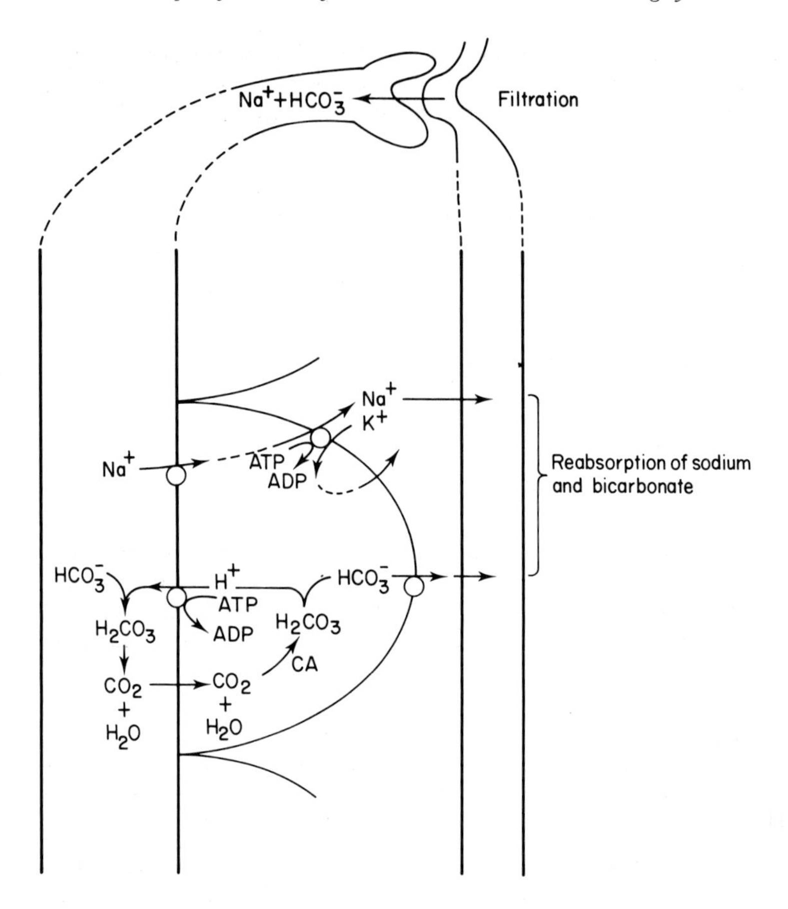

Fig. 7.3. Distal reabsorption of filtered sodium bicarbonate. There are three major differences between this mechanism and that operating in the proximal tubule (compare Fig. 6.4): 1, the hydrogen secretion is driven by a pump capable of generating large pH gradients; 2. the tight junctions are less leaky so that gradients are easier to maintain; and 3. carbonic anhydrase (CA) is present only inside the cell. Luminal carbonic anhydrase is unnecessary in the distal tubule and collecting system since the concentration of carbonic acid can be made high enough in the lumen by the low pH to drive dehydration by simple, uncatalysed mass action. Reabsorption of sodium bicarbonate merely restores filtered bicarbonate to the blood; it does not lead to acid excretion.

decrease with the delivered load of bicarbonate in order to avoid large fluctuations in the excretion of acid and base. Conversely, relatively small fractional changes in the rate of hydrogen secretion can, in the absence of a change in delivered bicarbonate, produce relatively large changes in excretion.

The distal tubule can normally secrete sufficient hydrogen ions to recover virtually all the bicarbonate which enters it. Note that even if the bicarbonate concentration stayed the same throughout the tubule and collecting duct, the urine would usually contain only about 1 per cent of that filtered since the urine flow is usually about 1 per cent of GFR. When the pH of the urine is reduced, the bicarbonate concentration is even lower and still less is excreted. The ability to reduce the pH of the luminal fluid considerably below that of plasma also means that there can be a net excretion of acid, mainly as dihydrogen phosphate and ammonium ions.

Factors influencing the rate of secretion of hydrogen ions

Net hydrogen secretion in the distal tubule, as in the proximal tubule, is the difference between an active secretion process and backleaks of hydrogen and bicarbonate. It is known to be affected by several factors.

1. The luminal concentrations of relatively impermeant anions such as bicarbonate, sulphate, phosphate, and β-hydroxybutyrate.
2. The rate of sodium reabsorption.
3. The luminal pH.
4. The plasma pH
5. The plasma potassium concentration.

(The effect of pCO_2 has not been examined critically in the distal tubule and collecting duct, see p. 67ff.) An increase in the concentration of impermeant anions or an increase in sodium reabsorption each makes the lumen more negative and this change probably accounts for the increased hydrogen (and potassium) secretion.

The important effects of the anion have been demonstrated in volunteers who had been sodium depleted by a low sodium diet and diuretics. Infusions of sodium chloride lead to little change in urine pH. By contrast infusions of either sodium sulphate or sodium phosphate, even when combined with sodium bicarbonate to ensure no fall in plasma pH, produce a rapid fall in urine pH from 7 to less than 5.

The effect of luminal and peritubular pH (points 3 and 4 above) are as expected for any pump-leak secretion process since both the pumping rate and the backleaks may be sensitive to the ion gradients (compare Chapter 6). The effect of plasma pH on the pump rate presumably occurs via changes in intracellular pH. The effect of potassium concentration are similar to those in the proximal tubule (and the mechanism is similarly not understood). Potassium and hydrogen appear to compete for a secretion process even though the actual transport mechanisms are quite separate and appear to occur in different types of cells.

Aldosterone stimulates both hydrogen and potassium excretion indirectly via the stimulation of sodium reabsorption.

Bicarbonate secretion

Bicarbonate transport in cortical collecting system segments isolated from rabbits and cortical collecting tubules prepared for microperfusion in rats varies with the pretreatment of the animals. Tubules from chronically acidotic animals reabsorb bicarbonate, probably by active hydrogen secretion as discussed above. This process does not require the presence of sodium. Tubules from chronically alkalotic animals secrete bicarbonate. The secretion mechanism requires the presence of sodium but not sodium reabsorption. Medullary collecting ducts always secrete hydrogen.

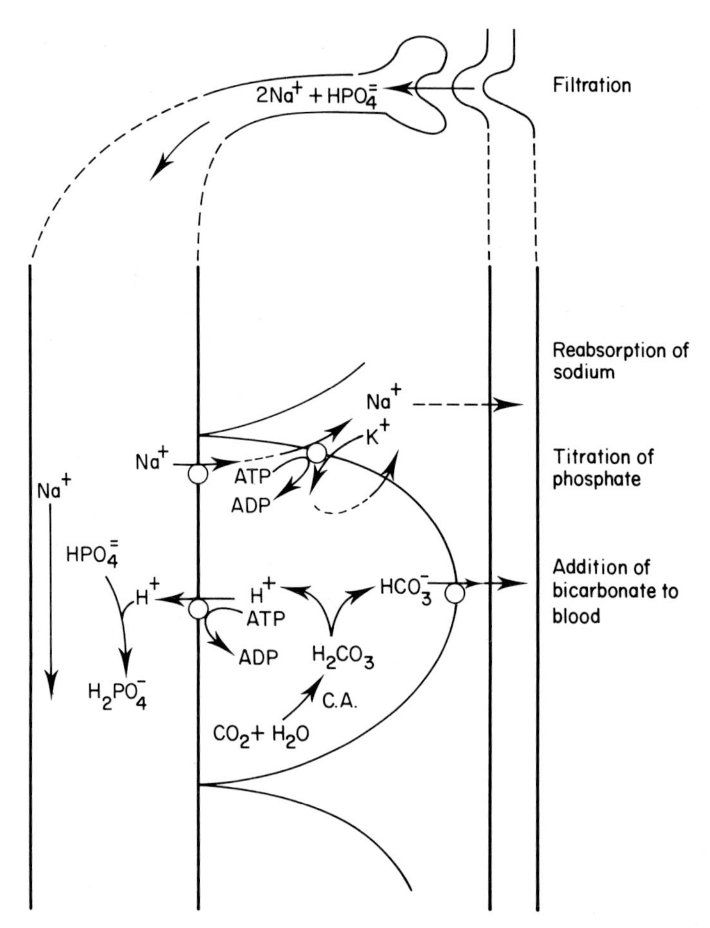

Fig. 7.4. Titration of buffers in the lumen to more acidic forms. For each secreted hydrogen ion that titrates a buffer and remains in the tubule a bicarbonate ion is added to the blood.

Bicarbonate secretion is unlikely to be important for normal control of acid or base excretion in man. However, it is currently attracting much attention as a means to obtain information about tubular mechanisms.

Excretion of acid

Excretion of significant quantities of acid is possible only when almost all of the bicarbonate has been reabsorbed, because none of the buffers that can be used to excrete acid will bind significant amounts of hydrogen ion until the tubular pH falls below 7. That cannot happen unless the bicarbonate concentration falls, which cannot happen unless bicarbonate reabsorption more than parallels fluid reabsorption. Reabsorbing bicarbonate prevents a decrease in plasma bicarbonate concentration but cannot increase it. By contrast for each hydrogen ion which actually remains in the tubular fluid and is excreted into the urine, 1 bicarbonate ion is added to the blood thus tending to increase plasma bicarbonate concentration. This addition of bicarbonate to the blood by excretion of acid allows the regeneration of the buffers which reacted with the acid while it was within the body (see Chapter 16).

The amount of acid excreted is determined by the amounts of buffers excreted and by the urine pH which in turn depends on the rate of hydrogen secretion. Fig. 7.4 shows the processes for acidifying luminal monohydrogen phosphate and the net return to the blood of bicarbonate. Polar organic acids such as β-hydroxybutyrate and acetoacetate can also be partially acidified in the same way and, again, with each hydrogen ion excreted a bicarbonate is regenerated. The amount of acid excreted in this way is the excess of the hydrogen ions bound to those buffers in the urine over the hydrogen ions that were bound to them in plasma, i.e. the amount of hydrogen ions required to titrate the buffer excreted in the urine from pH 7.4 (normal plasma pH) to the pH of the urine. The quantity of H^+ excreted depends on the amounts and the pKs (see p. 198ff) of the urinary buffers. In essence one excretes more acid with more buffer present and with lower urine pH.

Normally phosphate is the only titratable buffer present in the urine in significant amounts. The amount delivered into the distal tubule is usually the excess of input into the ECF over nonrenal losses. On a typical western diet about 30 mmol/day of acid are excreted as part of dihydrogen phosphate, roughly the same amount of acid as is released in the body by phosphate metabolism.

Excretion of acid as ammonium

The acid that can be excreted as free hydrogen ions is negligible since pH 4.5 is equivalent to only 30 μM H^+. Thus in 1.5 l of urine per day the kidney can only excrete 45 μmoles of free H^+. Metabolism can produce more than 25 mmol day of H_2SO_4 from sulphur containing amino acids. Fig. 7.5. summarizes the mechanism which removes sulphuric acid from the body as ammonium sulphate. Ammonium, at equilibrium with a small amount of ammonia, is produced in the renal cortex. Ammonia is a highly diffusable and highly water soluble gas that can pass rapidly from the cells to both the luminal fluid and the blood. These carry it to all parts of the kidneys. The tubular cells in the collecting ducts secrete hydrogen ions which combine with ammonia in the lumen to form ammonium. Ammonium ions are not permeant across the tubule and thus are trapped in the lumen and excreted in the urine. For each hydrogen ion excreted as ammonium one bicarbonate ion is regenerated and added to the blood and a sodium ion is reabsorbed.

The amount of ammonia trapped as ammonium in the collecting duct increases as the luminal pH falls (see Fig. 7.6) because more ammonia is converted to ammonium which leads to increased diffusion of free ammonia into the lumen. When the pH is low the luminal concentration of ammonium can be much greater than that in the tubular cells and the venous blood.

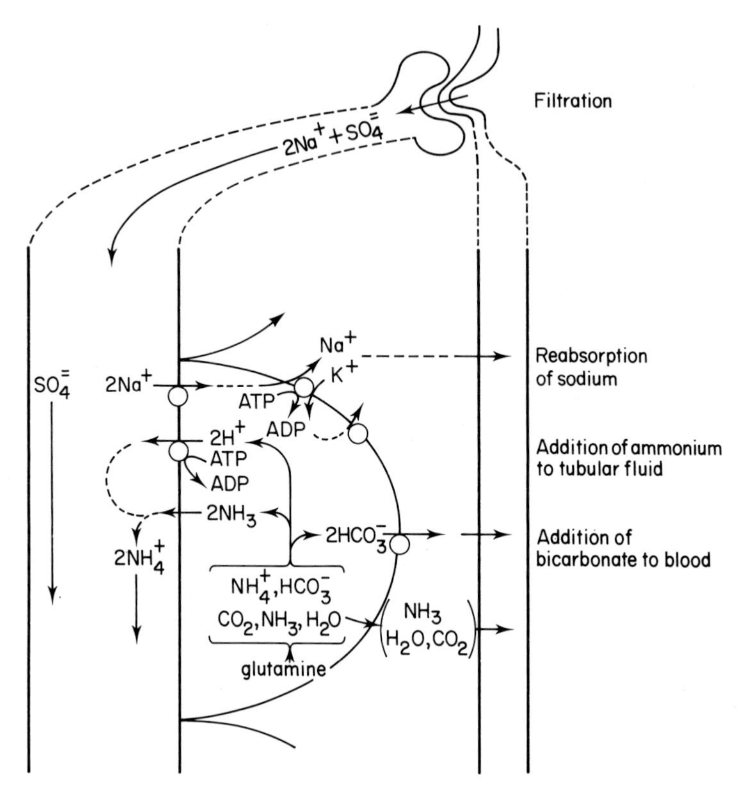

Fig. 7.5. The replacement of sodium by ammonium ions as a means of excreting acid. Ammonium ions are produced by deaminations, most frequently of glutamine. Subsequent metabolism releases bicarbonate. For each secreted hydrogen ion which remains in the tubule as part of an ammonium ion, a bicarbonate ion is added to the blood. In this figure the net effect of processes occurring in several cells in different parts of the kidney are shown as occurring in only one (see text).

This transfer of ammonium ions from the cells to the lumen by separate movements of nonionic ammonia and hydrogen ions is an example of the nonionic diffusion mechanism for transfer of weak acids and bases. An important property of this mechanism is that pH differences across a barrier can produce a large concentration ratio of the charged form of the weak acid or base (here ammonium). The necessary conditions are that

1. the charged form (ammonium) cannot cross the barrier;
2. the uncharged form (ammonia) can cross;
3. the pH on the high concentration side must strongly favour the charged form.

The ammonia which is produced in the kidneys leaves in either the urine or the venous blood. Because ammonia is so diffusable, it reaches virtually the same concentration in both. The ammonium concentration in each is then given by

$$[NH_4^+] = K_{NH_3}[H^+][NH_3]$$

or in other words the ratio of the ammonium concentrations is the same as that for the hydrogen ions. The ammonium concentration in urine increases less than proportionally with the hydrogen ion concentration because the increased rate of loss of

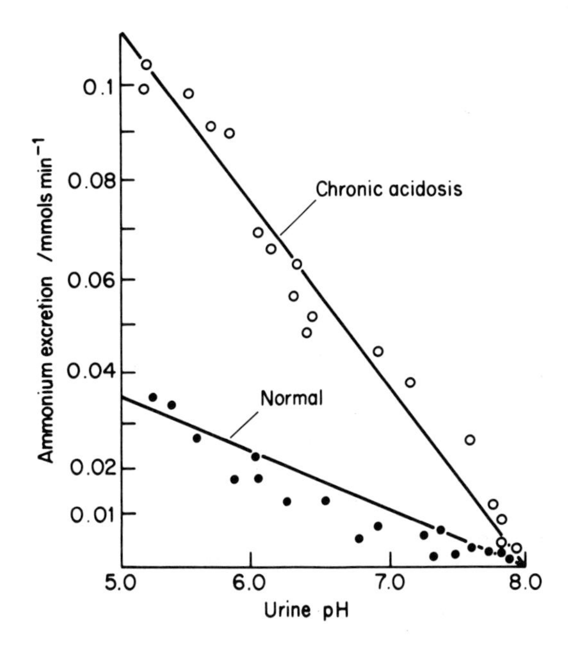

Fig. 7.6. Rates of ammonium ion excretion in acute and chronic metabolic acidosis. The increase in excretion rate reflects the increase in the rate of renal ammonium ion production. (Reproduced with permission from Pitts, R.F., 1948).

ammonium in the urine lowers the free ammonia concentration everywhere in the kidney. An increase in urine flow rate tends to increase the rate of ammonium excretion, but at high rates the increases are limited by the rate of ammonium production.

Ammonium production

Ammonium ions are produced in tubular cells primarily by deamination of glutamine first to glutamate, catalysed by glutaminase, then to α-ketoglutarate, catalysed by glutamate dehydrogenase. The glutamine is brought to the kidney in the blood. A secondary source of glutamate is transamination of α-ketoglutarate using other amino acids extracted from the blood. Bicarbonate ions are produced from the metabolism of the carboxyl groups of the glutamine and amino acids that were deaminated to produce the ammonium.

The mechanism of control of ammonium production is unknown. In chronic acidosis the plasma concentration of glutamine does not increase but the amount used by the cells increases. Thus the site of control appears to be intracellular. There are a number of possible sites including the entry step for glutamine into the mitochondria and inhibition of the deaminations by accumulation of products, perhaps α-ketoglutarate or ammonium ions. The stimulus for increased intracellular ammonium ion production during chronic acidosis (see Fig. 7.6) is also poorly defined. Tubular pH and plasma pH are the principal candidates.

Water

The early and late diluting segments always have a low water permeability and so in these segments solute reabsorption makes the fluid markedly hypoosmotic. How much water is reabsorbed in subsequent segments and how much is excreted depends on the plasma level of ADH. In the absence of ADH the collecting system is also relatively impermeable to water and urine flow is copious, up to 20 per cent of GFR, and dilute. The handling of ions and wastes is not greatly influenced by whether or not most of the water is retained in the tubule. This allows solute excretion and retention to proceed appropriately with very different excretion of water.

ADH increases the water permeability 10–100 fold in both the *cortical* collecting tubule, and the collecting duct. The dilute fluid entering the cortical collecting tubule can therefore equilibrate osmotically with peritubular plasma, by reabsorption of water, so that the fluid entering the medullary collecting duct is isosmotic and greatly reduced in volume, typically only 5 per cent or so of GFR. This effect of ADH to restore tubular fluid to isosmolality and reduce its volume as it passes through the cortex is of vital importance in the production of a small volume of concentrated urine as discussed in the next chapter.

Mechanism of action of ADH

ADH binds to hormone receptors on the basolateral membrane of cells in the collecting system and promotes the intracellular production of c-AMP. (Note that the ADH responsive cells in the cortex appear to form a separate population from those tubular cells that respond to parathyroid hormone). This second messenger stimulates a complex chain of intracellular processes, apparently culminating in the insertion of water permeability channels into the apical membrane.

Evidence for this mode of action of ADH includes the following. Electron micrographs show that ADH treated cells have extra membrane particles in their apical membranes, of which the number is related to the measured water permeability. Furthermore in the absence of ADH, changing the luminal osmolality has much less effect on collecting duct cell volume than does changing peritubular osmolality, implying that water flux occurs much more readily across the basolateral membrane, and that the impermeable membrane must be on the luminal side.

In the absence of ADH the collecting system is much less permeable to water than the proximal tubule. The main reason seems to be that the apical membranes in the collecting system have few microvilli and so the total surface area for water flux is much smaller per unit length of tubule than in the proximal tubule. Also the tight junctions in the collecting system are probably much less permeable to everything, including water.

ADH increases the urea and water permeabilities in the inner medullary collecting duct as discussed further in Chapter 8. Whether ADH has important effects on ion transport in the mammalian kidney is debatable. In mice and rats it is reported that sodium chloride reabsorption in the thick ascending limb is stimulated by ADH. This seems a sensible arrangement since this could enhance the operation of the medullary counter-current system (see Chapter 8).

However, there is little evidence in other species, including man, that at levels that maximally affect water permeability ADH can directly influence sodium reabsorption.

Hormones

Hormones known to have effects in the distal tubule and collecting system include ADH, aldosterone, and parathyroid hormone. In addition a natriuretic hormone may act here (see Chapter 14). ADH is discussed in the preceding section and in Chapters 8 and 13. The effects of parathyroid hormone on phosphate and general fluid reabsorption are primarily in the proximal tubule and are discussed in Chapter 6. The effect on calcium excretion is partly proximal, see Chapter 6, but primarily distal (see p. 85). Its role in calcium and phosphate homeostasis is considered in chapter 12. Aldosterone is implicated in the control of sodium and hence extracellular fluid volume, (see Chapter 14) and in the regulation of potassium levels, (see Chapter 12). Aldosterone also influences acid-base balance, (see Chapter 17).

Actions of aldosterone in the distal tubule and collecting system

There are many consequences of a fall in aldosterone levels.

1. Decreased sodium reabsorption, probably as a consequence of decreased synthesis and insertion into the luminal membrane of the sodium transporter which is sensitive to amiloride.
2. Less negative or even positive luminal potentials as a consequence of (1);.
3. Decreased chloride reabsorption, at least partly as a consequence of (2).
4. Decreased secretion of hydrogen, again at least partly as a consequence of (2).
5. Decreased Na, K–ATPase activity primarily because there is much less sodium to pump.
6. Decreased secretion of potassium as a consequence of the change in luminal potential, the reduced peritubular influx of potassium into the cell via the sodium pump and a fall in the luminal membrane permeability to potassium.
7. Decreased metabolic activity, presumably as a result of the decreased use of ATP by sodium pumping.

With the exception of the effect on potassium permeability, these actions of aldosterone require new protein synthesis. Aldosterone induced proteins have been isolated, but their functions are still unknown.

In addition to the primary and secondary effects discussed above, long term changes in aldosterone levels will lead to tertiary changes in excretion as well. For instance elevated aldosterone leads to excessive losses of acid and potassium and thus to increased plasma pH and reduced potassium concentration. The fall in plasma potassium acts back on the kidney to reduce potassium excretion but also to increase acid excretion. Thus the alkalosis of hyperaldosteronism is made considerably worse by the simultaneous fall in plasma potassium concentration.

Further reading

Bank, N. & Schwartz, W.B. (1960). The influence of anion penetrating ability on urinary acidification and the excretion of titratable acid. *J. Clin. Invest.* **39**, 1516–1525.

Burg, M. (1981). Renal handling of sodium, chloride, water, amino acids and glucose. Chapter 7, pp. 328–370 in *The Kidney*, 2nd edn, Brenner, B.M. & Rector, F.C. Jr., eds, Saunders, Philadelphia.

Clapp, J.R., Rector, F.C. Jr. & Seldin, D.W. (1962). Effects of unreabsorbed anions on proximal and distal transtubular potentials in rats. *Am. J. Physiol.* **202**, 781–786.

Cohen, J.J. & Kamm, D.F. (1981) Renal metabolism. Relation to renal function. Chapter 4, pp. 144–248 in *The Kidney*, 2nd edn, Brenner, B.M. & Rector, F.C. Jr., eds, Saunders, Philadelphia. (Discussion of amino acid metabolism in the kidneys and ammonium production.)

DeWardener, H.E. (1978). The control of sodium excretion. *Am. J. Physiol.* **235**, F163–F173.

Giebisch, G. (1978). Renal potassium transport. Chapter 5, pp. 215–298 in *Membrane Transport in Biology, Vols, IVA & IVB, Transport Organs*. Giebisch, G. ed, Springer-Verlag, Berlin.

Greger, R. & Schlatter, E. (1981). Presence of luminal K^+, a prerequisite for active NaCl transport in the cortical thick ascending limb of Henle's loop of rabbit kidney. Pflügers *Arch.* **392**, 92–94.

Koeppen, B., Giebisch, G. & Malnic, G. (1985). Mechanism and regulation of renal tubular acidification. Chapter 65, pp. 1491–1525 in *The Kidney. Physiology and Pathology*, Seldin, D.W. & Giebisch, G. eds, Raven, N.Y.

Laski, M.E., Warnock, D.G. & Rector, F.C. Jr. (1983). Effects of chloride gradients on total CO_2 flux in the rabbit cortical collecting tubule. *Am. J. Physiol.* **244**, F112–F121.

Malnic, G. & Giebisch, G. (1979). Cellular aspects of renal tubular acidification. Chapter 6, pp. 299–356 in *Membrane Transport in Biology, Vols. IVA & IVB, Transport Organs*, Giebisch, G. ed, Springer, Berlin.

Pitts, R.F. (1948). Renal excretion of acid. Fed. Proc. 7,418–426.

Pitts, R.F. (1973). Production and excretion of ammonia in relation to acid-base regulation. Chapter 15, pp. 455–496 in *Handbook of Physiology, Section 8, Renal Physiology*, Orloff, J. & Berliner, R.W., eds, American Physiological Society, Washington, D.C.

Pitts, R.F. (1974). *Physiology of the Kidney and Body Fluids*, 3rd edn, Yearbook Medical Publishers, Chicago. pp. 211–241 Excretion of acid.

Schafer, J.A. & Andreoli, T.E. (1976). The collecting duct. Chapter 35, pp. 707–737 in *Physiology of Membrane Disorders.*, Andreoli, T.E., Hoffman, J.F. & Fanestil, D.D., eds, Plenum, N.Y.

Schwartz, W.B. & Cohen, J.J. (1978). The nature of the renal response to chronic disorders of acid-base equilibrium. *Am. J. Med.* **64**, 417–428.

Sutton, R.A.L. & Dirks, J.H. (1981). Renal handling of calcium, phosphate and magnesium. Chapter 12, pp. 551–618 in *The Kidney*, 2nd edn, Brenner, B.M. & Rector, F.C. Jr., eds, Saunders, Philadelphia.

Tannen, R.L. (1978). Ammonia metabolism. *Am. J. Physiol.* **235**, F265–F277.

Tisher, C.C. (1981). Anatomy of the kidney. Chapter 1, pp. 3–75 in *The*

Kidney, 2nd edn, Brenner, B.M. & Rector, F.C. Jr., eds, Saunders, Philadelphia.

Warnock, D.G. & Eveloff, J. (1982). NaCl entry mechanisms in the luminal membrane of the renal tubule. *Am. J. Physiol.* **242**, F561–F574.

Warnock, D.G. & Rector, F.C. Jr. (1981). Renal acidification mechanisms. Chapter 10, pp. 440–494 in *The Kidney*, 2nd edn, Brenner, B.M. & Rector, F.C. Jr., eds, Saunders, Philadelphia.

8

The production of dilute or concentrated urine

Dilute urine

Higher vertebrates have probably evolved from ancestors who lived in fresh water and thus faced the challenge of continual influx of water and dilution of the body fluids. This challenge was met by the development of two systems for the transport of salt and water: skin and gills which can transfer salt from very dilute fresh water into the extracellular fluid and glomerular kidneys. In this type of kidney plasma is ultrafiltered into the tubules and nearly all the salts and desirable solutes can be reabsorbed to leave behind a large volume of dilute urine. The glomerular kidney has been retained by terrestial vertebrates.

In the early and late diluting segments of the mammalian kidney salts are always actively reabsorbed while water is held back. In the collecting system this dilution continues in the absence of antidiuretic hormone, ADH. Fig. 8.1 shows schematically the flows and concentrations of tubular fluid in the diluting kidney. Isosmotic fluid reabsorption in the proximal tubule removes about two-thirds of the filtrate. Approximately 30 ml/min re-enters the cortex from the thick ascending limb and may be reduced to about 20 ml/min by the time it enters the medullary collecting duct. The 10 ml of fluid reabsorbed between these points is strongly hyperosmotic which leaves behind a dilute tubular fluid. As the tubular fluid descends the medullary collecting duct, there is a large osmotic difference between it and the interstitium. As a result even though this part of the tubule has a low water permeability in the absence of ADH, there is still reabsorption of several ml/min of water and the final volume of urine is 10–20 ml/min. The collecting duct can avidly reabsorb sodium giving a final sodium concentration as low as 1–2 mM. The urine can be as dilute as 60 mosmolal with urea as the principal remaining solute.

Isosmotic urine

The same amount of solute can be excreted in a smaller volume of urine if some late part of the tubule is made sufficiently permeable to water that the tubular fluid osmotically equilibrates with plasma. The requisite permeability is achieved by the action of ADH. It would be possible to produce almost isosmotic urine even without the special folding or geometry of the nephron and collecting system.

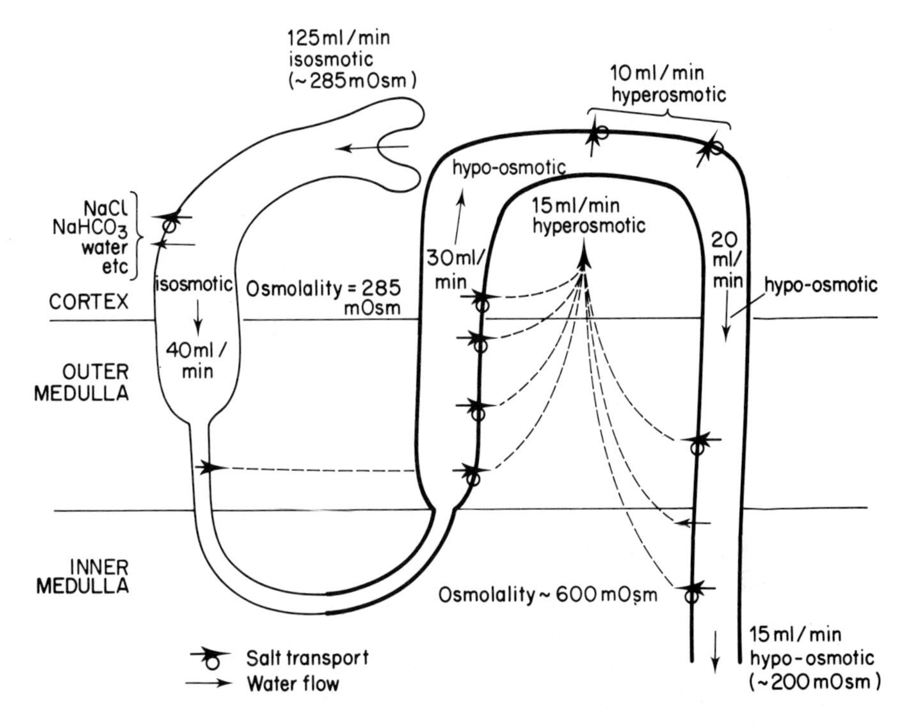

Fig. 8.1. The mechanism for producing a dilute urine. A single schematic nephron is used to indicate the average behaviour of all nephrons. Tubule walls with low water permeability in the absence of ADH are shown as heavy lines, salt transport is indicated by a circle with an arrow, and water movements are denoted by wide arrows. In all segments starting with the ascending limb of the loop on Henle, sodium chloride is transported out of the tubule while water lags behind since the water permeability of the tubular walls is low. The sodium chloride concentration in the urine can be as low as 1 mM. Urine flow rates above 25 ml/min are possible. The fluid reabsorbed in the cortical portions of the distal tubule and collecting system always has a higher osmolality than the tubular fluid, but it is not inevitably hyperosmotic to plasma. The sum of the reabsorbates, cortical and medullary, is, as it must be, hyperosmotic. mOsm = mosmols/kg.

Concentrated urine

For terrestrial species there is the constant risk of water depletion and it is clearly an advantage to be able to use very little water for the excretion of waste products. One way to avoid excreting water when it is scarce is to stop excreting wastes until water is again available. To a large extent this is done by reptiles. Another way to conserve water is to develop some mechanism for reabsorbing water from tubular fluid leaving behind a small volume of concentrated urine. The apparent difficulty for the vertebrate kidney in producing a concentrated urine is that the tubule is designed to pump solute away from the tubular fluid and not vice versa. However, if the tubule can dilute the luminal contents it must consequently be able to concentrate solute in the interstitium. If the solute removed from the lumen in a diluting segment of the tubule is confined to a small compartment, then the fluid in that compartment can be made significantly hyperosmotic. This hyperosmotic solution produced by removing salt from a relatively large volume of tubular fluid can then be used to extract water from a smaller volume of isosmotic fluid flowing through a later segment of the tubule. This, in its most basic terms, is the principle on which the concentrating kidney operates.

The principle is related to a schematic nephron in Fig. 8.2. Salt is removed from the tubular fluid in the ascending limb of the loop of Henle leaving water behind in the lumen. The salt enters the surrounding interstitium and the blood vessels of the vasa recta, together known as the medullary core, and makes this core hyperosmotic. The dilute solution in the lumen flows into the cortex where

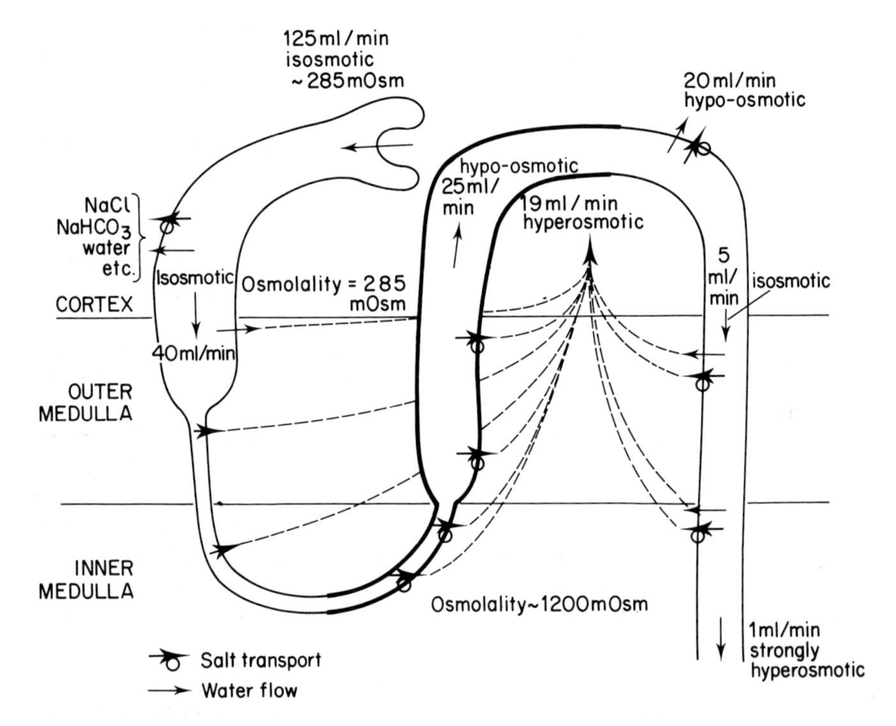

Fig. 8.2. The mechanism which concentrates urine is illustrated using a schematic 'average' nephron. The numerical values are rough approximations. Tubule walls with low water permeability in the presence of ADH are shown as heavy lines. Salt is pumped out of the ascending loop of Henle making the region outside the tubule hyperosmotic. The water left behind flows up the tubule into the cortex where most of it is reabsorbed. The isosmotic tubular fluid, greatly reduced in volume, flows from the cortical collecting tubule into the collecting duct. The high concentration of salt in the medulla extracts water from the collecting duct making the urine hyperosmotic. The salt and extracted water return to the body via the vasa recta as a hyperosmotic solution. The sum of the reabsorbates is, as it must be, hypo-osmotic. Salt transport in the thin ascending limb may be passive. Although the principles can be illustrated in terms of a single nephron, the mechanism actually used in human and rat kidneys may make use of the differences between superficial and juxtamedullary nephrons to make the processes more efficient.

in the presence of ADH the excess water is reabsorbed together with more salt. The tubular fluid, now isosmotic and greatly reduced in volume, then enters the collecting duct. Given the high levels of ADH the collecting ducts are relatively permeable to water and water flows out of the ducts into the hyperosmotic core until the osmolalities within the ducts and the core are almost equal. Since so little fluid flows into the collecting duct, the amount of water transferred to the core is small relative to the amount of salt pumped into it from the ascending limb and thus the core and the urine can be strongly hyperosmotic.

The water extracted from the collecting duct and the salt pumped from the ascending limb are removed from the medulla as a hyperosmotic solution and returned to the general circulation by the blood flow through the vasa recta.

It should be emphasized that the fluid flowing up the ascending limb is markedly hypo-osmotic and that the total fluid delivered to the cortex and thence to the renal venous blood is hypo-osmotic. Thus the kidneys return a dilute fluid to the blood as they produce a concentrated urine. To reiterate, salt is taken from a relatively large volume of fluid in the ascending limb of Henle's loop leaving water behind. In the presence of ADH, most of this water is removed from the tubule in the cortex and returned to the blood. A much smaller volume of fluid enters the collecting duct and is concentrated as water is drawn into the medulla.

In parallel with the passive movement of water, the collecting duct epithelium can also pump sodium chloride from the duct lumen into the core. Thus since both water and sodium chloride can be removed from the collecting duct, the osmolality of the urine can be almost entirely due to high concentrations of wastes with urea accounting for up to 600 mmol/litre. Alternatively when there is excess salt, sodium pumping in the duct is suppressed and the sodium chloride concentration can rise to 300 mmolar.

Fig. 8.2, also indicates that water is extracted from the descending limb of the loop of Henle. This water extraction increases the salt concentration at the bottom of the descending limb. In a manner which is not completely understood (see p. 101 and small print on p. 106), this increase in concentration assists salt transport from the thin ascending limb of the juxtamedullary nephrons into the deeper portions of the medulla which allows the core in this region to be made particularly concentrated. It is this high osmolality which determines the final concentration of the urine.

Urea and its effects on the concentrating mechanism

Excretion of urea at high concentrations

A high concentration of urea in the urine is achieved without compromising the ability of the kidney to concentrate other wastes. In the cortex and the outer medulla, the distal tubule and collecting system are always impermeable to urea, thus in these segments the urea delivered from the ascending loop of Henle is concentrated as water is extracted. In the presence of ADH, the late collecting duct is very permeable to urea. A portion of the concentrated urea therefore leaves the duct and enters the deepest portions of the medulla which tends to make the urea concentrations in the core and duct nearly equal. Water is extracted from the duct into the core until the total osmolalities are almost the same inside and out. The sum of the osmolalities of sodium chloride and urea in the core is therefore the same as the sum of the osmolalities of urea and the wastes in the duct. In effect, the osmolality of urea balances itself and the osmolality of the sodium chloride in the core is being used solely to concentrate the other, potentially toxic wastes in the urine. The energy to concentrate the urea is supplied by the processes which lead to water reabsorption in the distal tubule and collecting duct.

Urea leaves the medullary core both by diffusing into the thin limbs and via the vasa recta. A proportion of the urea from the vasa recta may diffuse across into the descending proximal straight tubule. Thus the concentration of urea in the medulla allows a recycling of urea (see Fig. 8.3) from the collecting duct to the core, to the loop of Henle, to the cortical collecting tubule, and back to the collecting duct. As a result of this mechanism the amount of urea entering the distal tubule and collecting system exceeds the amount delivered from the proximal convoluted tubule. Thus there is more urea to be concentrated and the concentration achieved in the collecting duct and inner medulla is high. Even though some urea leaves the duct into the core, that which remains allows ade-

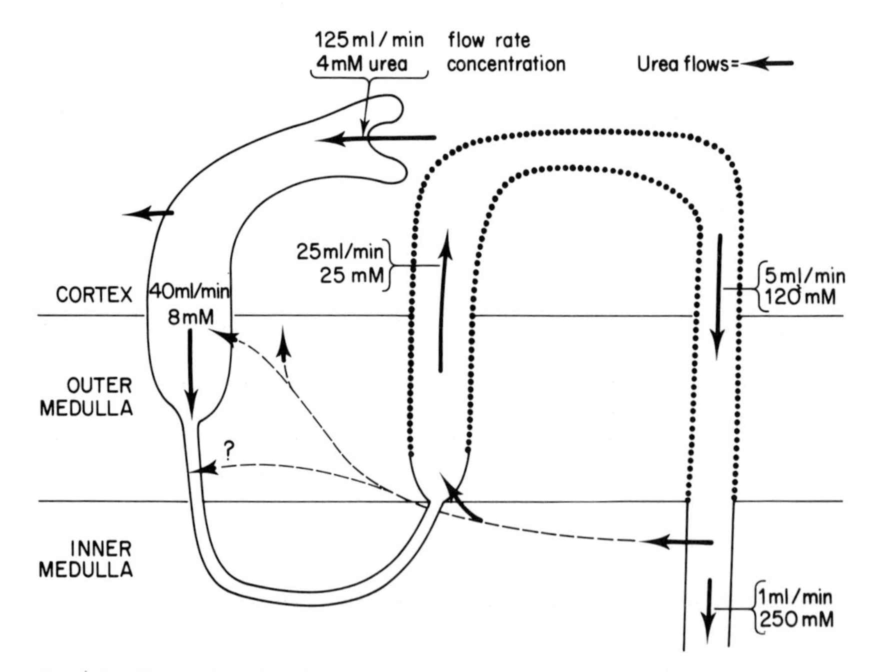

Fig. 8.3. The recirculation of urea through the medulla. The distal tubule, collecting tubule, and outer medullary collecting duct are impermeable to urea. Thus as water and salt are removed in these regions, urea becomes more concentrated. In the presence of ADH the duct wall is permeable to urea near the papilla, and urea leaves the duct into the medulla raising the concentration there. Urea leaves the medulla by diffusion into the thin ascending limb and via the vasa recta. Part of the urea carried away by the vasa recta finds its way into either the pars recta of the proximal tubule (in the region inaccessible to micropuncture) or the cortical end of the descending limb.

quate urea excretion. The high concentration of urea in the medulla depends on the presence of ADH. In its absence the medullary concentration falls many fold.

The effects of urea on the concentration of other solutes

When urea is present in the medulla, it increases the osmolality of the core which allows more extraction of water from the long descending limbs of the juxtamedullary nephrons. As noted earlier such extraction increases the concentration of sodium chloride within the descending limb and hence in the ascending limb. It is now established that this increase greatly assists the transport of sodium chloride from the thin ascending limb of the justamedullary nephrons into the papilla and inner medulla. This transport is essential for the production of a high sodium chloride concentration in the papillae and thus for the ability to concentrate toxic wastes in the urine. In man the ability to produce concentrated urine is impaired on low protein diets which result in reduced production of urea. There is then a lower concentration of urea in the urine and in the medulla and hence also a lowered osmolality of the remaining solutes. Evidence that it is the fall in urea concentration which reduces the ability to concentrate the other solutes in the urine has been obtained in perfused rat kidneys where the amount of urea in the glomerular filtrate can be controlled directly. The absence of urea markedly decreases the osmolality of the nonurea solutes. It has been proposed that when urea is present the salt concentration inside the long loops is increased sufficiently so that sodium chloride can be transported out of the thin ascending limb passively. This is described in more detail later (in small print on p. 106).

Influence of tubular flow rate

The production of a dilute or concentrated urine depends not only on the absence or presence, respectively, of ADH but also on the appropriate delivery of fluid to the distal tubule and collecting system. If the flow is greatly reduced, then even in the absence of ADH the fluid remains in the collecting system a sufficiently long time for water to equilibrate with the fluid in the core and approach or even exceed isosmolality. Thus with greatly reduced flow, as seen in severe extracellular fluid contraction, the kidneys cannot produce hypo-osmotic urine.

Inability to concentrate or dilute the urine during diuresis accompanied by natriuresis.

An excessive flow into the distal tubule and collecting system as might occur with extracellular fluid expansion or during osmotic diuresis, can so overload the system that little dilution or concentration can be achieved. In the absence of ADH there is little dilution because the delivery of sodium greatly exceeds the reabsorption capacity so that its concentration in the luminal fluid and in the urine is not much reduced. In the presence of ADH the excessive flow has several consequences.

1. If the diuresis originates in the proximal tubule, as with osmotic diuretics at high concentrations or extracellular fluid expansion, there is increased flow of fluid in the descending limb of the loop of Henle and thus more water must be extracted from the thin limb into the core to achieve any given increase in the concentration of the solutes within the loop. Furthermore for osmotic diuresis the solutes which are concentrated inside are now only partly sodium chloride since the osmotic diuretic is concentrated at the same time. This reduction in sodium chloride concentration within the loop reduces the transport of sodium chloride into the core.
2. In the ascending limb, distal tubule and cortical collecting tubule reabsorption increases but not enough to match the increased flow, i.e. the fraction of the flow which can be reabsorbed is reduced. Thus urea cannot be effectively concentrated by the mechanism described above. This then reduces the concentration of urea in the medullary core and, in turn, the concentration of sodium chloride in the loop of Henle and transport of sodium chloride out of the thin ascending limb into the core.
3. In the collecting duct the increased flow yields, in the presence of ADH, a large reabsorption of water.

Thus as a result of diuresis more water and less solutes are added to the core, the hyperosmolality is greatly reduced and the concentrating mechanism fails.

The vasa recta

Blood flow must be provided to the medulla to supply the ordinary needs of the cells of the loops of Henle and the collecting ducts and to remove the fluid which enters the core. Blood flow into the vasa recta is about 50–100 ml/min of which perhaps 5 ml/min reaches the papillae. In addition up to 30 ml/min of fluid is reabsorbed from the medullary interstitium. These large flows must be prevented from washing away the salt and urea gradients which make the medulla hyperosmotic. This end is accomplished by using countercurrent flow.

Blood enters and leaves the medulla, via the vasa recta, at the cortical boundary. As it descends towards the papillae, it becomes progressively more concentrated partly by solute entry and partly by loss of water. As the blood ascends again towards the cortex it becomes progressively less concentrated as it flows. The net movement of salt into the descending limb of the vasa recta at each level is only slightly greater than the net flow out of the ascending limb. Thus while there is fluid reabsorption, there is little net dilution or concentration of each level of the core. The net reabsorption of solutes and water over the entire vasa recta is governed by the Starling mechanism (see Chapter 3) which keeps the interstitial fluid pressure in the medulla low. Whenever fluid enters the interstitium from the tubules, which tends to increase the fluid pressure, more is reabsorbed into the capillaries.

When medullary blood flow is increased, solutes are washed away more rapidly and the core concentrations of sodium chloride and urea are reduced. The reduction in sodium chloride concentration then decreases water extraction from the collecting duct which decreases the ability to concentrate urea (see p. 99ff) thus reducing the urea concentration yet further. The decreased urea concentration leads to less water extraction from the thin descending limbs which reduces sodium chloride transport into the core (see pp. 99 & 106). The net effect is to reduce the distal reabsorption of both salt and water.

Mechanisms believed to operate in the kidney

The outline of the concentrating mechanism given above is sufficient for understanding the role of the kidney in osmoregulation. However many variations of this mechanism are possible and they differ greatly in how efficiently they make use of the metabolic energy consumed in pumping sodium chloride. The details of the actual mechanism used differ between species and are not completely understood for any species. They are also not important for considering any other topics in basic renal physiology and might well be considered beyond the scope of a book intended primarily for a first course. However, the organization of the process has an elegance which continues to attract the attention of students, researchers, teachers, and examiners alike. The details are thus further discussed here.

The advantage of an osmolality gradient

Inefficiency arises in the mechanism primarily in three ways.

1. It costs energy to concentrate the salt in the core fluid. This energy is stored as the excess osmolality of the fluid. To the extent that the portion of the core fluid returned to the body is hyperosmotic, part of this energy is wasted. Thus the hyperosmolality of the net fluid returned to the body by the vasa recta should be as small as possible.
2. Since it costs energy to create osmotic gradients, it is wasteful to extract water from the collecting duct using gradients any larger than necessary.
3. It is wasteful to have large gradients of osmolality across the wall of the ascending limb. The medulla can be hyperosmotic only if a hypoosmotic fluid leaves the medulla in the ascending limb. Large gradients across the wall of the ascending limb promote leakage of water out of this limb, thus dissipating the hypoosmolality of the ascending fluid before it reaches the cortex.

The inefficiencies resulting from these causes are greatly reduced in the kidneys by the use of a gradual osmolality gradient throughout the medulla. In human kidneys the osmolality varies from *c* 285 mosmolal at the cortical–medullary boundary to as much as 1200–1400 mosmolal at the tip of the papillae. The osmolality gradient was discovered by observing the melting point of frozen slices taken from different positions in the medullae of rats that had been deprived of water. This technique is known as *microcryoscopy*.

In a kidney producing a concentrated urine, a small volume of fluid, *c* 5 ml/min, enters the medullary collecting ducts. As it descends through the increasingly hyperosmotic medulla, water is extracted across the wall of the duct. At each level the difference in osmolality between lumen and interstitium is small. The water extracted together with the salt from the loop of Henle ascends through the medulla via the vasa recta towards the cortex. As it ascends this fluid encounters less concentrated fluid in the collecting ducts and extracts yet more water and becomes more dilute. Thus by using a medullary gradient of osmolality, water is extracted from the duct at each level using the lowest possible concentration of medullary solute, the medullary solute as it ascends in the core is used to extract more water at each level, the fluid which leaves the medulla in the vasa recta is only slightly hyperosmotic and the urine is concentrated. We must now consider how the gradient in osmolality is produced.

Production of the gradient: Counter-current flow in the limbs of the loop of Henle

The gradient in osmolality is produced by transport from the loops of Henle into the medullary interstitium. Many nephrons contribute to transport in the outer medulla but only the 15 per cent of nephrons which are juxtamedullary and possess long loops of Henle contribute in the inner medulla. The basic principle is shown in Fig. 8 .4 . In contrast to the ascending limb, the thin descending limb of the loop is highly permeable to water. Thus salt pumped out of the ascending limb extracts water from the descending limb (*c* 10–20 ml/min) as well as from the collecting duct (*c.* 5 ml/min). The water extraction from the descending limb increases the sodium chloride concentration within it so that the osmolalities of the core and descending limb fluids are almost equal at each level. At each level in the medulla salt is taken from the ascending limb diluting its contents, and water is removed from the descending limb making its solutes more concentrated. In both limbs and in the interstitium the concentration is therefore highest in the papillae and lowest near the cortex. Thus the differences in osmolality across the walls of the ascending and descending limbs are always much less than the maximal osmolality at the papilla. This arrangement allows efficient extraction of water in the descending limb using small osmotic gradients and minimizes leakage of water out of the ascending limb.

A gradient of hyperosmolality in the medulla can be produced either by water extraction from the descending limb as described above, or by letting part of the salt extracted from the ascending limb diffuse into the descending limb. In this alternative, called *solute recycling*, the descending limb must be permeable to salt rather than to water. Solute recycling is described in the textbook of Pitts and in many textbook diagrams derived from his presentation. Part of the uncertainty about the mechanism operating in humans is that in some nephrons salt may be added to the tubule in some part of the descending limb, perhaps in the pars recta of the proximal tubules. An informed guess is that most of the increase in osmolality *in nephrons which enter the inner medulla* is due to water extraction.

Solute recycling and water extraction can both dilute the fluid in the ascending limb and create an osmotic gradient in the medulla. However, they differ markedly in the net amounts of fluid and salt reabsorbed in the medulla and hence in the amounts which remain in the tubules to reenter the cortex. Water extraction reduces the volume of fluid in the tubule and hence minimizes delivery of salt. It is therefore very useful for an animal which must conserve sodium chloride since this mechanism reduces the total amount of sodium chloride which must be reabsorbed more distally. Solute recycling does not reduce the volume of fluid delivered (no water is reabsorbed from the loop) and a larger amount of sodium chloride reaches more distal parts of the tubule. This mechanism is therefore useful for an animal which routinely has to excrete large quantities of sodium chloride while conserving water. There appear to be species which offer examples of each mechanism. The desert rat, Psammonys, gets its water by eating plants which store both water and sodium chloride. It must excrete the salt while conserving the water and it uses solute recycling. Rabbits on the other hand eat ordinary plants and have little sodium chloride in their diets. They use water extraction. Laboratory rats use primarily water extraction with some solute recycling. Humans are probably most like rats.

The process of concentrating urine depends crucially on the ability to transport salt out of the ascending limb, leaving water behind. The thick ascending limb has a low water permeability and a high capacity active transport system for sodium chloride. The thin ascending limb of juxtamedullary nephrons also has a low water permeability, but convincing evidence for active salt transport has never been found. Although the partial pressure of oxygen in the inner medulla is adequate to support

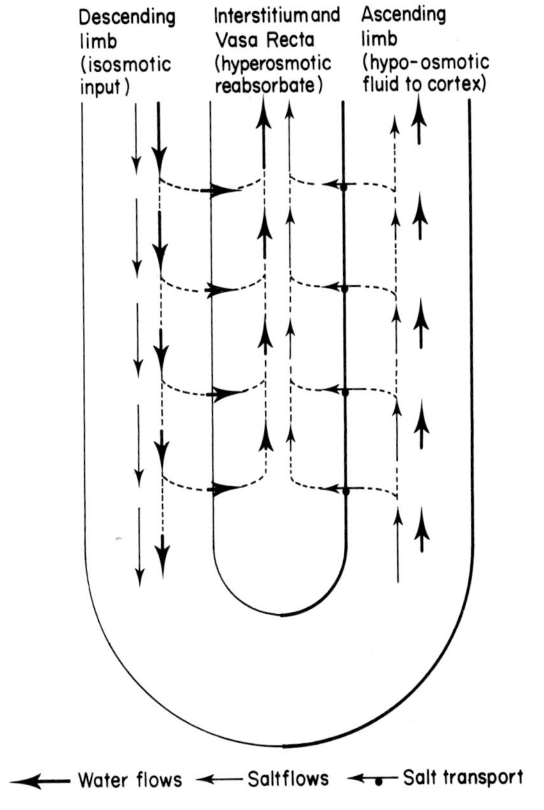

Fig. 8.4. Production of an osmolality-gradient by selective reabsorption of salt and water. In this simplified version of the process the walls of the descending limb are permeable to water but not salt, and nothing crosses the walls of the ascending limb except for salt which is actively pumped out of the lumen into the interstitium. The lengths of the arrows are proportional to the amount of salt or water passing that point. Thus the osmolality is given by the ratio of the lengths; the fluid is isosmotic when the lengths are equal. Fluid in the ascending limb of the loop is made dilute by the active transport of sodium chloride into the interstitium and vasa recta and thus at each level in the medulla the ascending limb removes a fluid which is less concentrated than its surroundings. This removal of water leaves an excess of salt which extracts water from the descending limb. The reabsorbate ascends towards the cortex via the vasa recta. The concentrated fluid in the descending limb goes deeper into the medulla thus making the deeper regions more concentrated. The overall result is that the difference in osmolality between the papilla and the cortex far exceeds the osmolality difference across the tubules at any point.

oxidative phosphorylation, the histological appearance of the cells in the thin segment does not suggest pumping activity, e.g. there is little membrane folding and there are very few mitochondria. It has been proposed that salt leaves the thin ascending limb passively.

In species, such as man, which use water extraction to concentrate sodium chloride in the descending limb, it is clear that urea augments the concentrating process in the inner medulla. This occurs since the presence of a high concentration of urea in the medullary core provides an osmolality additional to that of sodium chloride. Water is extracted from the descending thin limb of the loop until the osmolalities of sodium chloride plus urea balance across the tubule wall. If the permeabilities to urea and sodium chloride are low enough, the fraction of the osmolality contributed by urea remains higher outside than inside, and water extraction from the limb increases the sodium chloride concentration inside until it substantially exceeds that outside. The thin ascending limb is permeable to salt, slightly permeable to urea, and effectively impermeable to water. Thus, in the passive mode hypothesis, when the fluid enters the ascending limb at the tip of the loop, salt will diffuse out, down its concentration gradient, less urea will diffuse in, down its gradient, and water will hardly move. The osmolality of the fluid inside the ascending limb will therefore decrease and sodium chloride will be added to the core near the papillae as needed to make it strongly hyperosmotic. The energy to drive these processes is made available by the mechanism which concentrates urea in the medulla. Although this mechanism which uses only passive transport within the inner medulla is physically plausible, it is not clear that it is adequate to produce the amount of sodium chloride transport which must occur from the thin ascending segment. The actual mechanism may depend on transport of salt and water between nephrons whose loops of Henle have different lengths. In this regard it is interesting to note that the tubules and vessels in the inner medulla are arranged in a very orderly fashion.

In species such as Psammonys, which use solute recycling, urea may not be part of the concentrating mechanism since water extraction does not occur in the descending limb. Thus in Psammonys adding urea to the glomerular filtrate reduces the osmolality of the urine, towards isosmolality, since the urea acts as an osmotic diuretic.

Summary

1. Sodium chloride is added to the core by transport out of the ascending limb of the loop of Henle.
2. In the cortical collecting system in the presence of ADH, the volume of the tubular fluid is reduced, the osmolality increases to become isosmotic with plasma, water in excess of solute is returned to the blood, and urea is concentrated.
3. Urea is added to the core from the collecting duct by diffusion down its concentration gradient.
4. The high concentrations of urea and sodium chloride in the core are used to extract water from the fluid in the descending limb of the loop of Henle and the high concentration of urea assists sodium chloride transport from the thin ascending limb.
5. Water extraction from the descending limb, and sodium chloride transport from the ascending limb, produce a gradient of osmolality through the medulla, from isosmotic near the cortex to strongly hyperosmotic near the papillae.
6. The gradient of osmolality is used to concentrate progressively the fluid descending in the collecting duct.
7. The water and solutes extracted from the tubules and collecting ducts leave the core via the blood flow through the vasa recta.

Further reading

Burg, M. & Stephenson, J.L. (1978). Transport characteristics of the loop of Henle, pp. 661–679 in *Physiology of Membrane Disorders*., Andreoli, T.E., Hoffman, J.F. & Fanestil, D.D., eds, Plenum, N.Y. (This chapter gives an admirably clear account of the evidence before it dives into the depths of theory. Stephenson is largely responsible for putting the theory of the concentrating mechanism onto a sound physical basis.)

Jamieson, R.L. (1981). Urine concentration and dilution. Chapter 11, pp. 495–530 in *The Kidney*, 2nd edn Brenner, B.M. & Rector, F.C. Jr., eds, Saunders, Philadelphia. (Critical consideration of the evidence and the theories.)

Kokko, J.P. & Rector, F.C. Jr. (1972). Countercurrent multiplication system without active transport in inner medulla. *Kidney Int.* **2**, 214–223. (A clear presentation of the simplest version of the concentrating mechanism that uses passive reabsorption in the inner medulla.)

Pitts, R.F. (1974). *Physiology of the Kidney and Body Fluids,* 3rd edn, Yearbook Medical Publishers, Chicago. (Solute recycling told as well as anywhere. Fig. 7–14 is the prototype for many versions which have appeared elsewhere. Unfortunately it can be misleading. As Pitts notes in the text, the emergent fluid is dilute during the creation of the osmotic gradient. However so long as the loop is considered in isolation, in the steady state what goes in must come out. Thus, in the steady state, the figure would need to show a strongly hyperosmotic papilla but an isosmotic fluid emerging to the cortex. Of course once salt is allowed to leave the medulla via the vasa recta, the fluid in the ascending limb can be dilute as is in fact the case.)

Symposium (1983). *Federation Proceedings* **42**, 2377–2405. (Clear statements of different views of the present position. This collection is probably the best entry point for the student wishing to pursue the detailed mechanism further.)

Valtin, H. (1983). Chapter 8, *Renal Function*, 2nd edn, Little, Brown & Co., Boston. (It's always a good idea to read more than one account. However, beware of Fig. 8.2 which is adapted from Pitts' figure for solute recycling (*q.v.*). To make it work for water extraction, Valtin should have allowed the core fluid to flow upwards. As it is drawn, in all but the last frame the water extracted from the loop would blow up the medulla like a balloon.)

9

Hormonal and metabolic functions of the kidney

Renin and angiotensin

Renin is a specific proteolytic enzyme, MW 35 000, secreted from modified granule-containing smooth muscle cells of the afferent arteriole. These cells are part of the juxtaglomerular apparatus as indicated in Fig. 9.1. Renin acts on an α_2-globulin, angiotensinogen, to cleave off a decapeptide, angiotensin I. Then another enzyme (converting enzyme) splits off a dipeptide to leave the octapeptide, angiotensin II, which is the main biologically active form. Some of the renin is secreted into the renal interstitium where there are both angiotensinogen and converting enzyme. Angiotensin II is then produced in the region of the juxtaglomerular apparatus and acts as an intrarenal messenger. Renin is also secreted into the blood where it catalyses formation of angiotensin I from angiotensinogen in plasma. Converting enzyme is present in many tissues and angiotensin II is formed at many sites and can thus act like a distributed hormone. Angiotensin is inactivated by various peptidases called collectively angiotensinase.

In the kidney, angiotensin II has a vasoconstrictor action on the arterioles, reducing renal blood flow while tending to maintain glomerular filtration rate (see Table 5.1). Angiotensin II may also stimulate reabsorption of sodium chloride from the proximal tubule (see p. 73).

Systemic effects

As a hormone angiotensin II has a number of actions, including the following.

1. Angiotensin II is one of the most potent vasoconstrictor substances for arterioles and venules. However, only when renin release is stimulated above the resting level and angiotensin II levels are high, do the acute actions of the hormone contribute an important part of vascular 'tone'.
2. Angiotensin II stimulates aldosterone release from the zona glomerulosa cells of the adrenal cortex. It is, however, not the only stimulus. The physiological control of aldosterone release is still the subject of controversy and investigation.
3. Angiotensin II potently stimulates thirst when the plasma concentration is high or when it is applied directly to the third ventricle in the brain. Its

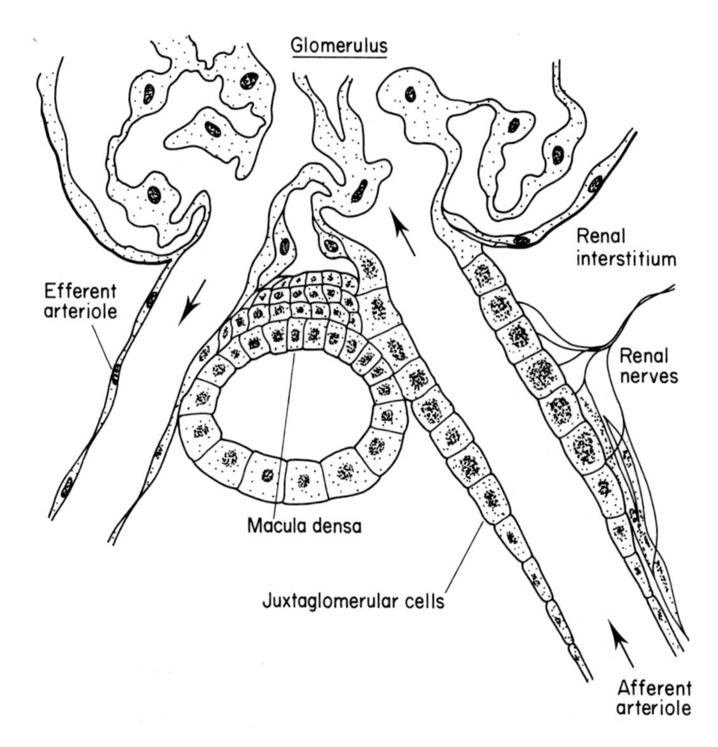

Fig. 9.1. Diagram of the juxtaglomerular apparatus. Renin is made and released from the granular cells of the afferent arteriole. These are modified smooth muscle cells and are innervated by postganglionic sympathetic nerves. The macula densa is a specialized region within the early diluting segment of the same nephron. (Reproduced with permission from Davis, J.O. 1971.)

possible role in the thirst that follows fluid loss or fluid deprivation is considered in Chapter 13.

4. In some circumstances angiotensin II may stimulate sodium appetite.
5. Many other actions of infused or injected angiotensin are reported, e.g. enhanced fluid reabsorption from gut and increased secretion of ADH from the posterior pituitary gland.

It is difficult to unravel the actual role of the hormonal effects of angiotensin in day to day physiological adjustments. One view would be that the renin–angiotensin system is primarily concerned with intrarenal control but that in response to certain stresses or emergency conditions, e.g. sodium deprivation or haemorrhage, plasma levels become sufficiently high for some or most of the general effects listed above to become important. The influence of the renin–angiotensin system in the control of extracellular fluid volume and blood pressure is considered in Chapters 14 and 15.

Control of release

A number of factors are known to be involved in regulating the release of renin from the juxtaglomerular apparatus. Note that there is a resting release so that secretion of renin can be either stimulated or reduced.

1. Noradrenaline released from the renal nerves can stimulate renin secretion by a β-adrenergic effect.
2. The pressure difference across the wall of the afferent arteriole seems directly to effect renin release. Decreased arterial pressure or increased interstitial pressure (produced experimentally by ureteral clamping) stimulates release. These responses are sometimes attributed to a 'renal baroreceptor'. The effects of adrenergic stimulation and reduced renal perfusion pressure together can be much greater than the sum of their separate effects.

   The stimulation of renin release by the renal baroreceptor may be mediated by the prostaglandin PGI_2 (or possibly PGE_2). Infusions of PGI_2 produce renin release and indomethacin (which blocks the formation of prostaglandins) prevents the increase in renin release caused by a fall in arterial pressure within the range of autoregulation. Further falls in blood pressure, however, still cause release presumably via the macula densa mechanism.

3. The flow and composition of tubular fluid passing the macula densa influences renin release. Decreased delivery of sodium chloride stimulates renin release into the circulation.

   The actual stimulus to the macula densa has not been established. Perhaps the most attractive hypothesis is that it is due to the rate of either sodium or chloride ion entry into the macula densa cells from the lumen. Since these cells are part of the early diluting segment (see p. 78), this would explain the requirement for sodium and chloride ions and the ability of frusemide to block the response of the macula densa to luminal sodium chloride.

   In the view of most experts decreased delivery of sodium chloride to the macula densa stimulates renin release, as noted above. However, as discussed on p. 55 decreased delivery is also thought to lead to afferent arteriolar dilation. Some experts feel that there must be something wrong with these views, since renin release leads to increased local angiotensin II production and angiotensin II is a potent vasoconstrictor.

4. Elevated angiotensin II levels appear to exert a negative feedback control by inhibiting renin release.
5. Increased levels of ADH reduce renin release.
6. Decreases in extracellular fluid volume appear to increase renin release even in the absence of measurable changes in arterial pressure, plasma sodium concentration, renal blood flow, and glomerular filtration rate. It is not known whether this release results from the superposition of several stimuli, each below the level of detection, or from some additional agent such as a hormone, colloid osmotic pressure, or venous pressure, acting on the kidneys (see Chapter 14 for further discussion).

Antagonists

Blocking the formation or the effects of angiotensin II is an important experimental manoeuvre and is increasingly showing promise as a therapeutic approach in the treatment of some forms of hypertension. Several peptides have

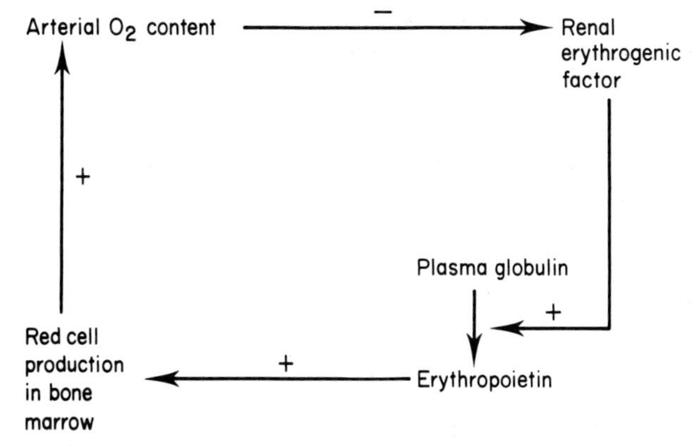

Fig. 9.2. Scheme for control of red blood cell production.

been produced which inhibit converting enzyme including captopril which is absorbed across the intestinal mucosa and thus can be administered orally. Analogues of angiotensin II such as saralasin can act as competitive inhibitors at the receptors. However, at the doses required to completely block the effects of angiotensin II these substances produce some of the same effects.

Erythropoiesis

The kidney plays an important part in the regulation of red cell production in the bone marrow. Fig. 9.2 outlines the control system believed to be involved in maintaining an adequate O_2 content of arterial blood. The O_2 content appears to be monitored by the kidney. A reduced O_2 content in the blood increases the secretion of renal erythrogenic factor, a proteolytic enzyme which cleaves erythropoietin off a circulating globulin. The hormone erythropoietin is a direct stimulant of the haemopoietic tissues of bone marrow. Two conditions in which this system can be demonstrated are: anaemia following haemorrhage where it acts to restore the normal haematocrit, and chronic hypoxia, as at high altitudes, where an elevated haematocrit can partly compensate for the incomplete O_2 saturation of arterial haemoglobin.

Neither the cells responsible for the response to altered O_2 content of the arterial blood nor those for secreting renal erythrogenic factor are yet identified, though the action appears to take place in the cortex and not the medulla. The anaemia of renal failure is partly due to reduced production of renal erythrogenic factor.

Vitamin D

Vitamin D plays an important part in regulating intestinal absorption of calcium and the reabsorption and deposition of bone. The principal form, cholecalciferol which is also called vitamin D_3, can be obtained from the diet or produced in the skin on exposure to ultra violet irradiation. It appears that to become active vitamin D_3 must be converted to the 1,25-dihydroxy compound,

1,25-DHCC. The first hydroxylation reaction occurs in the liver, the second in the renal tubular cells. This hydroxylation appears to be stimulated by low levels of phosphate or by elevated levels of parathyroid hormone. These processes and their place in the general regulation of body calcium are discussed in the companion volume in this series, *Endocrine Physiology*, by Hardy. We should note here that severe renal disease is associated with malabsorption of calcium in the gut due to the failure of production of 1,25-DHCC.

Gluconeogenesis

The liver is normally the major site of glucoenogenesis, but the kidneys are also important. When plasma glucose concentration is depressed glucose concentration in the renal veins markedly exceeds that in the renal arteries. Many substrates can be converted into glucose including pyruvate, lactate, glycerol, acetoacetate, alanine, and glutamate. Renal glucose production from amino acids may become particularly significant in starvation with its accompanying acidosis. The deamination of glutamine and glutamate in the kidney thus serves the dual purpose of gluconeogenesis and providing ammonium ions which are used in excretion of acid (see Chapters 7 and 17).

Conjugation

The condensation of many organic wastes and foreign substances with groups such as glycine, glucuronate and sulphate is of major importance as it frequently reduces toxicity and enhances excretion. Most conjugations occur in the liver; those in the kidney are primarily condensations of glycine with carboxylates or alcoholic groups. For instance, benzoic acid and its congeners are seriously toxic substances. When these are occasionally produced as metabolic end products, they are converted in the kidney into the more innocuous hippuric acids. The excretion of nitrogenous wastes and foreign substances is considered in Chapter 11.

Further reading

Davis, J.O. (1971). What signals the kidney to release renin? *Circulation Res.* **28**, 301–306.

Davis, J.O. & Freeman, R.H. (1976). Mechanisms regulating renin release. *Physiol. Rev.* **56**, 1–56.

Gibbons, G.H., Dzau, V.J., Farhi, E.R. & Barger, A.C. (1984). Interaction of signals influencing renin release. *Ann. Rev. Physiol.* **46**, 291–308.

Hollenberg, N.K. (1980). Angiotensin as a determinant of renal perfusion and function. Chapter 5, pp. 57–5 in *Captopril and Hypertension*, Case, D.B. Sonnenblick, E.H. & Laragh, J.H., eds, Plenum, N.Y.

Keeton, T.K. & Campbell, W.B. (1981). The pharmacologic alteration of renin release. *Pharmacol. Rev.* **32**, 81–227. (A detailed account with extensive references. It starts with sections on the physiology.)

Keeton, T.K. & Campbell, W.B. (1984). Control of renin release and its alteration by drugs, pp. 65–118 in *Cardiovascular Pharmacology*, 2nd edn,

Antonaccio, M. ed, Raven, N.Y. (Intended as an advanced textbook account of much of the material presented in the previous reference).
Lifschitz, M.D. & Stein, J.H. (1981). Renal vasoactive hormones. Chapter 14, pp. 650–720 in *The Kidney*, 2nd edn, Brenner, B.M. & Rector, F.C. Jr., eds, Saunders, Philadelphia.

10

The regulation of the body fluids by the kidneys

General principles

The constancy of the body fluids is continually being threatened by variable intake and unpredictable losses. To meet these challenges kidney function must be continually adjusted. The distribution and composition of the body fluids and the way the kidneys work have been considered in Chapters 1 to 9. Changes in the body fluids, the control of excretion in response to these changes, and the resulting regulation of the fluids are described in Chapters 10 to 17. The concepts of this control were brought to prominence in the late 1800s by the great French physiologist, Claude Bernard. The term *homeostasis* was devised much later by the American physiologist, Walter Cannon to describe 'the various physiological arrangements which serve to restore the normal state once it has been disturbed'. It has come to mean the maintenance of the correct concentrations, volumes, flows, etc. within the body.

For each substance in the extracellular fluid, homeostasis obviously requires the matching of output to input. If the kidneys fail to form urine, an untreated patient will die within a few days from continuing accumulation of wastes. Persistent mismatches between input and output lead to progressive change in the body and sooner or later are inevitably fatal. However, it is not enough that excretion of substances should match their inputs. The cells of the body function properly only when the concentrations of substances in their environment are correct as well as constant. Furthermore, adequate function of the cardiovascular system is possible only if the volumes of blood, plasma and the interstitial fluid are controlled. Thus for each substance in the extracellular fluid *homeostasis requires the matching of output to input at the normal plasma concentration and for the normal fluid volumes*. Homeostasis is grossly disturbed in chronic (i.e. long standing) kidney failure. Output via the urine then matches the net input but only for abnormal extracellular fluid volumes, dangerously elevated levels of wastes, and seriously disturbed levels of important ions, e.g. potassium and phosphate.

Routes in and out of the extracellular fluid

There is a continual passage of substances in and out of the extracellular fluid. The main routes through which this occurs are indicated in Fig. 10.1. For most

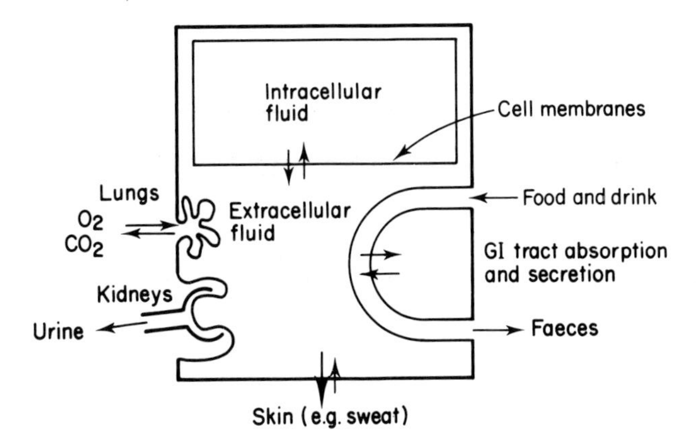

Fig. 10.1. The main routes for transport of substances in and out of the extracellular fluid.

of the substances we shall be considering, the main inputs in healthy adults are

1. food and drink;
2. production of metabolic wastes by the cells.

The main output is via the urine. Sometimes, however, other routes will dominate, e.g. a pregnant animal will deliver more calcium to the growing foetus than into the urine; a growing animal may transfer more potassium to its growing cells than it excretes; people with severe diarrhoea will lose much more water in their faeces than in their urine.

The role of the kidneys in homeostasis

The job of the kidneys is to vary the nature and amount of urine produced hour by hour and day by day so as to maintain the proper composition and volumes of the extracellular fluids. Under most circumstances *input* is not closely controlled and homeostasis is achieved by the regulation of renal *excretion*. Homeostasis is possible because excretion changes in response to changes in the extracellular fluids.

It might appear that excretion could be matched to input and the extracellular fluids controlled by directly monitoring the input and altering excretion whenever the input changes. However, this type of control is *never* used alone for several reasons.

1. The matching would have to be impossibly accurate since given enough time even very small mismatches would produce large cumulative changes.
2. The net non-renal input is often the sum of several variable processes that are hard to monitor.
3. Finally it would require a long memory of the deficits whenever there were a net non-renal loss so that subsequent input could be retained to remedy the deficiency.

For many substances, e.g. sodium, potassium and calcium, it is vital that the concentrations in extracellular fluid are kept within certain narrow limits, since cell function is disturbed by levels which are either too high or too low. For other substances, often metabolic end products, the requirement is for disposal rapid enough to prevent their accumulation. Some waste products such as urea and creatinine are relatively harmless and, as long as they do get excreted, the plasma levels reached are not critical. Other metabolic end products may be toxic and have to be excreted rapidly enough that plasma concentrations do not reach dangerous levels. (Toxic substances are often first rendered harmless by biochemical transformations, so that their excretion becomes less urgent, see pp. 112 and 131).

It is important to emphasize that regulated renal excretion of a substance will be able to keep the concentration in the extracellular fluid steady only so long as there is net input into the extracellular fluid via other routes. If the non-renal loss of a substance should exceed its total input then no change in urinary excretion can keep the levels constant. The best that the kidneys can then do is to excrete none. Normal levels can be restored only by extra intake, or suppression of the excess loss and continued normal intake. If you sweat profusely while running a marathon on a hot day, minimizing urine production will not maintain your body water. You get thirsty and drink to replenish the loss.

The major functions of the kidney: consequences of renal failure

The causes of death in renal failure give important clues as to the major functions of the kidneys. In acute renal failure, potentially fatal consequences include: water and sodium overload, hyperkalemia (elevated plasma potassium levels), acidosis (increased hydrogen ion levels), and the accumulation of a variety of toxic metabolic end products such as methylguanidine, benzoic acid derivatives and probably many others not yet characterized. It is worth noting that a fatal accumulation of one or more of these items would typically take several days, though fatal hyperkalemia, for instance, can develop more rapidly. In chronic renal failure there may additionally be arterial hypertension (see Chapter 15) and failure of the kidneys as endocrine organs (see Chapters 9 and 12). A much more detailed discussion of the consequences of renal failure can be found in *Disorders of the Kidney and Urinary Tract*, Chapters 3 and 4.

Renal mechanisms of homeostasis

The main principle of homeostatic regulation is that the regulated variable, e.g. the plasma concentration of a substance, must exert a key influence on the mechanisms, e.g. renal excretion of the substance, used to control that variable. The variation of urinary excretion with plasma level can be diagrammed as a 'renal function curve' such as that shown for creatinine in Fig. 10.2. The relationships between concentration and excretion differ for different substances as discussed later. The curve for creatinine is a relatively simple example where excretion increases in proportion to the plasma concentration (i.e. the clearance is a constant independent of concentration, see Chapter 4) and the curve is a straight line.

In the steady state the plasma level must lead to excretion which matches the input. This matching can be indicated in Figures like 10.2 as the intersection of the renal function curve with a horizontal line showing the steady input. The

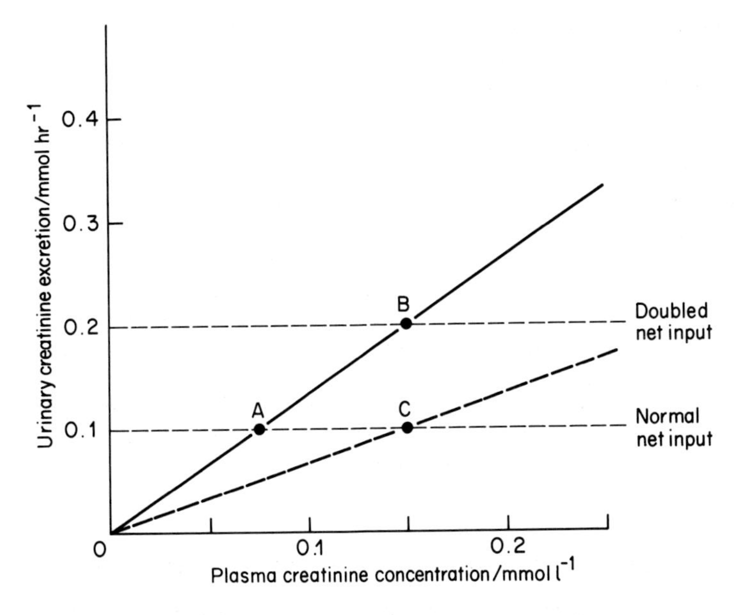

Fig. 10.2. Renal function curves for creatinine. The continuous line shows the normal relationship between creatinine excretion and its plasma concentration given constant GFR. The lower dotted horizontal line shows the normal net input into the ECF, mainly by release from muscle cells. The crossing point A gives the normal steady-state plasma concentration. If production of creatinine doubles, the input is as shown by the upper horizontal line and the crosssing point becomes B. The plasma concentration in this new steady state is twice normal. If creatinine clearance falls to half normal, the renal function curve becomes that shown by the dashed line. This altered output curve crosses the normal input at C, indicating a doubled plasma concentration.

plasma concentration at this intersection is the steady state concentration. The only ways in which the plasma concentration can be changed in the steady state are by changes in

1. the relation between plasma concentration and excretion or
2. the net input.

The diagram indicates the effects of reducing the slope of the renal function curve to a half (as would occur for creatinine in renal disease that halved the glomerular filtration rate) and also the effect of doubling the net input. Taking the latter example, when net input increases creatinine will accumulate in the extracellular fluid and its concentration will rise. But, as its concentration rises so does the rate at which it is excreted until once more excretion balances output – at the cost of an increase in plasma concentration. If, for any substance, net input exceeds the kidney's ability to excrete it there will be progressive, perhaps fatal, accumulation.

Plots like those in Fig. 10.2 show what happens in the steady state, but do not easily show what happens during transitions between steady states or with shor-lived changes in input. The consequences of such a change are shown in

Fig. 10.3 in which plasma concentration, net input and renal excretion are plotted against time. Panel (a) shows what happens with a maintained doubling of the net input into the extracellular fluid as might be achieved by a constant infusion. At first, input exceeds output and there is accumulation in the extracellular fluid and a rise in plasma concentration. As the plasma concentration increases so excretion increases until a new steady state level is reached at which the doubled plasma concentration results in a doubled rate of urinary excretion thus matching the doubled input. Reverse changes occur after the infusion is stopped. Fig. 10.3 (b) shows a similar analysis, but this time for a maintained change in the ability of the kidney to excrete the substance. The important point here is to note that an increased capacity to excrete, i.e. an increased rate of urinary excretion for a given plasma concentration, results in a transient increase in excretion but then a new steady state in which, naturally, excretion must again match net input. The persistent change is the reduced plasma level. We will return to this point when considering the influence of diuretic drugs on the renal excretion of sodium in Chapter 14.

Regulation of the type shown in Fig. 10.2 does not allow very close control of plasma concentration. A doubling of input causes a doubling of the plasma level. This is acceptable for relatively harmless end products such as creatinine or urea. It is not satisfactory for substances like potassium which must be closely regulated even though intake can vary by ten fold or more. A much steeper relation between the regulated variable, e.g. plasma potassium concentration, and renal excretion is needed (and provided) so that only small changes in plasma concentration lead to the requisite changes in urinary excretion. The mechanisms and implications of these much steeper relationships are discussed for specific solutes in subsequent Chapters.

Factors and agents that can affect kidney function

The important factors that act upon the kidneys to alter or control excretion can be subdivided into five not necessarily exclusive catagories:

1. plasma concentration of the individual solutes;
2. physical properties of the circulation, e.g. arterial blood pressure and colloid osmotic pressure;
3. nervous and hormonal influences;
4. pathological changes;
5. drugs (pharmacological agents).

It is also useful to consider here changes in excretion caused by changes in glomerular filtration rate and renal plasma flow. Diuretics are considered in chapter 14.

Plasma concentration

The plasma concentration of each substance can directly control the rate at which it is excreted. For creatinine, Fig. 10.2, or inulin, Fig. 10.4(a), other things being equal, the higher the plasma concentration the more that is filtered and excreted. Also shown in Fig. 10.4 are several other relations between

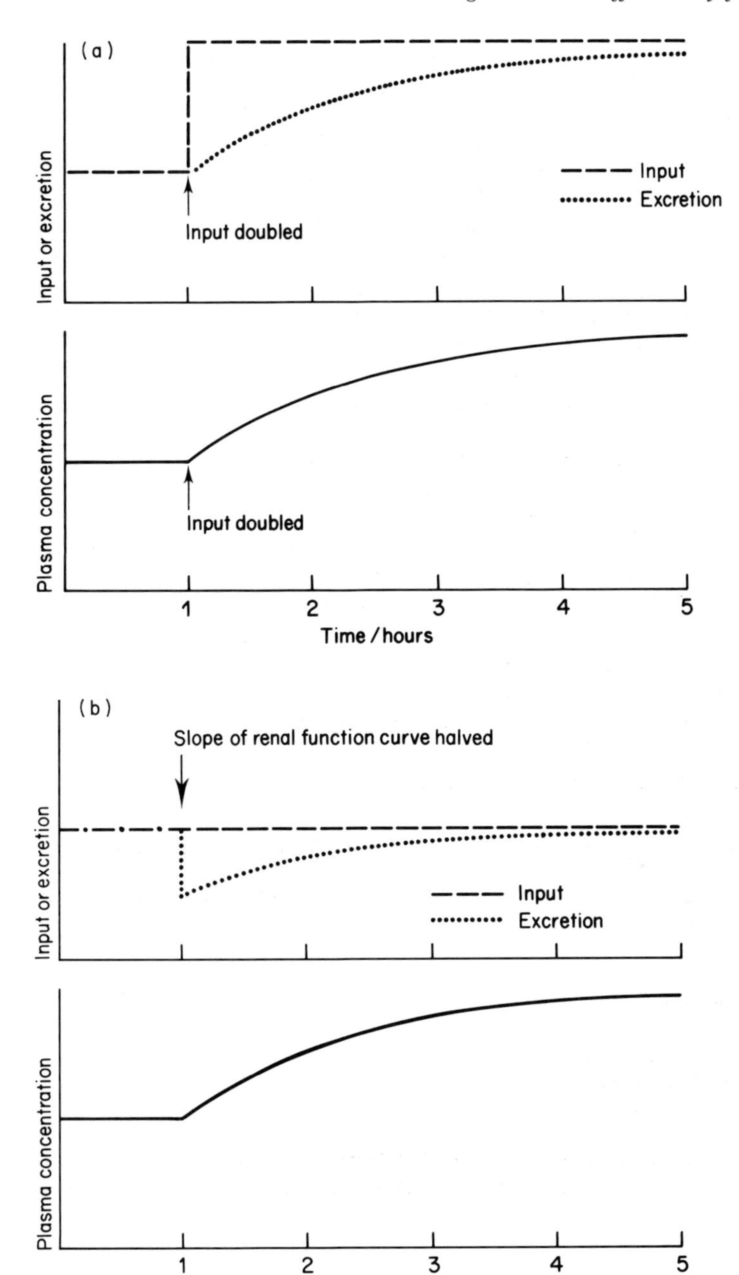

Fig. 10.3. Diagram to indicate the time course of changes in excretion and plasma concentration of creatinine following: (a) a sudden doubling of the rate of input into the ECF, or (b) a sudden halving of the renal clearance (e.g. as could follow ligation of the blood vessels to one kidney).

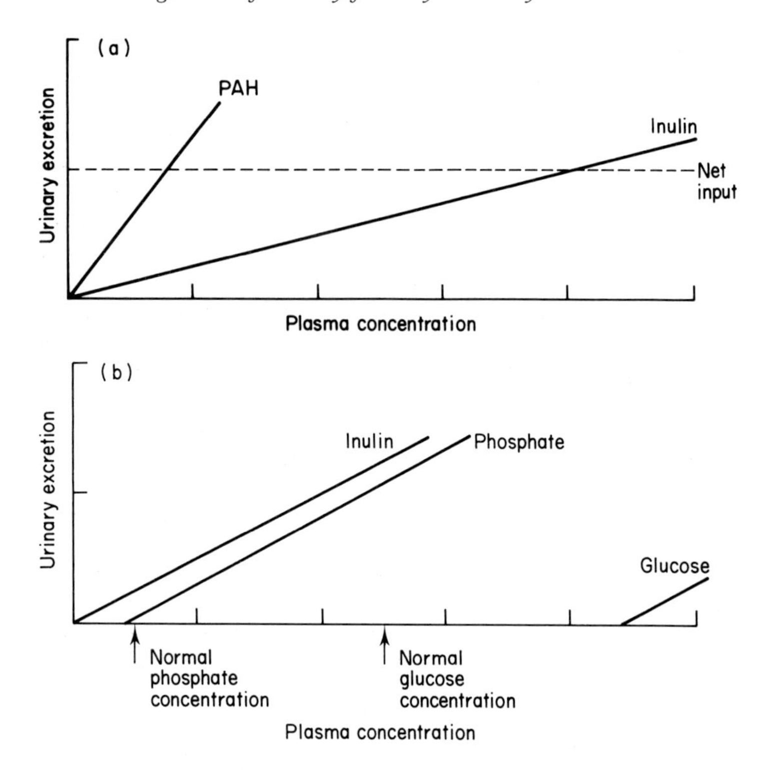

Fig. 10.4. Renal function curves for paraaminohippuric acid (PAH), inulin, phosphate and glucose. At plasma levels which do not saturate the secretion process for PAH, i.e. which are well below its T_m (see p. 39 ff), the slope for PAH is five times that for inulin because renal plasma flow is about five times larger than GFR (see Chapter 4). This means that for the same net input, e.g. infusion at the same rate, the plasma level will be five times lower for PAH than for inulin as seen from the crossing points. This illustrates the value of tubular secretion of potentially toxic metabolites. Phosphate and glucose share the same pattern, i.e. no excretion until T_m is reached and then increasing excretion along a line parallel to that for inulin. They differ however in the normal plasma concentrations. The concentration of phosphate normally sits at a point where the T_m is just exceeded and a small net input is matched by a small renal excretion. Glucose concentration is usually far below that for the T_m and normally none is excreted.

plasma concentration and excretion, each of which depends relatively simply on properties of the nephron. For a substance which is secreted into the tubules as well as filtered, e.g. PAH, the excretion is greater for each plasma level. Then as indicated in Fig. 10.4(a) for a given input into the extracellular fluid the plasma concentration in the steady state will be lower. Secretion reduces plasma levels (see also p. 131).

Some substances are normally mostly (e.g. phosphate) or almost completely (e.g. glucose) reabsorbed in the tubules as shown in Fig. 10.4(b). For these substances the kidneys are a kind of overflow control. For plasma levels that do not cause the amount filtered to exceed the T_m the maximum amount which can be reabsorbed, very little 'overflows' into the urine, and the kidneys play no part in regulating the plasma levels. This is the normal state of affairs for useful organic metabolites. Only when levels become pathologically high, or when reabsorption is defective, do substances such as glucose, amino acids and tricarboxylic acids overflow into the urine.

Substances like phosphate, as illustrated in Fig. 10.4(b), or sulphate (see p. 142) are normally present at concentrations at which the filtered load only slightly exceeds the T_m. This allows the normal small net input to be matched by the overflow excretion. Should plasma levels fall only slightly excretion virtually ceases; if the plasma level rises slightly there is a large increase in excretion since all the extra filtered load is excreted. For instance the increase from 1.0 to 1.1 mM phosphate concentration could more than double urinary excretion. This kind of relationship between plasma concentration and renal excretion is effective in preventing large increases in plasma levels when there are fluctuations in the input. An interesting feature of this type of overflow control is that the level of the overflow can be altered if the T_m can be changed. For example, parathyroid hormone reduces the T_m for phosphate which shifts the phosphate curve in Fig. 10.4 to the left. This reduction in T_m will therefore reduce steady state plasma levels for a given net input into the extracellular fluid.

In the examples shown above the mechanisms by which excretion varies in response to changes in plasma levels are relatively straightforward. For some substances such as potassium the plasma concentration, acting directly on the nephron, is a major influence on the urinary excretion, although the tubular mechanisms are largely unknown (see p. 83ff). The very steep renal function curves for potassium are shown and discussed in Chapter 12.

For two of the most important constituents of urine, water and sodium, the plasma concentrations appear to have little direct effect on the kidneys. Changes in water concentration, i.e. osmolality, influence water excretion via a complex neuro humoral feedback using ADH (see Chapter 13). Changes in plasma sodium *concentration* appear not to have much effect on sodium excretion (at least in man). Rather, changes in sodium excretion are caused primarily by the consequences of increased sodium (and water) *content* of the extracellular fluid (see Chapter 14).

Changes in glomerular filtration rate and renal plasma flow

For solutes like creatinine, for which the urinary output equals filtration, or phosphate for which loss is the excess of filtration over its T_m, the excretion varies with plasma concentration because excretion varies with the amount filtered. The amount of a substance filtered is equal to the product of its (free) plasma concentration and GFR. If GFR increases, excretion of the substance initially increases, and its plasma concentration falls. If GFR remains increased, the concentration continues to fall until the rate of excretion is reduced sufficiently to again equal the rate of intake. Thus for constant intake, the plasma concentration varies inversely with GFR.

The plasma concentrations of non-toxic substances, like creatinine and urea, are not critical. Only drastic depression of GFR such as can accompany severe kidney disease produces dangerous elevations in their concentrations. The levels of substances like phosphate, of which the plasma concentrations are subject to overflow control, are more critical. Small changes in GFR are then potentially more significant. Stabilization of GFR by autoregulation serves to reduce spurious fluctuations of excretion and hence to maintain the plasma concentrations at constant levels.

For solutes secreted by the organic ion transport systems of the proximal tubule, the amount excreted varies with renal plasma flow. As with GFR, changes in renal plasma flow are of concern primarily in severe kidney disease. Much higher than normal plasma levels are then required before excretion can match the net input into the extracellular fluid, and it is this fact that causes the accumulation of potentially toxic metabolic end products in chronic renal failure.

Many drugs are also excreted either by glomerular filtration or by filtration together with tubular secretion so that reduction of GFR and renal plasma flow will result in much slower elimination. Repeated doses of drugs, which would be appropriate for a patient with normal kidney function, can easily lead under these conditions to dangerous elevation of plasma levels. These important points are considered in more detail in *Disorders of the Kidney and Urinary Tract.*

Physical factors: arterial blood pressure and colloid osmotic pressure

Increases in renal perfusion pressure or decreases in colloid osmotic pressure markedly increase urine flow rate and sodium excretion (see p. 73) even though as a result of autoregulation GFR changes very little (see p. 54ff). The effects on sodium are considered in Chapter 14. The excretion of potassium, chloride, and bicarbonate are increased as consequences of the increases in sodium excretion and flow as discussed in Chapters 6 and 7.

Hormones

Antidiuretic hormone, angiotensin II, and aldosterone

These three hormones whose names all begin with the letter 'A' have particularly important effects on the kidneys. The mechanisms by which ADH alters the volume and concentration of the urine are considered in Chapters 7 and 8. The regulation of ADH secretion and its effect on body fluids is considered in detail in Chapter 13. Angiotensin acts on the vasculature within the kidneys and on the tubules to reduce salt excretion (see p. 73). In the circulation, acting as a hormone, it stimulates aldosterone release and produces a general vasoconstriction throughout the vasculature. Its effects on sodium regulation are considered in Chapter 14. Control of its production and its effects in the general circulation are discussed in Chapter 9. Aldosterone is a steroid hormone released from the *zona glomerulosa* (the outer region) of the adrenal cortex. It can be thought of as a sodium retaining and potassium excreting hormone (see pp. 84 and 93 and Chapters 12 and 14).

Natriuretic factors

There appear to be two, or more, humoral factors in addition to those listed above that contribute to the regulation of sodium excretion. These are discussed in Chapter 14.

Parathyroid hormone

Increasing levels of parathyroid hormone increase the excretion of phosphate, decrease (at constant plasma calcium concentration) the excretion of calcium, and decrease proximal reabsorption of most solutes (see pp. 72, 73, & 84–5). The role of parathyroid hormone in the homeostasis of calcium and phosphate is considered in Chapter 12.

Other hormones

Growth hormone appears to stimulate tubular reabsorption of sulphate, as mentioned on p. 142. Glucocorticoids, primarily cortisol and corticosterone, and the thyroid hormones have effects in the kidneys, but physiological variations in their levels are not known to be part of normal control. As with most other organs, adequate levels of glucocorticoids are needed for normal function, the so called permissive effect. One consequence of glucocorticoid deficiency is impaired excretion of a water load; this deficit apparently results partly from an effect in the collecting system and partly because of inappropriate ADH secretion. Excessive levels of glucocorticoids cause sodium retention and potassium loss as a result of their mineralocorticoid (aldosterone-like) effects in the distal tubule. Hypothyroidism leads to reduced GFR and renal blood flow and apparently to excess excretion of ADH which impairs excretion of water. Hyperthyroidism leads to increased GFR and renal blood flow but no obvious abnormality of plasma composition. The mechanisms of these pathological changes are still obscure.

Other chemical influences

Many naturally occurring messenger substances, other than those discussed above, can influence renal function. These include dopamine, the prostaglandins, and the kallikrein–kinin system. These substances can be formed in or secreted within the kidneys and probably have important roles in local regulation or in mediating or modifying the influence of external agents.

Dopamine

Specific dopaminergic, D_1 receptors have been identified in the renal vasculature. Some of the renal sympathetic nerves appear to be dopaminergic and the kidney can convert circulating L-dopa to dopamine using the tubular cell enzyme, dopa decarboxylase. The main effects of infused dopamine seem to be vasodilator and natriuretic by virtue of both increased GFR and reduced tubular reabsorption. Just how dopamine is involved in the physiological regulation of kidney function is still unclear, as are the detailed mechanisms by which it exerts its effects. Dopamine is used as a drug in certain forms of acute renal failure and as a pretreatment for donor kidneys prior to transplantation. These points are discussed further in *Disorders of the Kidney and Urinary Tract*.

Prostaglandins

Prostaglandins play numerous roles as cellular regulators in many tissues and the formation of several types including PGE_2, PGI_2 and thromboxane has been demonstrated in kidney tissues. PGI_2 and PGE_2 stimulate renin release and it is thought that one or the other may mediate the stimulation produced by a fall in renal perfusion pressure and also possibly play a role in the macula densa control of renin secretion. PGE_2 is formed in the medulla in response to a number of influences including angiotensin. This prostaglandin is vasodilator and may modulate the constrictor effects of angiotensin. Inhibition of prostaglandin synthesis by agents such as indomethacin or aspirin tends to lower plasma renin levels and to compromise medullary blood flow as might be expected from the actions stated above. Severe haemorrage is then more likely to result in ischaemic damage to the renal medulla. Some such mechanism may underly the severe damage, the so called analgesic induced papillary necrosis, that can occur in the renal medulla of some patients who have taken large quantities of this type of drug over many years.

ADH promotes the formation of PGE and PGE appears to counteract the effects of ADH. It is therefore found in experimental animals and in man that inhibition of prostaglandin synthesis can enhance the renal response to fluctuations in plasma levels of ADH.

Despite an enormous amount of work, the role of the prostaglandins in normal physiological regulation and in pathalogical conditions is still not well understood. Even in the presence of sufficient inhibitor completely to prevent the formation of prostaglandins there does not appear to be serious perturbation of renal function under reasonably normal conditions. The ability of the kidneys to respond to severely stressful conditions may be seriously diminished in the absence of prostaglandin formation.

Kallikrein

The kallikreins are a family of enzymes found in many tissues, which can cleave biologically active peptides from plasma globulins as does renin. One of the best known products is bradykinin, a potent vasodilator. Infusion of bradykinin into the renal artery causes renal vasodilatation and an increase in sodium excretion; also many procedures which increase the excretion of sodium are associated with increased amounts of kallikrein in the urine. It has therefore been proposed that kallikrein is in some way involved in the regulation of sodium excretion. However the evidence is somewhat controversial, and up to the present time no clear picture as to the physiological and pathophysiological role of kallikrein has emerged.

The renal nerves

The efferent nerve supply to the kidneys is mainly sympathetic postganglionic. There is a rich supply to the vasculature including the afferent and efferent arterioles, and it is now established that the tubules, at least near the glomerulus, are also innervated. The main neurotransmitter is probably noradrenaline though some of the fibres are dopaminergic. Increased renal nerve activity appears to have two main functions: control of renal blood flow in times of emergency, when all nonessential blood flows are reduced, and antinatriuresis. The role, if any, of the latter in normal control is considered in Chapter 14. Stimulation of renin release is considered in Chapters 9 and 14.

Further reading

Cannon, W.B. (1947). *The Wisdom of the Body*, Kegan Paul Tench, London.
Currie, M.G. & Needleman, P. (1984). Renal arachidonic acid metabolism. *Ann. Rev. Physiol* **46**, 327–341.
Lee, M.R. (1982). Dopamine and the kidney. *Clin. Sci.* **62**, 439–448.
Lifschitz, M.D. & Stein, J.H. (1981). Renal vasoactive hormones. Chapter 14, pp. 650–720 in *The Kidney* 2nd edn, Brenner, B.M. & Rector, F.C. Jr., eds, Saunders, Philadelphia.
Margolius, H.S. (1984). The kallikrein-kinin system and the kidney. *Ann. Rev. Physiol* **46**, 309–326.

11

Nitrogenous wastes and foreign substances

One of the main jobs for the kidneys is to remove metabolic end products and exogenous materials that are toxic or simply not wanted. Quantitatively the major task is excretion of the nitrogenous end products of protein and nucleic acid catabolism.

Urea

Formation

Intracellular catabolism of protein and intestinal absorption both add to the pool of free amino acids available in the body. Some of these are used for the synthesis of new protein. Most of the rest are made available for energy metabolism in the Kreb's cycle by deamination. These deaminations release the equivalent of one ammonium ion for each amino group removed. Ammonium itself, however, is highly toxic and the concentrations in the body fluids must be kept very low. Therefore in the tissues most amino groups are removed by transfer from the amino acids to carrier molecules which are then taken in the blood to sites where the ammonium or its equivalent can be released and dealt with by excretion or more specific reactions. An important example of such a carrier is α-ketoglutarate which can be transaminated to glutamate in almost all cells. The α-ketoglutarate is regenerated at the site of the subsequent deamination and transported back to the tissues.

In aquatic animals the oxidative deamination directly produces free ammonium which is rapidly excreted into the surrounding water. Terrestrial animals use more complicated reactions which allow them to convert the ammonium into a less toxic form. In mammals amino groups on carriers and the free ammonium generated in the rest of the body are delivered to the liver where the deamination is linked to the synthesis of urea by the reactions of the urea cycle. Only half of the ammonium is ever released in free form, the other half enters the urea cycle as the α-amino group of aspartate. This cycle and the web of reactions surrounding it are described in all standard biochemistry textbooks. Together they achieve the equivalent of releasing one ammonium ion for each amino group and incorporating the ammonium into urea.

$$2NH_4^+ + CO_2 \rightarrow H_2N{-}C({=}O){-}NH_2 + 2H^+ + H_2O$$

Urea production occurs almost exclusively in the liver, the only tissue containing one of the necessary enzymes, arginase.

On a typical western diet human systemic blood plasma has an ammonium concentration less than 0.1 mM and thus the total amount of free ammonium in the body (excluding urine and faeces) is less than 10 mmol. Since the production of ammonium ions from amino acids can easily exceed 1 mol/day, which is far greater than the ammonium content of the body, it is clear that the rate of urea synthesis is tied closely to the rate of ammonium production (see pp. 203–4). The rate of both reflects

1. a small obligatory catabolism of body proteins;
2. the positive nitrogen balance of the individual, i.e. the excess of protein intake over requirements.

Urea production is thus reduced on a low protein diet and vice versa.

Properties

Urea is very water-soluble and extraordinarily non toxic. Thus a lot of urea can be excreted in very little urine without precipitating, and its concentration in body fluids can be permitted to fluctuate over a fairly wide range, roughly 2–6 mM, in normal individuals. Alterations in urea concentration do not cause shifts of water between intra- and extracellular compartments because

1. changes in urea concentrations are usually relatively small and slow;
2. cell membranes are rather permeable to urea (some cells are exceedingly permeable, see below) so that urea equilibrates across cell membranes and shifts of fluid volume are avoided.

Excretion

Despite its innocuousness, urea does have to be eliminated by the kidneys. It is freely filtered. The proportion of the filtered load which is excreted varies with conditions, mainly with the concentration of ADH (antidiuretic hormone) and with urine flow. At moderately high urine flows urea clearance is about 60 per cent of the filtered load. At low urine flows urea clearance falls owing to increased urea permeability in the inner medullary collecting duct as described in Chapter 8. The reduced clearance of urea can double the plasma concentration during antidiuresis. The concentration of urea in human urine might typically be about 200 mM, in antidiuresis 600 mM and during water diuresis 40 mM. In some desert mammals urinary urea concentration may be as high as 2 M.

Urea in renal failure

With decreasing GFR, the plasma concentration of urea must rise proportionately to keep the rate of excretion equal to the rate of production. Large rises occur only with severely reduced filtration. The syndrome of chronic renal failure is sometimes known as uraemia (too much urea in the blood). Most of the pathological effects cannot be attributed to urea. But grossly elevated urea may contribute to the nausea and vomiting in renal failure, perhaps by its presence in the gut altering gut bacteria and leading to ammonia production. High urea may cause a tendency to bleed. Renal failure is discussed in Chapters 3 and 4 of *Disorders of the Kidney and Urinary Tract.*

Infusions of hypertonic urea solutions have sometimes been used clinically to reduce cerebral oedema by osmotically removing water from the brain. This works because the blood-brain barrier is only poorly permeable to urea and the kidneys excrete most of it before much can equilibrate into the brain. Mannitol infusion would now be used instead.

Mammalian red blood cells have an exceedingly high permeability to urea. Their special urea transporter may have evolved to protect them from excessive cell shrinkage during the passage down the vasa recta into the medulla where urea concentrations can exceed 0.5 M. Osmotic equilibration by entry of urea into the cells, rather than extraction of water, avoids the severe shrinkage which would greatly reduce red cell deformability and prevent their passage down the capillaries. It has also been pointed out that the very high permeability is also important in allowing the urea that gets into the red cells on the way down the vasa recta to get out on the way up. This avoids a wash-out of urea from the inner medulla.

Purines

The purine residues of the nucleic acids are degraded in a series of steps with different compounds being excreted by different groups of animals, see Fig. 11.1. Most mammals possess the enzyme uricase in their liver which converts uric

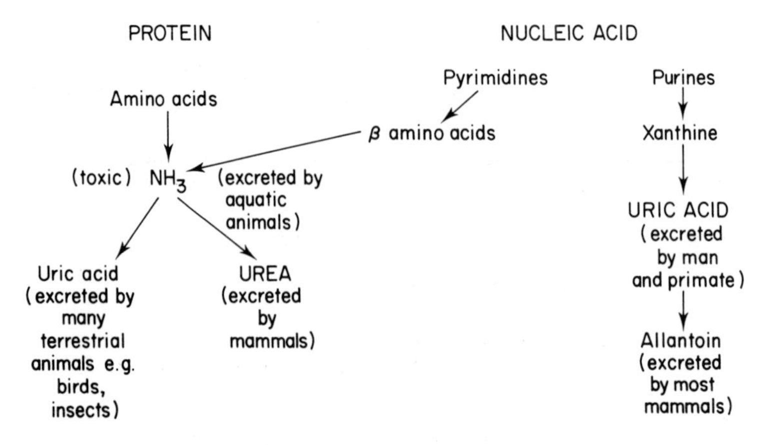

Fig. 11.1. Major pathways of catabolism of nitrogenous compounds.

acid into the relatively nontoxic, soluble and easily excreted compound, allantoin. Primates, including man, lack this enzyme and so the main product of purine metabolism is uric acid.

Unlike urea, uric acid has a low solubility in the body fluids, and it is potentially quite toxic by virtue of its tendency to form precipitates in soft tissues which gives rise to gout, a very painful and damaging condition.

Uric acid is very largely excreted by the kidneys though some may get into the faeces via secretion into the gut. Only a small proportion of uric acid is bound to plasma protein and so it is present in glomerular filtrate at nearly the concentration as in plasma. As discussed in Chapter 6, the tubular handling of uric acid is complex; the net result in humans is to leave approximately 10 per cent of the filtered load to be excreted in urine. Fig. 11.2 shows urate excretion curves for a normal person and also for a subject with reduced tubular secretion of urate. Such a disorder of urate excretion would increase plasma urate level. Drugs that inhibit reabsorption of urate, such as probenicid, steepen the excretion curve and reduce plasma levels. Another way to reduce elevated plasma urate is to use allopurinol, a compond which inhibits xanthine oxidase and so reduces urate production at the expense of an increase in the concentration of the less toxic xanthine.

One supposes that there must be some strong selective pressure on primates favouring the production and circulation of uric acid at dangerous levels when other mammals apparently sensibly convert most of it to allantoin. One suggestion is that urate secreted in the digestive juices combines with toxic compounds in certain plants and prevents their absorption, so increasing the range of plants available as food.

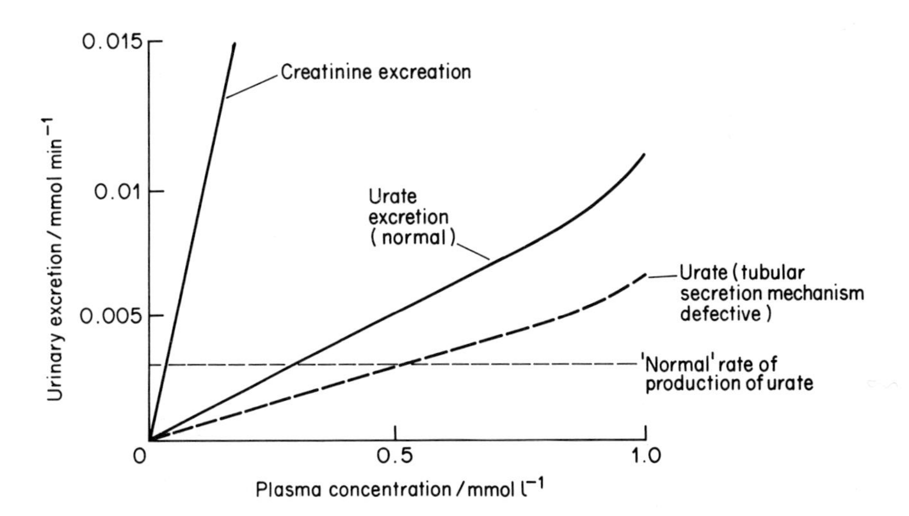

Fig. 11.2. Diagram to show the relation between uric acid concentration in plasma and its excretion. The normal rate of production is shown so that it can be seen that excretion will match production at a plasma level around 0.25 mM. If tubular secretion is defective, a higher plasma level is required for balance. The renal function curve for creatinine is shown for comparison. Note that with a clearance some 10 times greater than that of uric acid, creatinine would have a plasma level 10 times smaller for the same rate of production.

In some terrestrial species uric acid is not only the end product of purine metabolism but also the means for eliminating the ammonium ions produced by protein catabolism. These so called uricotelic animals include birds, some reptiles, insects and land-snails. These turn the insolubility of uric acid to advantage and use it to convert ammonium ions into a solid form which can be excreted without loss of water. Such excretion requires structures like the cloaca of birds into which uric acid can be avidly secreted to hold down plasma levels, and from which a paste like semisolid material can be ejected. The use of uric acid is also a particular advantage for embryos developing inside eggs with impervious shells since it can be laid down as crystals without compromising the limited supply of water.

Ammonium

Even in mammals some nitrogen is excreted in the urine as ammonium salts in amounts which vary with the pH of the urine (see pp. 89ff and 211ff). Most of this ammonium (always more than two-thirds, a much larger proportion at high excretion rates) is produced within the kidneys. On a standard diet the amount of nitrogen normally excreted as ammonium in human urine amounts to only some 50 mmol/day, much less than the hundreds of millimoles excreted as urea. But in chronic acidosis urinary ammonium excretion can be greatly elevated and urea excretion is reduced. The ammonium then represents a sizeable fraction of the excreted nitrogen.

The nitrogen of the excreted ammonium arises from deamination within the kidneys of glutamine and various amino-acids. However, these are replaced by reactions which depend on transaminations from amino acids in the rest of the body. The excretion of ammonium in the kidney therefore depletes the pool of amino acids. The decrease in the rate of urea synthesis may be a consequences of this change.

Creatinine

This nitrogenous compound is discharged from muscle tissue at a relatively constant rate. It is freely filtered and there is additionally a small tubular secretion so that its clearance should exceed that of inulin. The use of creatinine clearance as an estimate of glomerular filtration rate is discussed on p. 38 and in Chapter 1 of *Disorders of the Kidney and Urinary Tract*.

Under normal conditions urinary creatinine accounts for less than 10 per cent of the nitrogen excretion.

Small proteins and polypeptides

Peptides which are smaller than molecular weight *c* 50 000 and not bound to larger proteins will be filtered into the tubular fluid. In addition even a small amount of plasma protein does get filtered, possibly through defects in the capillary walls. These proteins and polypeptides are normally returned to the blood as their component amino acids, as discussed on p. 64. This process removes biologically active peptides such as insulin from the blood while conserving the amino acids. In renal failure with severe reduction in GFR the half-times of disappearance of insulin and some other peptide hormones are increased.

Increased filtration and excretion of protein occurs following extensive intravascular haemolysis when the urine contains haemoglobin, and in nephrotic syndrome where the glomerular membrane becomes leaky even to plasma proteins.

Substances secreted into the nephron

As has been discussed in Chapter 6 (p. 64), many metabolic end products and other organic ions are actively secreted into the tubular fluid. This arrangement can achieve very rapid excretion even for substances largely bound to plasma proteins and so it can both eliminate rapidly a given amount of substance added to the extracellular fluid and hold plasma levels very low in the face of a continued input. A secretory process with an adequate transport rate can lower the free plasma concentration of the substance. This lowering leads to net release of bound substance which can then also be removed from the tubule by the secretory process. Thus avid secretion can remove virtually all of a substance from plasma, while filtration can only remove a fraction of that which is free. The combination of binding to plasma proteins and secretion into the tubules is therefore excellent for dealing with rather toxic compounds whose free concentration in plasma must be kept low while they are transported to the kidneys, but which must still be excreted at a substantial rate.

Effects of Conjugation

Many foreign compounds are conjugated with groups such as hippurate and glycine either in the liver or to a lesser extent in the kidneys. This conjugation affects their excretion in two ways.

1. Non-polar compounds are frequently substantially bound to plasma proteins and thus are not freely filtered through the glomerulus. They can also back-diffuse from the lumen into the blood. Making such compounds more polar may increase the amount filtered and reduce passive reabsorption, and thus enhance the excretion in urine.
2. Conjugates are often actively secreted into the tubules, a process which greatly increases the rate of their elimination in the urine.

Effect of pH on the excretion of weak acids and bases

Efficient excretion of toxic or unwanted substances needs a large clearance which is only possible if most or all of what gets filtered or secreted stays in the tubule right to the end. Polar compounds will stay in the luminal fluid so long as there are no specific transporters to reabsorb them. The kidneys are very efficient at eliminating foreign polar substances such as penicillin, mannitol, and inulin. Lipophilic compounds will diffuse back across the tubule as their luminal concentrations rise with progressive fluid reabsorption and thus renal clearances for these are very small. For instance the kidneys do not contribute significantly to the elimination of ethanol or volatile anaesthetics from the body.

Many weak acids or bases have a charged hydrophilic form in equilibrium with an uncharged lipophilic form. The position of this equilibrium depends on the pH, and the pH therefore determines whether most of the substance will be trapped in the lumen as the charged form, or be able to diffuse back into the blood. These effects are discussed for ammonia and ammonium on p. 89ff.

Urine pH is of some importance in the elimination of certain drugs, including some that are commonly subject to deliberate or accidental overdose. Aspirin and barbiturates are weak acids whose excretion can be increased by making the urine alkaline. Opiates and amphetamines are weak bases, best excreted in an acid urine.

Further reading

Chonko, A.M. & Grantham, J.J. (1981). Disorders of urate metabolism and excretion. Chapter 20. pp. 1023–1055 in *The Kidney*, 2nd ed, Brenner, B.M. & Rector, F.C. Jr., eds, Saunders, Philadelphia.

Irish, J.M. III & Grantham, J.J. (1981). Renal handling of organic anions and cations. Chapter 13, pp. 619–649 in *The Kidney* 2nd edn, Brenner, B.M. & Rector, F.C. Jr., eds, Saunders, Philadelphia.

Pitts, R.F. (1973). Production and excretion of ammonia in relation to acid base regulation. Chapter 15, pp. 455–496 in *Handbook of Physiology, Section 8, Renal Physiology*, Orloff, J. & Berliner, R.W., eds, American Physiological Society, Washington, D.C.

Pitts, R.F. (1974). pp. 217–235, Excretion of Ammonia, in *Physiology of the Kidney and Body Fluids, 3rd Ed.*, Yearbook Medical Publishers, Chicago.

Schmidt-Nielsen, B.M. & Mackay, W.C. (1972). Comparative physiology of electrolyte and water regulation, with emphasis on sodium, potassium, chloride, urea and osmotic pressure. Chapter 2, pp. 45–93 in *Clinical Disorders of Fluid and Electrolyte Metabolism*, 2nd ed, Maxwell, M.H. & Kleeman, C.R., eds, McGraw-Hill, N.Y.

Schmidt-Nielsen, K. (1983). pp. 390–404 in *Animal Physiology: Adaptation and Environment*, 3rd edn, Cambridge University Press, Cambridge.

Stryer, L. (1981). *Biochemistry* 2nd edn, Freeman, San Francisco (pp. 407–415 consider deamination of amino acids and the production of urea.)

12

Potassium, calcium, magnesium, phosphate and sulphate

Potassium

Fig. 12.1 outlines the distribution of body potassium and shows typical values of dietary intake, fecal excretion, and urinary excretion for a man on a normal western diet. Over 98 per cent of the potassium is in cells and more than half of that in skeletal muscle. However, the small amount of extracellular potassium is vitally important for two reasons. Firstly if the extracellular concentrations are correct, the cells will accumulate the correct amounts. Secondly the concentration ratio for potassium is a principal determinant of the membrane potential.

Plasma potassium concentration is normally near 4.5 mM, and values outside the range 3.5–5.5 mM would be considered pathological. Levels below

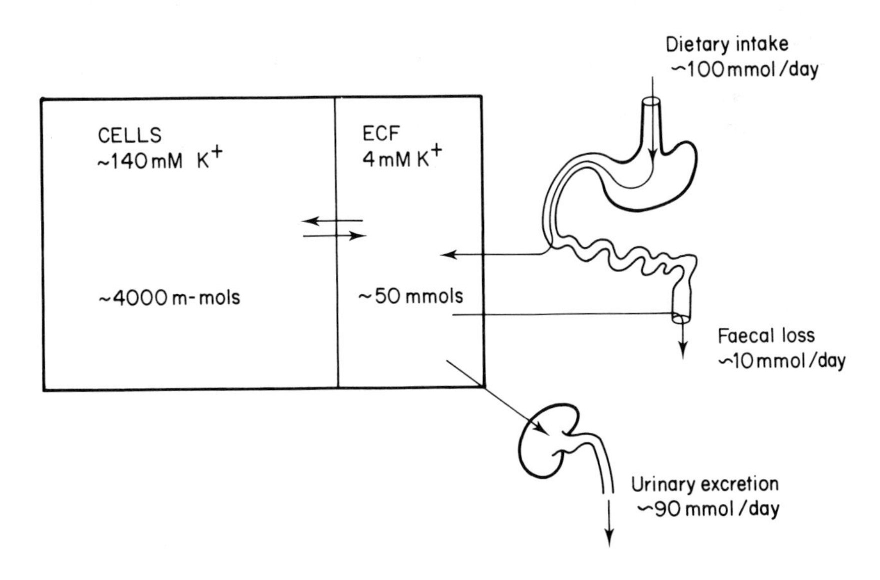

Fig. 12.1. Diagram to show distribution of potassium and typical values for dietary intake and renal and faecal loss.

2 mM or above 8 mM are likely to have serious consequences in many different tissues.

Effects of low potassium levels (hypokalemia) include the following: skeletal muscular weakness or even paralysis; disturbances of cardiac contraction and rhythm and increased sensitivity to the toxic effects of cardiac glycosides such as digitalis; weakness of intestinal smooth muscle with dilatation and ileus (cessation of bowel movements); severe structural and functional damage to renal tubular cells with particular impairment of the ability to dilute or concentrate urine and of the tubular secretory mechanisms. Effects of elevated potassium levels (hyperkalemia) include muscular weakness and most importantly disorders of cardiac excitability. Levels above 8 mM can depress atrioventricular and bundle of His conduction and promote ventricular tachycardia, and finally fibrillation.

The pattern of the ECG is a useful indicator of altered potassium levels. As potassium concentration rises, T-waves become taller and peaked, the PR interval lengthens showing the slowed A-V conduction, and the P-waves may disappear. Then the ventricular dysrhythmias may become apparent. In hypokalemia there may be S-T segment depression and reduced T-wave with prominent U-waves, though these changes are not as reliably seen as the changes associated with hyperkalemia.

It is clear from Fig. 12.1 that in order to maintain a steady extracellular potassium concentration there must be a closely regulated balance of potassium movements in and out of cells and also the dietary intake must be matched by excreted losses. The presence of a large intracellular pool is both a benefit and a threat. Excess input into the extracellular fluid can be temporarily 'buffered' in the cells, and after ingestion of large amounts of potassium this occurs mainly in the liver. But conversely it does not take much tissue destruction to flood the extracellular fluid with potassium. Factors which can alter the bulk distribution of potassium between the intra- and extracellular compartments are mentioned below.

The diet, being composed largely of cells, almost always contains excess potassium but in very variable amounts. So the kidneys must be able to vary the excreted potassium from as little as 5–10 mmol/day to over 500 mmol/day, while maintaining the plasma concentration in the normal range. Fig. 12.2 shows that in the intact animal there is, indeed, a very steep relation between plasma potassium concentration and its excretion. Fig. 12.2(a) shows the response in a dog to infusion of potassium chloride solution. Potassium excretion increased 10 fold while the plasma potassium level rose only about 20 per cent from 3.8–4.6 mM. To emphasize this achievement, consider that to increase creatinine excretion 10 fold would require a 10 fold increase in its plasma concentration. One could say that the kidneys can stabilize plasma potassium 50 times better than they can stabilize creatinine. Fig. 12.2(b) shows that in human subjects, one can also see an extremely steep potassium excretion curve in response to altered potassium input in the diet. The responses of the dog to 30 minute infusions indicate that potassium excretion increases in parallel with the increase in plasma concentration. It has also been found that prolonged administration of high potassium diets increases the ability of the kidneys to excrete potassium while potassium deficient diets reduce this ability. In addition, with high potassium intake there is an increased faecal loss of potas-

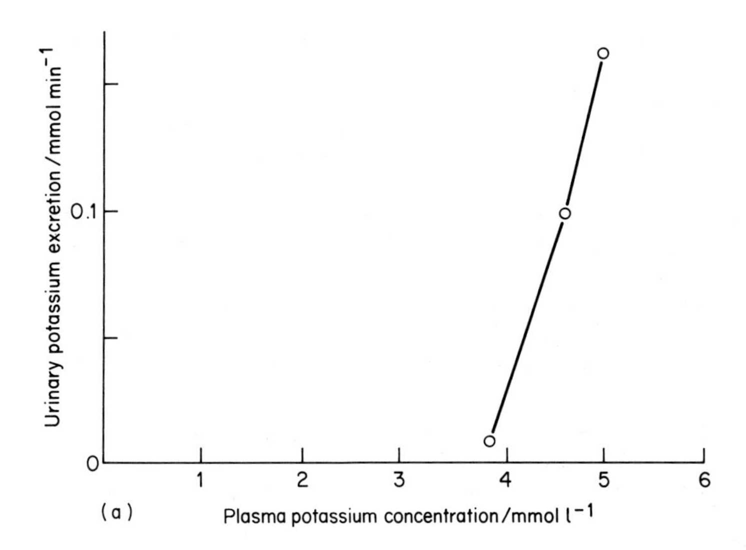

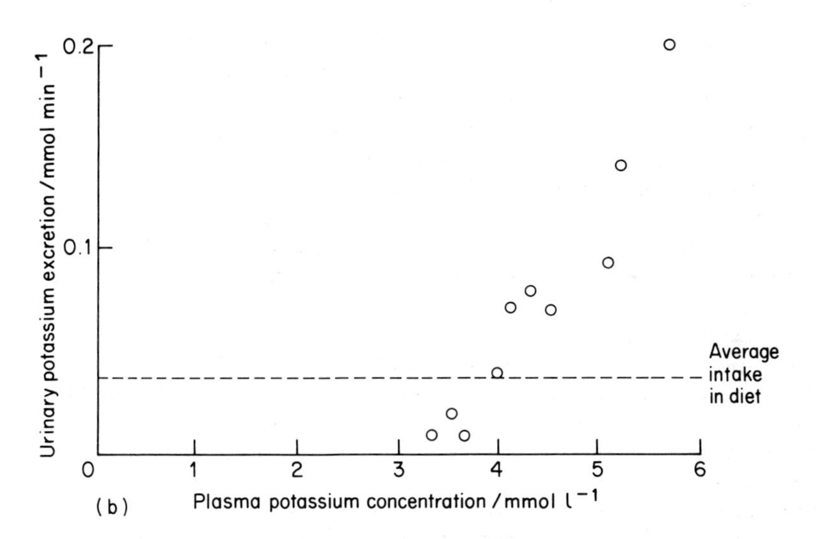

Fig. 12.2. Relation between plasma potassium concentration and potassium excretion. (a) In a dog whose plasma potassium was rapidly increased by intravenous infusion of potassium chloride. (b) In humans on diets containing varying levels of potassium. Data from O'Connor, 1962 and 1982.

sium so that the kidneys are the main, but not the only, regulated excretory route.

What controls renal potassium excretion?

Aldosterone

Potassium excretion can be partly regulated by a hormonal feedback mechanism. Elevated plasma potassium in the relevant range is a potent direct stimulus to the secretion of aldosterone from the adrenal cortex. Aldosterone in turn acts on the distal tubule to enhance potassium secretion and excretion which, as shown in Fig. 12.3(a) completes a negative feedback loop. In fact, some authorities think that aldosterone is more important as a regulator of potassium homeostasis than in controlling sodium excretion. However, the rate of potassium excretion reaches its maximum within an hour following an abrupt elevation of plasma potassium which seems too fast to be explained by variations in aldosterone.

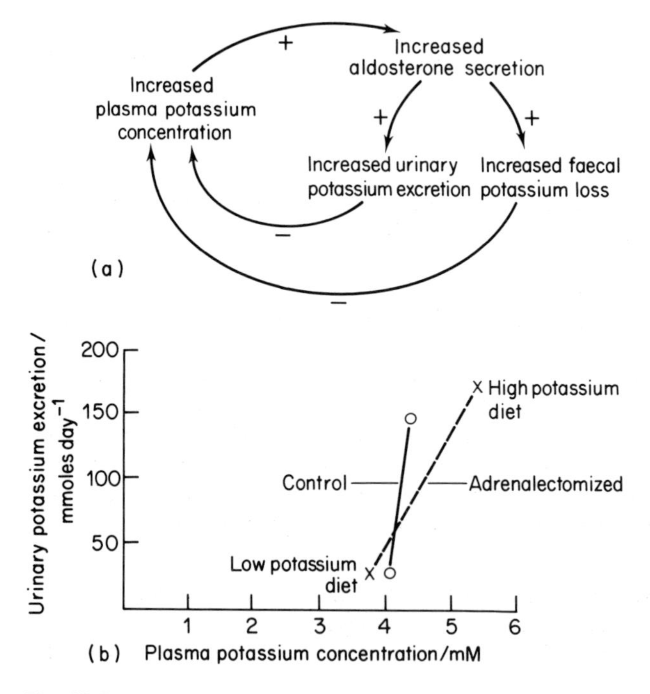

Fig. 12.3. Aldosterone and potassium excretion. (a) Diagram of the relations between plasma potassium and aldosterone secretion, and the level of aldosterone and potassium output. (b) The relation between plasma potassium concentration and urinary potassium excretion in two groups of dogs given either low or high potassium diets. The control animals, O, were able to vary their secretion of aldosterone in response to changes in potassium levels. The other animals, X, had their adrenal glands removed and received a constant infusion of aldosterone; in other words they could not alter their aldosterone levels in response to varying potassium levels. (Data from Young et al, 1976.)

Aldosterone may be important in maintaining the proper relation between potassium excretion and plasma potassium concentration in the face of altered sodium excretion. The secretion of potassium into the distal tubule depends on, among other things, the rate of sodium reabsorption (see Chapter 7). With extracellular fluid depletion delivery of sodium to the distal tubule is greatly reduced which will reduce the rate of sodium reabsorption and hence the secretion of potassium. The increase in aldosterone level can act as a compensatory factor to stimulate potassium secretion and maintain excretion at the required level. Conversely, in sodium overload the excessive delivery of sodium to the distal tubule could result in excessive potassium excretion; an effect which can be countered by the reduction of aldosterone levels.

Intrinsic renal response to potassium.

Despite the undoubted role of aldosterone, recent experiments with dogs have indicated that even when aldosterone levels are artificially prevented from changing, excretion of potassium still rises very steeply with plasma potassium concentration. Fig. 12.3(b) illustrates schematically the findings. Since no other important hormonal or nervous regulation of potassium excretion is known, this suggests that the nephron itself somehow senses plasma potassium and responds accordingly.

Disorders of potassium homeostasis

It is virtually impossible to find a diet sufficiently poor or rich in potassium to cause depletion or overload in a healthy animal. However, a number of other factors can upset this regulation and disorders of potassium homeostasis are not uncommon in medical practice.

Potassium deficiency can be produced by abnormal losses in urine, gut secretions, or occasionally from the skin in sweat or following extensive burns. Excess urinary potassium can result from many factors including: diuretic drugs that increase the sodium load to the distal tubule, e.g. the loop diuretics (see pp. 173–5); excess aldosterone which enhances potassium secretion in the distal tubule and collecting system (see p. 93); and alkalosis which likewise enhances potassium secretion (see p. 84). A reduction of extracellular potassium concentration can also result from an increased uptake into cells which can be caused by

1. alkalosis, with exchange of intracellular H^+ for extracellular potassium;
2. excess insulin (see Hardy, *Endocrine Physiology*.)
3. unknown mechanism in the inherited condition of 'hypokalaemic periodic paralysis'.

Retention of potassium can occur when renal excretion is compromised in renal failure, when there is a lack of aldosterone secretion, and sometimes in acidosis. Large shifts of potassium out of cells can rapidly cause hyperkalemia. This is seen with extensive cell destruction, e.g. intravascular haemolysis or crush injury of large masses of tissue. There may also be a large loss of potassium from cells in acidosis where the uptake of H^+ into cells is partly in exchange for potassium. Remember that it requires the potassium from only about 3 per cent of the cellular compartment to double the extracellular concentration to potentially fatal levels.

Calcium, magnesium, and phosphate

The renal handling of these substances constitutes only a part of the complex interrelationship of processes involved in their homeostasis. For each of them the amount contained in the extracellular fluid is only a tiny proportion of the total body content, calcium and phosphate being the main mineral components of bone and magnesium being a major intracellular cation. The extracellular concentrations are important and fairly closely regulated, especially that of calcium. The kidneys must therefore excrete, day by day, the excess that gets into the extracellular fluid and conversely in deficit these ions must be conserved.

Calcium

Fig. 12.4 outlines the distribution of body calcium and shows a typical daily input and output for a man on a standard western diet. Note, though, that for a child during growth or for a woman during pregnancy or lactation, the net intake from the gut may greatly exceed the output in the urine with the excess going into deposition of bones or the milk.

It is the free calcium in the extracellular fluid that is immediately available either to be bound or to enter cells. It is, thus, the concentration of free calcium that must be controlled. Deviations of about 20 per cent from the normal value can produce distinct symptoms. Lowered free calcium causes increased excitability of nerve and muscle membranes which can lead to twitching and spasms due to spontaneous motor nerve activity and bizarre sensations due to spurious impulses in sensory nerves. Raised calcium levels have serious effects on the kidneys interfering with tubular reabsorption and the urinary concentration process which causes polyuria (excess volume of urine) and consequential thirst and polydipsia (excess drinking). There may also be various neurological disorders and, if the elevation is prolonged, there may be 'metastatic calcification', due to calcium phosphate precipitating inappropriately in various soft tissues. The clinical pictures produced by disorders of calcium homeostasis and detailed consideration of hypo- and hypercalcemia, are discussed in *Disorders of the Kidney and Urinary Tract* and *Clinical Endocrinology*.

Normally only 5–10 mmoles of calcium are excreted in the urine per day. Even at this level various calcium salts in urine can be close to their solubility limits, and any increased excretion of calcium (hypercalciuria) whether due to an increase in the filtered load or to decreased tubular reabsorption can be associated with the formation of renal 'calculi' or 'stones' of calcium oxalate or phosphate in the renal pelvis, ureter or bladder. However, the factors leading to precipitation are complex and in many individuals calcium salts remain dissolved in the urine at concentrations well above their apparent solubilities. These points are considered more fully in *Disorders of the Kidney and Urinary Tract*.

Urinary excretion

It is clear from Fig. 12.4 that changes in the deposition and resorption of calcium from bone and in the absorption of calcium from the gut are likely to be much more important in the short term than changes in renal excretion in regulating extracellular free calcium levels. In the long run of course an adult must excrete the net input of calcium to remain in balance, but we might note that the rapidly exchangeable pool of bone calcium represents about 20 days excretion and the whole of the skeletal content about 15 year's worth. Indeed, renal failure actually causes lowered plasma calcium rather than the elevation one might initially expect from the failure of an excretory mechanism. The processes by which this occurs are discussed below, after we have considered excretion of phosphate.

Under normal circumstances over 95 per cent of the calcium filtered into Bowman's capsule is reabsorbed by the mechanisms discussed on pp. 72 and 84–85. The normal filtered load just exceeds an apparent T_m giving an overflow control as indicated in Fig. 12.5(a). As plasma levels rise above normal, excretion increases and if levels fall excretion virtually stops. Also shown is the effect of increased secretion of parathyroid hormone on the relationship between plasma concentration and excretion. Parathyroid hormone stimulates tubular reabsorption, increasing T_m, and shifts the whole curve to the right. For a maintained net input of calcium this will tend to elevate the steady-state plasma level. Conversely, parathyroid hormone deficiency will reduce tubular reabsorption, increase excretion and so tend to lower plasma levels. Parathyroid hormone also increases plasma calcium levels in two other major ways; it enhances calcium resorption from bone and it increases renal production of 1,25-dihydroxycholecalciferol, which itself promotes calcium uptake from the gut and calcium resorption from bone. These can increase the plasma concentration sufficiently so that the rate of excretion increases despite the renal effects of parathyroid hormone which tend to increase reabsorption.

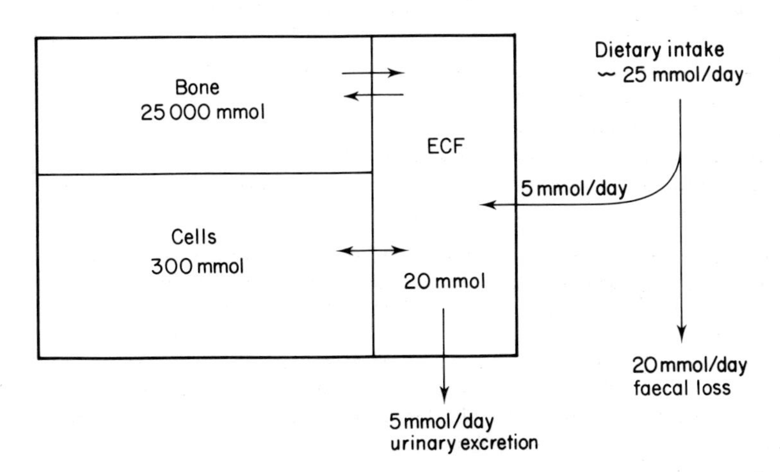

Fig. 12.4. Diagram to indicate distribution of body calcium and typical inputs and outputs for an adult male.

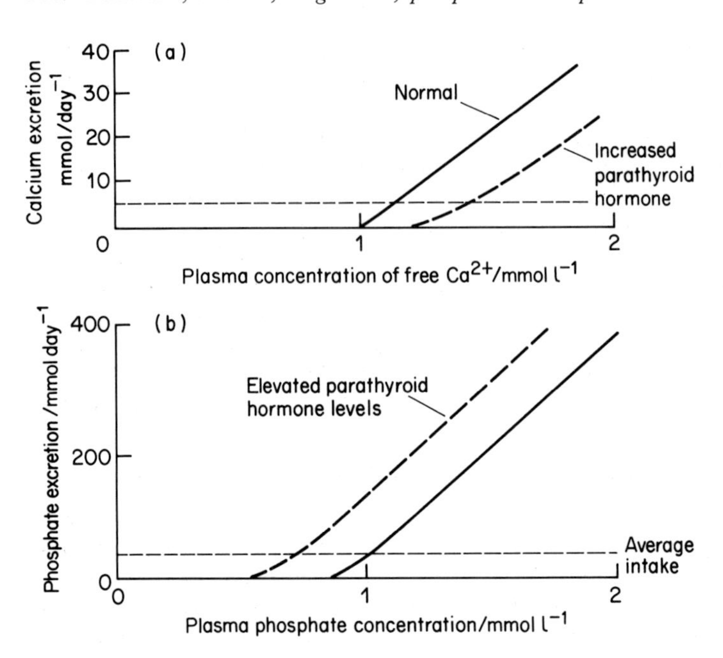

Fig. 12.5. The relations between plasma concentrations of calcium and phosphate and their renal excretion. Also indicated are the effects of parathyroid hormone.

Various other factors can incidentally influence calcium excretion from the kidneys. For instance, calcium reabsorption tends to follow that of sodium, so that the reduced sodium reabsorption in volume expansion or in the presence of diuretic drugs tends to be accompanied by increased urinary excretion of calcium.

Phosphate

Plasma phosphate concentration is normally near 1 mM and only a small proportion, *c* 10 per cent, is bound to macromolecules. There is an enormous store in bone and also a very high content inside cells where tens of millimoles per litre of cell water may be present as part of organic phosphate compounds. Extracellular concentration is not as closely regulated as that of calcium and might vary ± 40–50 per cent with age and with the metabolic state of the body. Plasma phosphate concentration, for instance, may be substantially decreased after a meal or during exercise in association with the cellular uptake of glucose and phosphate to make glucose-6-phosphate. Long term elevations of phosphate can be deleterious because of their effect on plasma calcium levels. Extracellular calcium phosphate is normally near its solubility limit, so that if phosphate levels rise deposition into bone is favoured, precipitation in soft tissues may occur, and free calcium levels can be dangerously depressed. Phosphate deficiency and seriously depressed plasma phosphate levels can be associated with muscular weakness and impairment of function of many different cells and tissues, possibly due to interference with the uptake of glucose and with the lack of high energy phosphate compounds within the cell.

The kidneys seem to play a more central role in phosphate regulation than they do in the regulation of calcium. A typical dietary intake for a man may be 25–50 mmol/day which represents more than the total extracellular phosphate pool. Fig. 12.5(b) indicates the relationship between plasma phosphate concentration and its excretion. As with calcium, it shows overflow behaviour with an apparent T_m just a bit less than the normal filtered load. Parathyroid hormone exerts a significant influence on the tubular handling of phosphate (see p. 72). In this case increased levels of the hormone depress phosphate reabsorption and increase excretion, tending to lower plasma levels. This drop favours resorption of calcium phosphate from bone which tends to elevate plasma calcium levels.

Changes in plasma calcium and phosphate in renal failure

Severe loss of renal function, with GFR and RPF below 10 per cent of normal, tends to cause phosphate retention since normal dietary input now exceeds the filtered load and even if reabsorption were totally suppressed (which it would not be) there would be progressive phosphate accumulation and elevation of plasma levels. We have seen that such an elevation of phosphate levels can depress calcium levels. Thus high phosphate levels are one of the causes of hypocalcaemia in renal failure.

The low calcium caused by the elevated phosphate stimulates excess secretion of parathyroid hormone which tends to enhance the uptake of calcium from the gut and also the reabsorption from bone in an attempt to restore plasma calcium levels towards normal. In the presence of elevated phosphate these effects may so increase the calcium phosphate product as to produce precipitation in various soft tissues producing the so called metastatic calcification, while the increased parathyroid hormone levels actually demineralize the bone itself.

The other major problem of calcium homeostasis in severe kidney disease is caused by the failure of the tubular cells to produce 1,25 dihydroxycholecalciferol despite elevated parathyroid hormone level. This deficit may prevent the elevated parathyroid hormone levels increasing calcium absorption from the gut and so compound the various causes of the hypocalcaemia. Renal failure, renal disease and their consequences are discussed in Chapters 3 and 4 of *Disorders of the Kidney and Urinary Tract.*

Magnesium

Magnesium homeostasis seems not to be quite as critical as that of calcium. It has not been studied so much and is not understood so well. Total plasma magnesium concentration is around 1 mM but as with calcium about half is bound or complexed, leaving 0.5 mM free. Its concentration is not as closely regulated as that of calcium although levels below one-half of normal or more than twice or three times normal can produce serious symptoms. Low magnesium levels can be associated with various signs of neuromuscular overactivity with tremors and mental confusion. High magnesium levels tend to depress neuromuscular function and can lead to respiratory failure and coma with bradycardia (slow heart rate) and finally cardiac arrest.

Average dietary magnesium is around 10 mmol/day with about half of this being absorbed across the gut, and half passing out with the faeces. The net intake in an adult is excreted in the kidneys (see p. 81). In renal failure the plasma levels of magnesium tend to rise as opposed to the falls seen with calcium. Magnesium phosphate is well below its solubility level and so magnesium retention, due to the depressed excretion and to the elevated parathyroid hormone levels, actually causes the plasma magnesium to rise. Very occasionally a massive intake of magnesium in antacid preparations can cause a fatal hypermagnesemia in patients with severe renal failure.

Sulphate

Sulphate, even more than magnesium, is somewhat neglected. Its plasma concentration is normally less than 1 mM. The tubular reabsorption shows a T_m just below the normally filtered load which gives an overflow control. Sulphate reabsorption can be enhanced by growth hormone and this may be associated with an increased requirement for sulphate in the formation of the mucopolysaccharide component of the ground substance of growing tissues. Disorders due to disturbances of extracellular sulphate concentration or sulphate retention in renal failure do not appear to have been described.

The sulphate in plasma is normally added to it, in effect, as sulphuric acid derived from the metabolism of sulphur-containing amino acids. The stimulation of acid excretion by sulphate ions in the tubules is thus of considerable importance in acid-base balance. It is considered further on pp. 87ff and 211.

Further reading

Giebisch, G., Malnic, G. & Berliner, R.W. (1981). Renal transport and control of potassium excretion. Chapter 9, pp. 408–439 in *The Kidney*, 2nd edn, Brenner, B.M. & Rector, F.C. Jr., eds, Saunders, Philadelphia.

Sutton, R.A.L. & Dirks, J.H. (1981). Renal handling of calcium, phosphate, and magnesium. Chapter 12, pp. 551–618 in *The Kidney*, 2nd edn, Brenner, B.M. & Rector, F.C. Jr., eds, Saunders, Philadelphia.

O'Connor, W.J. (1982). *Normal Renal Function*, Croom Helm, London. (Chapter 5, pp. 77–86 Excretion of sulphate, Chapter 6, pp. 87–96 Excretion of phosphate, Chapter 7, pp. 97–110 Excretion of potassium, Chapter 15, pp. 265–272 Intake of sulphur and excretion of sulphate, Chapter 16, pp. 273–282 Intake of phosphorus and excretion of phosphate, Chapter 17, pp. 283–298 Intake and excretion of potassium.)

O'Connor, W.J. (1962). *Renal Function*, Edward Arnold, London.

Pitts, R.F. (1974). *Physiology of the Kidney and Body Fluids*, 3rd edn, Yearbook Medical Publishers, Chicago. (pp. 78–80, Phosphate, pp. 80–81, Sulfate, pp. 117–124, Potassium.)

Young, D.B., McCaa, R.E., Pan, Y. -J. & Guyton, A.C. (1976). Effectiveness of the aldosterone-sodium and -potassium feedback control system. *Am. J. Physiol.* **231**, 945–953.

13

Osmoregulation

The principles of osmoregulation

Plasma osmolality is one of the most closely regulated physiological variables. In any one person it is normally held within extremely narrow limits, e.g. 286 ± 4 mosmol/kg, and it also shows remarkably small variation between healthy individuals. This close control is achieved by very sensitive control of ADH release, which regulates water loss, and when necessary by thirst. Osmolality is so tightly regulated because the osmotic pressure of the body fluids critically influences cell volume.

Osmolality and cell volume

As discussed on p. 20ff, cell membranes are relatively permeable to water and do not usually support a significant hydrostatic pressure. This means that water rapidly equilibrates across the membranes and matches intracellular osmotic pressure to that of the interstitial fluid. Changes in extracellular osmolality therefore cause changes in intracellular volume, at least temporarily. Increased extracellular fluid osmolality draws water out of the cells and the cells shrink. Reduced osmolality swells cells.

Most cells can tolerate 10–20 per cent osmotic swelling or shrinking without noticeable impairment of function. The swelling does not stress the membrane since the cells are not spherical and indeed many cells have membrane folds which can be opened out to accommodate the extra volume. The brain, however, is enclosed in a rigid box, the skull, and if the cells swell something else has to give. Even a little swelling in brain tissue can compress blood vessels sufficiently to cause malfunction and permanent damage. Shrinkage of brain tissue is not much better since it can pull on fine vessels which may rupture and cause diffuse bleeding.

The importance of extracellular sodium concentration

Sodium salts constitute more than 90 per cent of the osmoles in the extracellular fluid and thus of necessity regulation of either sodium concentration or plasma osmolality tends to stabilize both. It is the sodium concentration which appears to be controlled and it is also sodium concentration which is more closely tied to cellular volume. Sodium salts are excluded from cells (by virtue of the low sodium permeability of cell membranes and the presence of the sodium pump) and therefore changes in sodium concentration will produce maintained changes in cell volume unless and until there are secondary changes in the cell solutes. The other solutes, urea and glucose, which can sometimes significantly increase the total osmolality of the extracellular fluid enter most cells relatively rapidly. An increased extracellular concentration of either will therefore produce only a short lived shrinkage due to osmotic water loss; the water returns as the urea or glucose equilibrates into the cell.

Long term effects of osmotically induced changes in cell volume

The initial changes in cell volume produced by alterations of extracellular osmolality result from water movement to equalize the osmotic pressures inside and out. At least for a few seconds the total solute content of the cell is unchanged. In most cells, however, it is found that in the longer term the initial changes in cell volume are followed by slow (minutes, hours, or even days) alterations of the solute content appropriate to return the cell volume towards its original value. For example, cells swollen by hypo-osmotic solutions tend to lose potassium. This loss of intracellular solute with consequent osmotic loss of water counteracts the initial cell swelling. Cells shrunken by hyperosmotic solutions may increase their intracellular sodium or potassium content, or sometimes synthesize extra organic molecules to increase the total intracellular solute. The osmotic influx of water then corrects the loss of cell volume. In some cells, e.g. lymphocytes, this restoration may take place in a matter of minutes. In the brain, where such effects are most important, volume restoration seems to take many hours or even days.

Rapid changes in osmolality are the most dangerous

A fall of plasma osmolality of around 10 per cent (a fall in plasma sodium to below *c* 126 mM) over the course of a few hours usually gives rise to symptoms of water intoxication, e.g. headache, nausea and, possibly, coma and fits. Greater dilution can be fatal. By contrast, patients have had slower falls in plasma sodium concentrations to as low as a 110 mM, without experiencing symptoms and showing signs of serious brain malfunction. Presumably the slow reduction in osmolality gave time for the brain cells to lose intracellular solutes and thus minimize the changes in cell volume thereby avoiding the effects of compression of blood vessels. A rapidly developing hypernatraemia (increased sodium concentration) is normally thought to cause problems when the sodium concentration passes 155 mM. At this point there is usually raging thirst and then lethargy, perhaps coma and convulsions, and often severe fever in the patient. Again, a hypernatraemia developing over days rather than hours is less damaging. A sodium concentration as high as 190 mM has been recorded with apparent complete recovery of the patient.

Control of extracellular sodium concentration

Regulation of sodium concentration is achieved very largely by the control of water loss in the kidneys and by water intake in response to thirst. It may seem paradoxical that the extracellular sodium concentration should be regulated by control of water input and output, rather than by control of sodium excretion. There are a number of observations which may show that this arrangement makes sense.

1. The most common causes of an abnormal sodium concentration are an excess or a deficit of water. These abnormalities are corrected by *excreting or drinking water*.
2. The concentration of sodium is regulated chiefly to control cell volume. When sodium concentration is too high the cells are shrunken. They need *water* to regain their normal volume. Conversely, when the cells are swollen water must be excreted in order to restore their volume.
3. The amount of sodium in the extracellular fluid cannot be controlled as rapidly as the amount of water. Thus faster control of osmolality and cell volume is possible through changes in *water* input and output.

Sometimes an incorrect osmolality results from excess or lack of sodium. Using water intake and excretion for rapid correction of osmolality, in order to defend cell volume, will then increase or decrease the water content and volume of the *extracellular* fluid. These changes in extracellular volume lead to subsequent excretion or retention of sodium to restore the normal extracellular fluid volume. These processes and the interaction between osmoregulation and control of extracellular fluid volume are further considered in Chapter 14.

Water balance

Table 13.1 shows a typical water balance for a man in a temperate environment. Daily input excedes non renal output by perhaps 1.5 to 2.1, well above the approximate 500 ml/day minimal urine flow. Obviously the balance sheet can vary greatly. Large volumes can be lost, in sweat, in milk during lactation, and even by prolonged hyperventilation, not to mention the pathological losses that occur in haemorrhage or diarrhoea. Similarly large quantities can be drunk.

Table 13.1 Water balance chart

Input			*ml/day*		
Drink			1 500		
Water content of food			1 000		
Metabolic water production			200		
			2 700		
Output		*ml/day*			
Evaporation:	lungs	500		very dependent on temperature	not subject to osmoregulation
	skin	400			
Faeces		200			
		1 100			
Urine		1 600			

Water intake normally exceeds obligatory, or unregulated, losses. Balancing water intake and output and osmoregulation are therefore normally achieved by adjusting water loss in the urine. When extracellular osmolality falls below normal, i.e. the body fluids become diluted and the cells tend to swell, ADH secretion is reduced and a large volume of dilute urine is produced to excrete the excess water. So long as the urine contains a lower concentration of sodium salts than arterial plasma, the renal venous blood must be slightly more concentrated in sodium than the arterial blood and the extracellular fluid sodium concentration will rise back towards normal. When osmolality rises more ADH is released and the kidney produces a small volume of concentrated urine. Now the renal venous blood can be more dilute than the arterial blood and this slightly diluted venous blood tends to correct the elevated osmolality and sodium concentration.

In principle, a rising sodium concentration caused by water deprivation (or excessive water loss) can be corrected and thereby intracellular volume can be restored by renal excretion of sodium. In animals like man which cannot produce highly salt rich urine, the cost is a rapid loss of extracellular volume. It is therefore not surprising that humans do not attempt to osmoregulate by increasing sodium excretion. The only solution is to drink water.

Consider a human subject who is deficient in water by 2 litres and therefore is about 5 per cent hyperosmotic. To restore normal osmolality he will need to excrete an equivalent amount of salt. Since he can, at best, produce urine with 300 mM sodium salts, he would actually have to excrete about 2 litres of such urine to restore a normal extracellular sodium concentration. Now, however, his extracellular fluid would have been depleted by 4 litres which would leave a dangerously low volume.

Those animals that do excrete salt in response to a water deprivation can:

1. provide a higher sodium concentration in the urine;
2. better tolerate the loss of extracellular fluid volume;
3. in any case do so for only about 24 hours.

The relative inability of human kidneys to excrete salt rich urine also accounts for the inability to survive long periods when only sea water is available to drink. Sea water has about 500 mM salt and absorbing sea water will rapidly increase the osmolality of the body fluids. We cannot excrete any significant quantity of urine which is more than about half as concentrated in sodium as is sea water and so cannot restore osmolality without disastrously depleting body water. In fact drinking sea water results in progressive hypernatraemia and a raging thirst. Drinking fresh water is the correct and only answer.

Antidiuretic hormone

Control of urine osmolality and volume by ADH.

Fig. 13.1 shows how powerfully urine osmolality and flow are controlled by ADH. The crosses on the graphs indicate typical values for a normally hydrated man showing how increasing ADH levels two or three fold can increase urine concentration and reduce urine volume about four times. Suppression of ADH release can lower osmolality to approximately 50 mosmol/kg and greatly increase water loss. The kidney mechanisms involved in the effects of ADH are

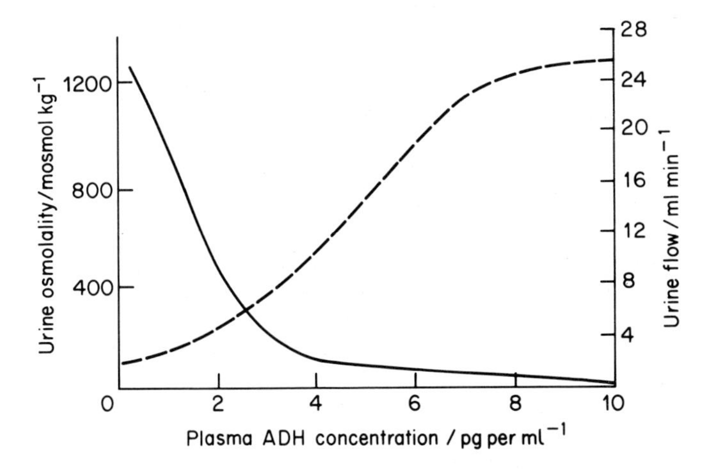

Fig. 13.1. Diagram to indicate the effect of ADH levels on urine osmolality and flow.

discussed on pp. 92–93. ADH controls water excretion with only small and secondary effects on solute excretion (see p. 172).

Secretion of ADH

ADH is a peptide hormone released from the posterior pituitary gland (or neurohypophysis). This gland is a downward extension of the hypothalamus and consists mainly of nerve endings whose axons come from cell bodies in hypothalamic nuclei. ADH is synthesized mainly in the supraoptic neurones and packaged into granules which are transported down to the neurohypophysis. When action potentials are conducted into these nerve terminals, ADH is discharged by calcium-dependent exocytosis. Details of the endocrinology of the posterior pituitary can be found in Endocrine Physiology by Hardy.

The secretion of ADH is strongly dependent on body fluid osmolality. One of the classic experiments by Verney which first demonstrated that the osmoreceptors are in the head is outlined in Fig. 13.2. More localized infusions of hyperosmotic saline suggested to Verney and Jewel that the responsive area lies in the hypothalamus. It now seems that both the supraoptic neurones, which are the ADH secreting cells, and other hypothalamic neurones that connect to them respond to small increases in osmotic pressure with increased firing. Certain cells in the lateral hypothalamus are particularly sensitive.

Infusions of hyperosmotic solutions of NaCl, Na_2SO_4 and sucrose are about equally effective in suppressing a water diuresis. Hyperosmotic urea and glucose are much less effective. It thus appears that the solutes which are confined to the extracellular fluid and are expected to maintain osmotic shifts of water and cell shrinkage are effective, whereas those expected to equilibrate across the cell membrane and give only a transient volume change are much less so. The receptors can therefore be cells whose activity is a sensitive function of their volume.

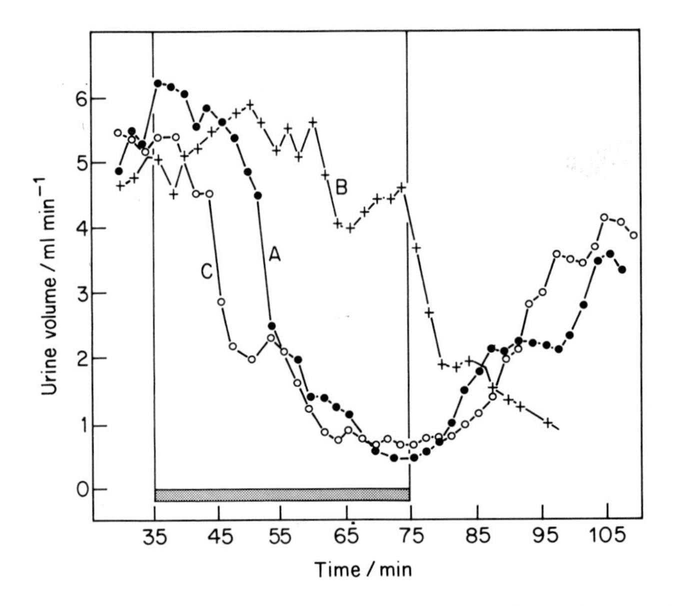

Fig. 13.2. A comparison of the antidiuresis induced by an intracarotid hyperosmotic saline infusion with that induced by an intravenous hyperosmotic saline infusion with or without the addition of pituitary extract, i.e. ADH. A conscious trained dog was given an intragastric dose of water at time ''O'' to induce a water diuresis. The urine flow was measured and plotted on the vertical axis. Test infusions were given during the period indicated by the heavy bar. When 1.25M NaCl was infused slowly into the right carotid artery (A, filled circles), marked antidiuresis occurred within twenty minutes. The same infusion intravenously (B crosses) produced a much more delayed effect indicating that the more rapid antidiuresis following intracarotid infusion resulted from an effect produced within the head. When a small amount of pituitary extract was added to the intravenous infusion, the results (C open circles) were very similar to those obtained with intracarotid infusion, suggesting that the effect of the intracarotid infusion was to release an agent, i.e. ADH, from the pituitary. (Simplified from Verney (1947)).

There has been considerable debate about whether osmoreceptors respond to the total osmolality of the plasma or extracellular fluid or to its sodium concentration. While this discussion may be relevant to the mechanism of the osmoreceptors, it has little practical significance since physiological, as opposed to experimental, alterations of osmolality parallel changes in sodium concentration. Exceptions can occur pathologically in renal failure with a massive rise in plasma urea concentration and in diabetes mellitus with a vast increase in glucose levels. However, both of these solutes are poor stimuli to ADH release. In fact, large infusions of hyperosmotic glucose solutions can actually suppress ADH release, perhaps because the combination of glucose uptake into osmoreceptor cells and dilution of extracellular sodium actually swells the cells.

The speed of the response to changes in osmotic pressure suggests that the cells in question respond to plasma osmolality rather than that of the cerebrospinal fluid. Osmoreceptive cells are presumably in that group of privileged hypothalamic neurones which lie outside the blood-brain barrier. This would explain why hyperosmotic urea, which does not readily permeate the blood-brain barrier, is not a good stimulus to ADH release, but can extract water from the brain and has been used clinically for this purpose in treating cerebral oedema.

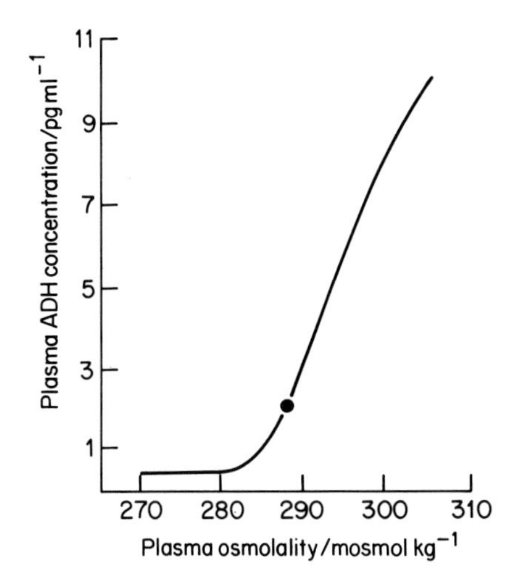

Fig. 13.3. Relation between plasma osmolality and plasma ADH concentration. O = Normal value. (Data taken from Robertson, et al, 1976.)

A major advance since Verney's experiments has been the development of a sensitive radioimmunoassay for ADH which has permitted a quantitative analysis of the way the plasma osmolality and other factors control its release in humans and in other animals. Fig. 13.3 shows the average relationship for healthy adults between plasma osmolality and plasma ADH levels. Of course plasma levels depend on the balance between ADH secretion and its loss from the extracellular fluid by breakdown and renal excretion. However, in health the rate of loss is fairly constant for any individual, the half-life being around 6–10 min, so that plasma levels are altered by, and reflect changes in pituitary release. As expected from Verney's experiments, plasma ADH concentration is an exceedingly steep function of plasma osmolality. There is an apparent threshold for ADH secretion near 280 mosmol/kg below which ADH levels are undetectable and urine flow and dilution will be maximal. For higher osmolalities ADH levels increase roughly linearly until by 295 mosmol/kg ADH levels are reached which produce maximum urinary concentration and minimum water excretion. Thus a change of ± 7 mosmol/kg (or ± 2.5 per cent) from 'normal' osmolality encompasses the entire renal response of water loss and water conservation. This is emphasized by combining the data of Figs. 13.1 and 13.3 as shown in Fig. 13.4 which gives urinary osmolality as a function of plasma osmolality. Note that for an adequately hydrated man with ADH levels of approximately 2.5 pg/ml and a plasma osmolality of 287 mosmol/kg, the curves in Figs. 13.1 and 13.4, indicate sensitive responses to both dilution and concentration of the body fluids.

Experiments like those shown in Fig. 13.2 where ADH was infused into a water-loaded animal, show that the response to a large secretion of ADH can start within a few minutes (especially allowing for the dead space of the ureter and bladder when collecting samples for measurement) and that the response is largely complete within 20 minutes. The experiment in Fig. 13.2 also indicates that changing plasma osmo-

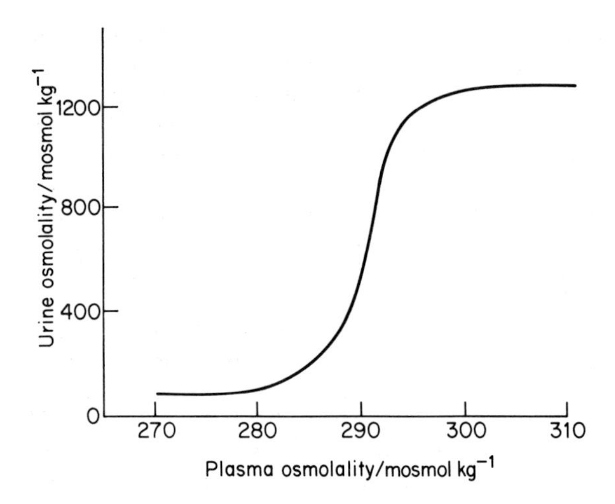

Fig. 13.4. Relation between plasma osmolality and urine osmolality.

lality can very rapidly stimulate ADH release; line A barely lags behind line C.

The speed of switching from urinary concentration to dilution must be limited by the time taken for the loss of ADH from extracellular fluid, in other words by the half-life of ADH. We would expect going from near maximal concentration to full dilution to take around 30 mins., i.e. about three half-lives to get from 4 pg/ml to 0.5 pg/ml.

Water diuresis following a large drink

The excretion of water following a large intake is a remarkably rapid occurrence. A fairly typical time course of urinary excretion following the intake of a substantial amount of water that the subject neither needed nor wanted, is shown in Fig. 13.5. This response is commonly attributed to a suppression of ADH release, consequent upon the dilution of body fluids. However, the

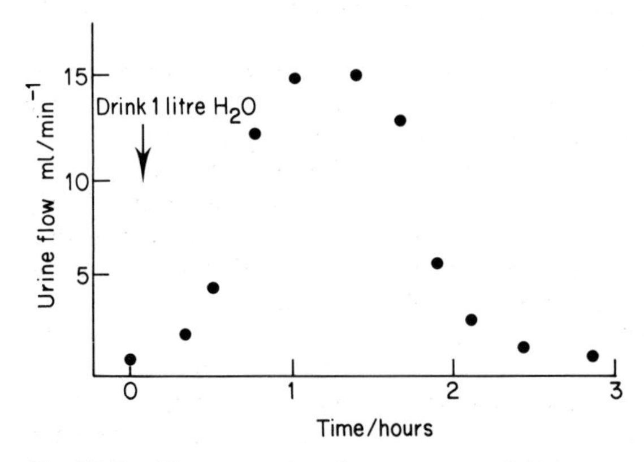

Fig. 13.5. Water excretion after an unwanted drink.

response is probably too fast for this to be the complete explanation since the delay is largely accounted for by the half-life of ADH in the plasma, leaving no time for the absorption of water from the gastrointestinal tract to have occurred. The available evidence suggests in fact that water absorption takes 10–30 min to occur. It seems likely therefore that a rapid, reflex suppression of ADH release follows the ingestion of large amounts of fluid. This idea is supported by the finding that ingestion of isosmotic saline (by a relaxed subject, free of apprehension) can produce a water diuresis of similar rapid onset and initial magnitude to that produced by the ingestion of the same volume of water. These initial effects of isosmotic saline cannot be due to a change in osmolality nor to volume expansion since the fluid is absorbed much more slowly than is water. Probably the stimulation of sensory receptors in the mouth, throat and gullet during the drinking and swallowing of a liquid and the stimulation of receptors in the stomach due to the presence of fluid in the stomach reflexly inhibits ADH secretion. Recent experiments in dogs have provided strong evidence for this mechanism. It seems likely that the pathways for this are similar to those concerned with the rapid satiation of thirst that follows drinking and which are discussed below. The role of this rapid suppression of ADH release could be to prevent dangerous falls in osmolality which might follow excessive drinking, by starting the excretion of the water load at the earliest possible moment.

The effect of blood volume on ADH release

Although ADH release is only weakly sensitive to modest changes in blood volume, it is massively stimulated by a severe blood loss. As shown in Fig. 13.6 ADH release is sensitive to 1 per cent changes in osmolality, but it takes approximately 10 per cent changes in blood volume to produce comparable effects.

There are two main candidates for the receptors which mediate the effects of altered blood volume, atrial or 'low-pressure' baroreceptors and arterial or 'high pressure' baroreceptors. Other things being equal, blood loss reduces and excessive blood volume increases atrial volume and hence the firing of vagal nerve fibres from atrial stretch receptors. The evidence that afferent nerve impulses in the vagus can influence ADH release is convincing but the effects seem to be small. Atrial volume receptors may have more important roles in the control of extracellular fluid volume.

Arterial baroreceptors and possibly chemoreceptors are important in the vast release of ADH that occurs on severe blood loss. Certainly when pressure in the region of the carotid bodies and sinuses is lowered in experimental animals ADH release is massively stimulated. The levels reached are sufficient for ADH to act as a powerful vasoconstrictor and therefore to be part of the circulatory defence against severe hypotension. Indeed ADH is also named vasopressin. There are patients who completely lack osmotic control of ADH release but still possess a normal ADH response to lowered blood pressure.

Osmolality is the principal factor regulating ADH release and influencing the concentration and volume of urine. The total osmolality and extracellular sodium concentrations are normally kept within very tight limits, while quite large variations in blood volume are tolerated. These points are considered in more detail on p. 172.

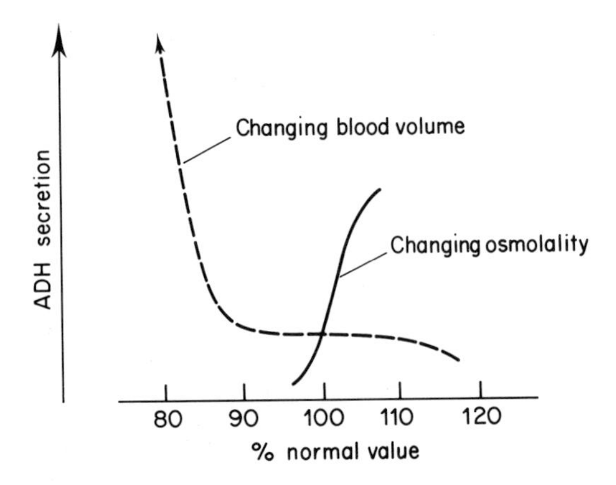

Fig. 13.6. Diagram to indicate the very sensitive response of ADH secretion to changes in osmolality, the insensitivity to small changes in blood volume, and the massive stimulation for severe blood loss.

Non-regulatory influences on ADH release

Various factors can influence the secretion of ADH in ways apparently unrelated to body fluid homeostasis. Alcohol suppresses ADH release so that the water loss after an alcoholic drinking session often exceeds the water intake. It is probable that the consequent dehydration, with elevation of body fluid osmolality and extracellular sodium concentration is partly responsible for the symptoms of the hangover.

Fear, surprise and pain can powerfully stimulate ADH release. Verney's water loaded dogs interrupted their water diuresis when he blew a trumpet in their ears. Robertson reports a subject in whom the pain of a suddenly slipped disc similarly stopped a brisk water diuresis.

Diabetes insipidus

Various pathological or experimental conditions can interfere with ADH release or its action on the kidneys. Diabetes insipidus is characterized by the production of copius volumes of dilute tasteless (insipid) urine. It usually results from defective secretion of ADH from the posterior pituitary following damage to the gland or nearby parts of the hypothalamus. At a normal plasma osmolality ADH secretion is then far below normal and the urine is nearly maximally diluted and produced in large volumes. Plasma osmolality therefore rises with only a marginally increased ADH level while extracellular fluid volume falls. The increased osmolality stimulates thirst which lends to the intake of the vast amounts of water needed to keep the subject in water balance. The resulting plasma osmolality is slightly raised above the normal and is, of course, much higher than normally associated with such a large urine flow. Diabetes insipidus is discussed in Chapter 14 of *Disorders of the Kidney and Urinary Tract*.

Such patients sometimes fail to present to a physician, being prepared to go to bed with two buckets - one being full of water which is consumed during the night, and the other empty to be filled with the urine that is produced. This condition can be ameliorated by treatment with an analogue of antidiuretic hormone, which is conveniently absorbed through the nasal mucosa. This can greatly reduce the urine output of these patients and reduce the amount of water they have to drink to remain in balance.

Most patients with diabetes insipidus have some residual ADH secretion, and if access to water is restricted the patient may come into osmotic balance at, say 310 mosmol/kg, where sufficient ADH is released to produce a concentrated urine but at the price of sustaining the most fearful thirst. Robertson estimates that approximately 90 per cent deficit in ADH secretory capacity is required before overt diabetes insipidus is seen. The alert reader may have realized that the key point is that overt symptoms occur when the concentration of sodium in urine is less than that in plasma for a plasma concentration that stimulates thirst. A normal thirst mechanism is critical for patients with diabetes insipidus. Should the osmotic drive to thirst be defective in addition to the defect of ADH release, as sometimes happens with extensive lesions of the hypothalamus, survival is exceedingly precarious in the absence of careful monitoring of body fluids by repeated blood sampling and weighing.

The converse problem of production of inappropriately concentrated urine with dilution of the body fluids can occur due to excess or inappropriate secretion of ADH. Sometimes this reflects erratic secretion of ADH from the posterior pituitary gland or sometimes subjects are found to have shifted their whole ADH response curve to a lower plasma osmolality, so that osmoregulation is in fact occurring, but around an abnormally low value. Another cause of the syndrome called 'inappropriate antidiuretic hormone secretion' is the production of an ADH-like peptide by certain cancers; most commonly 'oat-cell' carcinoma of the lung.

Thirst

Thirst is essentially an emergency response

Most of the time most animals take enough water by habitual or, as Fitzsimons has termed it, secondary drinking to more than cover non-regulatory water losses. Water balance is then maintained by regulating water excretion via the kidney. The mechanisms of this habitual drinking are not known, but there seems to be a fairly strong and persistent drive since animals provided with more than sufficient fluid by intravenous infusion still drink quite large amounts of fluids. Partly this drinking is prandial, i.e. associated with the intake of food, presumably to ease chewing and lubricate food for swallowing.

Secondary drinking alone cannot be relied upon for survival. All terrestrial vertebrates seem to have mechanisms of 'need-induced' thirst that makes them seek out and drink water to replenish a deficit. A hint of the power of this sensation and behavioural drive may be familiar, but most of us have not experienced the overwhelming character of thirst in the final stages of water deprivation. Horrific accounts of shipwrecked sailors are quoted, for example, in Wolfe's classic book on thirst. Coleridge's poem 'The Rhyme of the Ancient Mariner' also vividly describes the misery of water deprivation and the special agony of being thirsty while surrounded by sea-water.

> 'Water, water, everywhere nor any drop to drink..... and every tongue through utter drought, was withered at the root; We could not speak no more than if we had been choked with soot.'

There appear to be two main stimuli to thirst. Raised total osmolality and extracellular fluid sodium concentration which produces cellular dehydration are of more importance than loss of extracellular fluid volume, i.e. extracellular dehydration. The importance of the sensations from a dry mouth and throat in stimulating thirst in water deficit is still debated. Rinsing the mouth with cold water without swallowing briefly relieves thirst.

Osmotic or cellular dehydration thirst

The triggering of thirst by elevated osmolality is entirely appropriate since the ingestion and absorption of water can restore the osmolality to normal and correct the cellular dehydration. Osmotic thirst appears to involve hypothalamic osmoreceptors similar to, but probably anatomically separate from, those driving ADH release. Raising plasma osmolality by infusion of hyperosmotic saline has long been known to stimulate drinking in both experimental animals and in humans. The receptors have been localized to the anterior hypothalamus by methods analogous to those used in the investigation of ADH osmoreceptors. Electrical stimulation in these areas of the hypothalamus or local microinfusion of hyperosmotic solutions can cause copious drinking in conscious animals. Experimental lesions of these areas in animals, or their destruction by disease in humans, can abolish osmotic stimulation of thirst.

As with ADH release, drinking is much more strongly stimulated by increases in extracellular fluid sodium concentration than by equivalent increases in osmolality produced by urea or glucose. These osmoreceptors seem to respond to changes of cell volume. As mentioned previously, the threshold osmolality for induced drinking is higher than that for stimulation of ADH release, so that thirst is not triggered until osmolality is about 2 per cent above normal. This is just about the point where ADH levels are causing maximum urinary concentration and where extra water intake becomes mandatory to maintain osmolality within acceptable limits.

Osmotic thirst does not seem to adapt. A given increment in extracellular fluid sodium concentration causes similar drinking in animals allowed immediate access to water and in animals to whom water is given many hours later. This has obvious survival advantages, for the failure to find water rapidly when thirsty is a reason to look harder, not to give up. In fact, the accounts in Wolfe's book, referred to above, relate that with continued water deprivation thirst becomes progressively more agonizing and overwhelming. It is worth noting that people on hunger strike nearly always continue to take fluid. This may be partly deliberate to prolong the procedure. After all, a man can survive without food for up to two months, but even in temperate conditions total water lack is likely to be fatal in a week. But also, thirst is a much more powerful, persistent and less resistable drive than hunger.

Drinking the right amount of water

The amount of water taken in following an experimental elevation in extracellular sodium concentration or a period of water deprivation is roughly appropriate to restore the concentration to normal. Rats tend to slake their thirst over a period of many minutes, probably giving time for water absorption from the gut to dilute their body fluids and switch off their thirst drive. Other species, however, including dogs, monkeys and man, tend to drink roughly what is needed rather rapidly after getting access to water, and then stop drinking long before sufficient water could be absorbed to lower body fluid osmolality below the thirst threshold. There seems to be a rapid mechanism whereby sensory information from the mouth, throat and stomach, caused by drinking and swallowing fluid, is able temporarily to switch off the thirst drive. Thus in the control of osmolality by thirst, not only is the osmolality monitored, but so also is the process being used to correct it. This can greatly improve the accuracy and speed of the response of the control system. If drinking were not monitored and it continued while the osmolality of the body fluids slowly (over e.g.. 30 min) dropped below the thirst threshold, then even after osmolality had fallen, there would be continuing reabsorption of the water remaining in the gut and water excess would follow the deficit.

Experiments with dogs suggest that about half of the satiety signals come from sensory receptors in the mouth and throat and about half from the distension of the stomach. The crucial experiments involved making oesophageal fistulas (holes) in dogs so that any ingested water spilled out onto the floor while water could be instilled through the hole directly into the stomach without having to be swallowed by the animal. As has been emphasized above, after water deprivation dogs normally take in a volume approximating the water deficit within a minute or two of being given water to drink. Animals in whom the swallowed water immediately ran out from the oesophageal fistula were found to drink fairly rapidly about twice the volume of the deficit. If water was not placed in the stomach of the animals, about half an hour later the animals went back and drank again. This indicates that the satiety arising from signals in the mouth and throat is relatively short lived.

When water sufficient to make good a water deficit was placed directly in the stomach of animals with oesophageal fistulas, they still drank a roughly similar volume to their deficit. However, a volume of about twice the water deficit placed in their stomachs appeared to be sufficient to slake their thirst completely so that they no longer wanted to drink.

More recently, roughly similar findings have been obtained in experiments with primates.

Volume or extracellular dehydration thirst

Loss of extracellular fluid volume can stimulate thirst in experimental animals, but as with ADH release volume changes seem less effective than changes in osmolality. These observations are as expected, because loss of extracellular fluid is not appropriately corrected simply by increased water intake. However, in the face of circulatory collapse restoring extracellular fluid volume may be worth the price of a lower osmolality and the risk of cellular overhydration. In man thirst is apparently rarely a symptom of haemorrhage, although it is often a symptom of severe, painful injury.

Extracellular dehydration thirst may be triggered by signals from the low pressure baroreceptors or volume receptors in the atria and great veins, or the high pressure or arterial baroreceptors. It has also been found that elevated angiotensin levels can stimulate thirst. Angiotensin probably acts on specialized vascular tissues that lie at least partly outside the blood-brain barrier at the anterior aspect of the hypothalamus. The relative contribution of these mechanisms has been difficult to assess. It is probably fair to say that sufficient

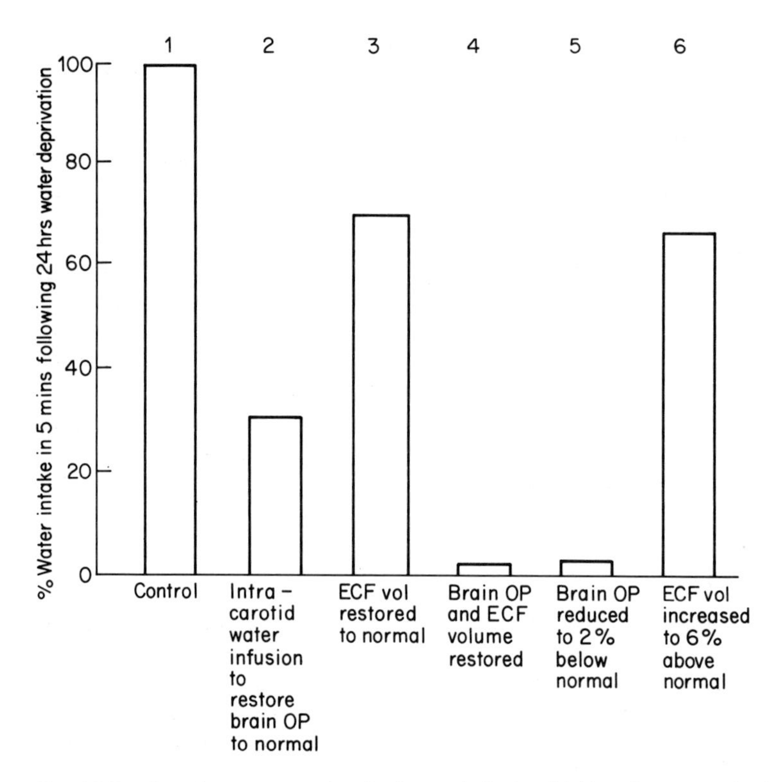

Fig. 13.7. Experiment to examine the factors inducing drinking after water deprivation (which causes ECF volume depletion and osmolality increase) in dogs. Dogs were deprived of water for 24 hours and then the intake during five minutes access to water was measured. In the control group about 400 ml was drunk, and this is designated 100 per cent. In group 3 the ECF volume was restored to normal by i.v. saline infusion. In group 4 brain OP and ECF volume were both restored to normal. In group 5 brain osmolality was reduced to 2 per cent below normal with intracarotid water. In group 6 the ECF volume was increased to about 6 per cent above normal. (Data simplified from Ramsay, et al, 1977.)

Conclusions: In these dogs about 70 per cent of the drinking was due to the increase in osmolality which was about 1–2 per cent. About 30 per cent of the drinking was due to ECF volume depletion (of around 5 per cent). Low osmolality can override volume depletion thirst but expansion of volume (by 6 per cent) does not diminish the osmotic thirst response.

renin release to give plasma angiotensin levels high enough to cause drinking, occurs only with substantial volume loss and significant arterial hypotension.

Interactions of osmotic and volume thirst

Often water deficit will lead to both elevated osmolality with cellular dehydration, and a reduced extracellular fluid volume. The available evidence suggests that the thirst drives from both these stimuli are additive. But when osmotic and volume signals are in conflict the osmotic drive will normally dominate. Thus infusion of isosmotic saline equal to one-third of the volume of the extracellular fluid of rats did not noticeably reduce the drinking response to a few percent elevation of osmolality. A small reduction in osmolality below normal can readily inhibit the drinking caused by a decrease in extracellular fluid volume. Very strong stimulation of low pressure baroreceptors, achieved with experimental animals by expanding a balloon-tipped catheter in a pulmonary vein, can depress, though not abolish, drinking in response to elevated osmolality. But afferent activity under these conditions may well be beyond the range that could be achieved under more physiological circumstances.

Some of these points are brought out in the elegant experiments which are summarized in Fig. 13.7. These were designed to assess quantitatively the factors that were responsible for the drinking in dogs that followed a 24 hour period of water deprivation. It is seen that approximately 70 per cent of the drinking could be attributed to the raised plasma sodium concentration and about 30 per cent to the reduction in extracellular fluid volume. More recent experiments along the same lines, in monkeys, suggest that in these animals and perhaps in man, the drinking that follows water deprivation depends even more on elevated sodium concentration with even less contribution from the loss of ECF volume.

Further reading

Denton, D. (1982). *The Hunger for Salt*. Springer-Verlag, Berlin. A monumental and comprehensive treatise.

Fitzsimons, J.T. (1972). Thirst. *Physiol. Rev.* **52**, 468–561.

Fitzsimons, J.T. (1976). The physiological basis of thirst. *Kidney Int.* **10**, 3–11.

Fitzsimons, J.T. (1979). *The Physiology of Thirst and Sodium Appetite*. Cambridge University Press, Cambridge.

Hays, R.M. & Levine, S.D. (1981). Pathophysiology of water metabolism. Chapter 16, pp. 777–840 in *The Kidney*, 2nd edn, Brenner, B.M. & Rector, F.C. Jr., eds, Saunders, Philadelphia.

O'Connor, W.J. (1982). *Normal Renal Function*, Croom Helm, London. Chapter 10, pp. 163–178. The antidiuretic action of vasopressin, Chapter 11, pp. 179–207. Release of antidiuretic hormone from the neurohypophysis, Chapter 12, pp. 209–228 Acute experiments on the volume of the urine; Chapter 13, pp. 229–246. Acute experiments on drinking by dogs, Chapter 21, pp. 349–374. Water balance Chapter 22, pp. 375–386. Experimental diabetes insipidus.

Ramsay, D.J., Rolls, B.J. & Wood, R.J. (1977). Thirst following water deprivation in dogs. *Am. J. Physiol.* **232**, R93–R100.
Robertson, G.L., Shelton, R.L. & Athar, S. (1976). The osmoregulation of vasopressin. *Kidney Int.* **10**, 25–37.
Rolls, B.J. & Rolls, E.T. (1982). *Thirst.* Cambridge University Press, Cambridge. (Excellent brief monograph.)
Thrasher, T.N., Brown, C.J., Keil, L.C. & Ramsay, D.J. (1980). Thirst and vasopressin release in the dog: an osmoreceptor or sodium receptor mechanism? *Am. J. Physiol.* **238**, R333–R339.
Verney, E.G. (1947). The antidiuretic hormone and the factors which determine its release. *Proc. Roy. Soc. Lond. B.* **135**, 25–106.
Wood, R.J., Rolls, B.J. & Ramsay, D.J. (1977). Drinking following intracarotid infusions of hypertonic solutions into the dog. Am. J. Physiol. 232, R88–R92.

14

Control of extracellular fluid volume, blood volume, and the intake and excretion of sodium

Principles of extracellular fluid volume regulation

The volume of plasma or interstitial fluid can decrease by 10 per cent or increase by 20 per cent in the short term without serious effects. This is just as well because after a meal a man might secrete 1–2 litres of digestive juice into the gut and then absorb all this plus a litre extra from his food and drink. By contrast, over days, weeks and months cumulative changes must not be allowed to occur. It is thus not surprising that the physiological control of extracellular fluid volumes occurs over a longer time course than adjustments of osmolality. If a person drinks an unwanted litre of water, the osmolality will be corrected by excreting the excess water in about two hours; a litre of isosmotic saline infused into a vein might be eliminated over 12–24 hours.

Oedema and the factors which govern the distribution of the extracellular fluid between the plasma and the interstitium are considered in Chapter 2. Extracellular fluid volume must be regulated to avoid oedema, but more importantly to keep plasma and blood volumes within acceptable limits. Too low a circulating volume reduces first venous return and cardiac output, and then arterial pressure. A rapid loss of 30–40 per cent is likely to be fatal. A larger than normal circulating volume will increase cardiac output and arterial pressure. Up to 50 per cent increases can be tolerated in the short term, but in the long term even much smaller increases would produce arterial hypertension (see Chapter 15).

Extracellular fluid volume is determined by the amount of exchangeable sodium in the body

As discussed in Chapter 13, extracellular sodium concentration is held almost constant by controlling water excretion and intake. The amount of sodium in the extracellular fluid then determines the amount of water present and thus the volume. Remember that sodium salts constitute the bulk of the extracellular solutes and that

$$\text{extracellular sodium concentration} = \frac{\text{amount of sodium in the extracellular fluid}}{\text{extracellular fluid volume}}$$

Given that the sodium concentration is kept within narrow limits by the ADH mechanism and thirst, the extracellular fluid volume is directly proportional to the amount of sodium in the extracellular fluid.

Most of the sodium in the body is present either free in extracellular fluid or bound in the structure of bone. If an isotope of sodium is injected, it will mix or exchange places with sodium in the extracellular fluid within about half an hour, but exchange with all but a small proportion of the sodium in bone is negligible for hours. Thus extracellular fluid volume is proportional to the amount of exchangeable sodium in the body (see p. 5).

Sodium distribution and turnover

The main routes by which sodium can enter or leave the extracellular fluid are shown in Fig. 14.1(a). Fig. 14.1(b) indicates the sodium distribution and typical inputs and outputs for a 70 kg man on a standard western diet in an equable environment. Intake of food and drink exceeds non renal output, so that sodium homeostasis is achieved by regulating renal excretion.

Sodium intake and sodium appetite

Sodium intake in most environments is more than adequate, because most mammals apparently have an inborn preference for salty foods and many foods contain salt. Marine animals may have to contend with an enormous sodium

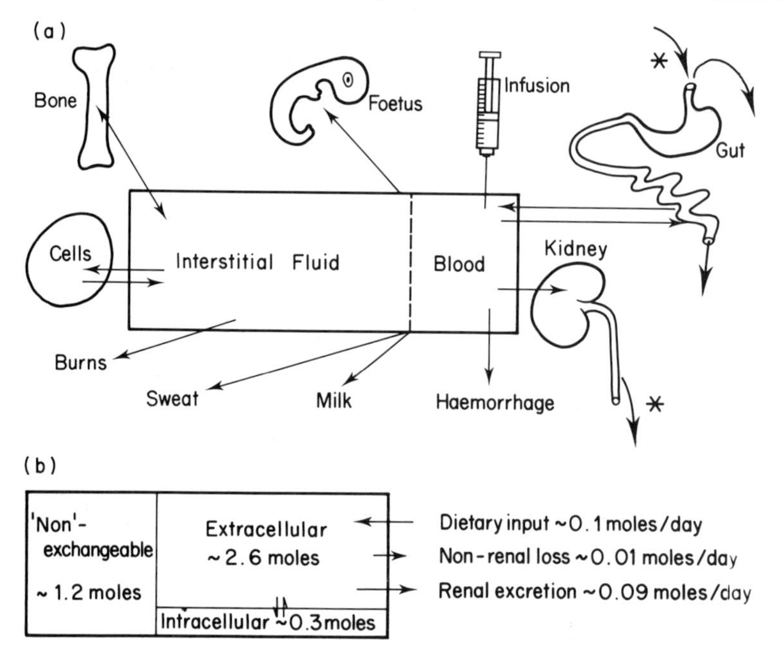

Fig. 14.1. The routes by which sodium can enter and leave the extracellular fluid are indicated in (a), while the amounts in the body and typical inputs and outputs are indicated in (b). Most of the nonexchangeable sodium is part of the structure of bone.

input. On the other hand herbivores, particularly in mountain areas, may have an almost sodium free diet. These animals hunt out salt licks and thus can be said to show a salt appetite. Behaviour that seems to indicate the presence of a salt appetite can also be seen in other animals when they are experimentally deprived of salt or made to suffer extracellular volume depletion. For instance, they may start to drink strong salt solutions that they had previously avoided.

It is not clear that salt appetite occurs in humans. Subjects made to lose salt by sweating but allowed to drink only water report an unpleasant sensation which is not the same as thirst, is not recognized as a desire for salt, but can be relieved by eating salt. Eating the extra salt does not come naturally to most people. It is interesting that last century, men working in hot humid conditions, e.g. in boiler rooms, were given salt in a ration of beer to ensure that they took in enough. More recently armies have had to issue orders that soldiers on desert patrol must take salt tablets; the soldiers do not demand the salt themselves.

There can be a clear craving for salt. Patients lacking adequate glucocorticoid and aldosterone secretion may eat salt in handfuls. This is necessary for their survival since they lose excessive salt in the urine. Salt craving also occurs in some patients required to have a very low salt diet while being treated for renal failure by intermittent haemodialysis. In this case the craving appears to be a psychological response to the imposed deprivation.

The mechanisms of salt appetite are not well understood. The finding of something like a salt appetite in humans depleted of salt but not deprived of water, suggests that a combination of low extracellular fluid volume together with a reduced sodium concentration might be the most effective stimulus. This fits in with the findings in sheep that perfusion of the cerebral ventricles with a solution of lowered sodium concentration appears to promote an appetite for salt. An attractive idea is that angiotensin levels might serve as an intermediate signal, since high angiotensin levels are associated with salt depletion.

Sodium loss

Large amounts of sodium rich fluid can be lost from the body as indicated in Fig. 14.1(a) by haemorrhage, by loss of gut fluids in diarrhoea or vomiting, or by profuse sweating. These can become life threatening within seconds, minutes and hours respectively. In some species, like cattle, there is a significant sustained loss of sodium during milk production. This loss is minor for women since human milk has a low sodium concentration. Large losses of sodium can occur via the kidneys in some forms of chronic renal failure or following inappropriate administration of diuretic drugs.

If non-renal sodium losses exceed intake, there will of course be progressive sodium depletion. The best that the kidneys can do then is to stop excreting sodium. Making good the loss requires either an extra input of sodium or a reduction of the non-renal loss with continued normal intake.

Sodium overload

Large amounts of sodium and extracellular fluid can accumulate as a result of either excessive input of sodium rich fluid e.g. accidental over-transfusion of blood or saline, or, more commonly, depressed excretion with a continued normal input. Excretion can be reduced either when renal function is impaired because of damage to the kidneys or as a consequence of cardiovascular disturbances such as congestive cardiac failure.

The rate of accumulation of excessive extracellular fluid is limited by the net intake of sodium. On a normal diet containing say 130 mmol/day of sodium this amounts to about one litre of extracellular fluid per day. Gross oedema therefore indicates a long standing defect of sodium excretion.

Sodium excretion

Renal sodium excretion in man can be altered over a huge range, from less than 10 mmol/day to over 500 mmol/day. With very low sodium intake, renal excretion is minimized and in addition losses in the faeces and sweat are reduced under the influence of aldosterone. Sodium retention is so efficient that even supposedly sodium free diets will not produce progressive sodium depletion unless there is substantial sweating or some abnormal loss of sodium from the body. Conversely, healthy kidneys can excrete so much sodium that it is hard to eat enough salt to produce any progressive accumulation of sodium.

Control of sodium excretion

Homeostasis of sodium and the extracellular fluids requires that when the exchangeable sodium content of the body increases, sodium excretion must increase and when the content decreases excretion must decrease. The changed excretion then restores sodium content to its controlled value. Changes in the exchangeable sodium content of the body normally change extracellular fluid volume, interstitial fluid volume, plasma volume, and hence also blood volume in the same direction. The control of sodium excretion might thus be based on a system which monitors any of these volumes or the content of sodium in the body. Of these, blood volume is most closely linked to the mechanisms detailed below which govern sodium excretion. Direct evidence that blood volume per se is the principal factor controlled is derived from observations when red cell mass is reduced, i.e. in severe anaemia. Blood volume is then rapidly restored to within normal limits by an increase in the plasma volume.

The mechanisms by which a change in exchangeable sodium can affect sodium excretion include direct effects on the kidneys of colloid osmotic pressure, plasma sodium concentration, arterial pressure and possibly central venous pressure, and indirect mechanisms whereby changes in these variables somehow alter secretion of humoral factors or change the activity of the renal nerves. These various mechanisms are indicated in Fig. 14.2 and outlined below. Because there are so many, the role of each one is still uncertain. Deleting or blocking any one mechanism often produces little change in excretion since changes in the others compensate. The numbers in the headings refer to the circled numbers in Fig. 14.2.

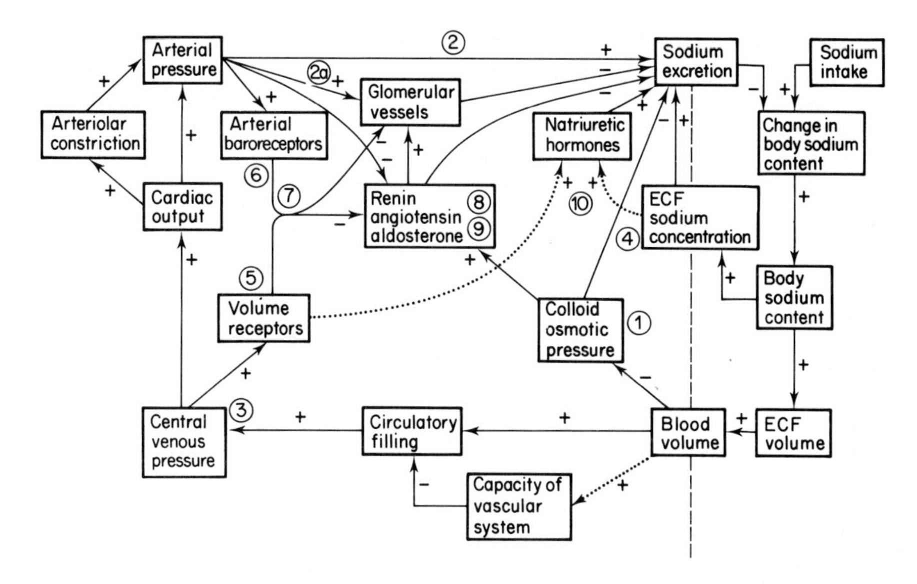

Fig. 14.2. Summary of the control of extracellular fluid and blood volumes by the regulation of sodium excretion. Arrows with plus signs denote that a change at the base of the arrow produces a change in the same direction at the head; for those with minus signs the changes are in opposite directions. The quantitative details of the relations shown to the left of the dashed line are complex, but, where indicated, the directions of the effects are not in doubt. As shown on the right changes in sodium excretion or intake immediately change the body content of sodium and hence the volumes of the total extracellular fluid, the plasma, and blood. It should be noted that changes in sodium excretion produce alterations in blood volume in the opposite direction and that the extracellular fluid volume can be constant only if sodium excretion matches sodium intake. Thus the approach of body size to a constant value after a disturbance is proof that excretion is controlled to match input. Variations in blood volume change sodium excretion in the same direction by many mechanisms as indicated by the arrows in the left portion of the figure. Some arrows and blocks have numbers which refer to the sections of text where they are explained. In the complete loop any change in blood volume changes sodium excretion in the same direction which produces a counter change in the extracellular fluid volumes, i.e. these volumes are controlled by negative feedback. The steps linking changes in blood volume to changes in arterial pressure are discussed in the next chapter.

Plasma colloid osmotic pressure (1)

Any change in extracellular fluid volume not accompanied by an equivalent change in the amount of circulating plasma protein will change plasma protein concentration and colloid osmotic pressure. For example, loss of gut secretions will elevate colloid osmotic pressure, and over-transfusion of isosmotic saline will reduce it. As discussed in Chapters 5 and 6, increased colloid osmotic pressure reduces renal sodium loss, and decreased colloid osmotic pressure increases it. The effects can occur by direct action on glomerular filtration and proximal reabsorption and indirectly via release of renin which in turn leads to altered sodium excretion (see (8) and (9) below). A decrease in colloid osmotic pressure suppresses renin release and reduces renal blood flow. There may also be redistribution of renal blood flow as discussed briefly on p. 56.

Persuasive evidence that colloid osmotic pressure is important in short term sodium regulation arises from comparison of the effects of infusions of saline and plasma (or of dextran saline solutions of the same colloid osmotic pressure as plasma). When blood volume is expanded equally by addition of a small volume of saline or plasma the natriuresis is much greater after the saline. The saline dilutes the plasma and lowers colloid osmotic pressure while additional plasma, of course, does not. In kidneys artificially perfused with blood, dilution of the blood with saline increases the rate of sodium excretion.

Reduction of colloid osmotic pressure in dogs from 22 to 13 mmHg, by periodic removal of plasma proteins leads to sodium retention rather than depletion. However with this severe decrease, blood pressure falls slightly and renal blood flow drops markedly. Presumably the sodium conserving effects of these changes more than offset the sodium losing effect of the fall in colloid osmotic pressure.

It is unclear whether or not changes in colloid osmotic pressure are important in long term sodium regulation. If, regardless of extracellular fluid volume and plasma volume, colloid osmotic pressure is eventually returned to normal by control of the synthesis or degradation of plasma proteins (see pp. 13–14) then there will be no long term change in colloid osmotic pressure and colloid osmotic pressure cannot exert a long term control over sodium excretion.

Arterial blood pressure (2)

Urine flow rate and sodium excretion are markedly affected by the prevailing arterial blood pressure as shown in Fig. 14.3. The mechanisms are discussed in Chapters 5 and 6. To recapitulate briefly: despite autoregulation of renal blood flow and glomerular filtration rate (2a), minor changes in GFR and fluid reabsorption and possibly redistribution of blood flow within the kidney can still lead to changes in delivery of sodium to the distal tubule, to changes in renin release, and to large changes in urinary sodium excretion. In the short term (less than a day) the pressure is normally held almost constant despite variations in blood volume. Arterial pressure variations are thus probably not important in normal short-term regulation. By contrast in the long term the effects of pressure changes may be critical. These effects are discussed in the next chapter.

Arterial pressure can directly influence renin release through the so called renal baroreceptors. These receptors are some part of that segment of the renal vasculature, presumably the afferent arteriole, which senses alterations in arterial pressure. They respond to an increase in pressure by suppressing renin release and to a decrease by enhancing release as discussed in Chapter 9. These changes in renin would help to influence urinary sodium loss in the appropriate direction (See 8 below).

Central venous pressure (3)

The effects of central venous pressure usually thought to be important in the regulation of sodium excretion are mediated by 'volume receptors' as discussed below (5).

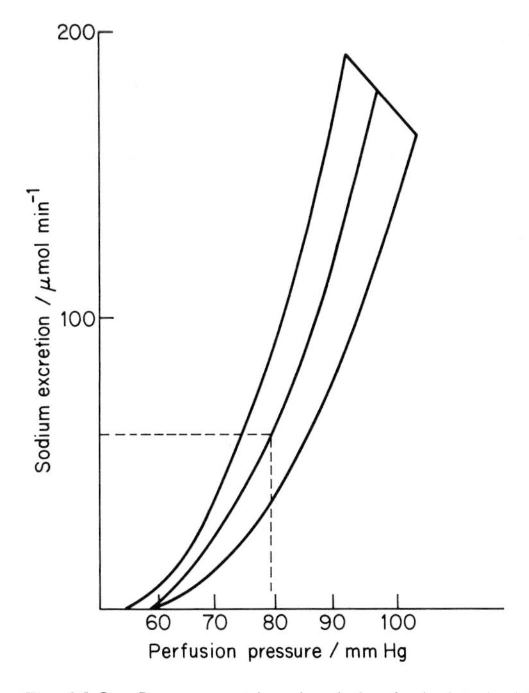

Fig. 14.3. Pressure-natriuresis relation for isolated rabbit kidneys perfused with blood from a normal anaesthetized rabbit. (Reproduced with permission from Thompson, J.M.A. and Dickinson, C.J., 1976.)

Increased venous pressures may lead directly to increases in the hydrostatic pressures in the peritubular capillaries, the renal interstitium, and the lumens of the tubules. By the mechanisms discussed in Chapters 5 and 6 these changes in pressure would lead to decreased glomerular filtration but also to decreased sodium reabsorption in the proximal tubules. Changes in intrarenal pressures may also affect renin release (see (8) below). The sizes of these effects and thus their importance in the regulation of sodium excretion are not known, and they are not indicated in Fig. 14.2. Direct effects of venous pressure on renin release and sodium excretion may be important in congestive cardiac failure (see p. 173).

Extracellular sodium concentration (4)

The concentration of sodium in plasma is kept within narrow limits by the ADH and thirst mechanisms, but small sustained changes can still occur. The available evidence suggests that changes in sodium concentration have little effect on sodium excretion by humans in the short term. A small, long-term effect might be significant in maintaining sodium balance.

When dietary sodium intake is increased, it may not be accompanied by enough water to make the additions isosmotic with plasma. The additional load of salt and water which must then be excreted by the kidneys requires an increase in the sodium concentration in the urine. As described in Chapter 13 this would occur as a result of raised ADH levels in response to slightly increased plasma sodium concentration. Either or both of these small changes may affect sodium excretion.

Plasma sodium concentration may have three effects which could be significant. Firstly if more sodium is filtered more may survive in the tubule to be excreted. Secondly more sodium may reach the macula densa which could suppress renin release, and thereby reduce the levels of angiotensin and aldosterone. As discussed below under (8) and (9) these changes would increase sodium excretion. Thirdly, the change in sodium concentration may affect plasma levels of a natriuretic hormone. In dogs, a 2 per cent increase in the sodium concentration of cerebrospinal fluid in the third ventricle can more than double the rate of sodium excretion. The effect persists with denervated kidneys. The sparse evidence available suggests that this effect is much less marked in humans.

Humoral and nervous influences on sodium excretion: Afferent pathways

'Volume' receptors (5)

Over a wide range on either side of normal the volumes of the great veins and the atria, and hence the distensions of their walls, vary with blood volume. The walls of these low pressure regions of the circulation contain numerous receptors whose activity increases with stretch. It is widely believed that the activities in these stretch receptors and their vagal afferent nerve fibres modulate humoral and nervous influences on sodium excretion. These atrial receptors are indeed often known as volume receptors. The recent discovery of atrial natriuretic factor suggests an additional hormonal link independent of the vagus between atrial distension and renal sodium excretion (see pp. 169–70).

It is clear from direct experiments, most convincingly those carried out in dogs, that altering the stretch of the atria can have the expected effects on renal sodium excretion, namely that increasing stretch enhances sodium excretion and decreasing stretch tends to cause sodium retention.

This apparently simple and sensible arrangement for detecting volume and altering renal excretion is in fact highly complex and indeed controversial. For example, elevation of left atrial pressure reliably increases urine flow and sodium excretion in resting relaxed dogs, particularly after a meal, but the response can be difficult or impossible to obtain if the animals are unwell, anxious, or undertaking any form of exercise. Furthermore, these responses appear to vary between species. In man and primates the effect of atrial receptors seems to be less marked, perhaps because changes in posture in bipeds are liable to produce changes in atrial pressure quite unrelated to fluid balance. However, the response to total body immersion argues that an atrial receptor effect on excretion still exists. If the body is immersed in water up to the neck there can be up to a three fold increase in sodium excretion. This increase is plausibly attributed to the shift of blood from the lower limbs where it normally pools under the influence of gravity, into the central circulation which distends the atrial receptors.

It must be supposed that in congestive cardiac failure the effects of atrial distension are overridden, because in such failure there is a large increase in atrial pressure and atrial size, but a decrease in renal sodium excretion.

Arterial baroreceptors (6)

Changes in blood volume can influence arterial pressure and hence elicit changes in the afferent impulses from arterial baroreceptors in the carotid sinuses and the aortic arch. Reflex effects of these impulses acting via nerves and hormones should operate in the same direction as the direct effects of arterial pressure on renal function, and could help stabilize extracellular fluid volume.

Adaptation

Stretch receptors adapt to maintained changes in their length. Thus while both the atrial and arterial receptors are important in ensuring a rapid response to changes, it is not known whether they have any effect on the long-term average values of mean arterial pressure and blood volume.

Hormonal and nervous influences on sodium excretion: Effector pathways

Renal nerves (7)

Decreased blood volume and/or arterial blood pressure stimulates activity in the renal sympathetic nerves via the afferent pathways discussed above. This activity is clearly important in the response to severe loss of blood volume when the reduction in renal blood flow and glomerular filtration can completely suppress urine production. As discussed on pp. 55–6 and 110 experimental nerve stimulation decreases GFR, increases the filtration fraction, increases renin release, and appears to increase sodium reabsorption in the proximal tubule. Thus normal nerve activity is expected to be antinatriuretic. It seems likely that there is normally some resting tone (continual impulse activity). If this is suppressed there can be a modest increase in sodium excretion.

It is often pointed out that transplanted kidneys, lacking a sympathetic nerve supply, can adequately maintain body fluid homeostasis and the inference is drawn that the renal nerves cannot be all that important physiologically even in the control of sodium excretion. Firstly the observation may be overstated; many transplant patients require diuretics or other drugs to control their blood pressure. Secondly because there are so many control systems for sodium excretion some redundancy is to be expected. The defect may become apparent only when the system is exposed to extreme tests. One compensation which is likely to occur is a form of 'denervation hypersensitivity' which could make the transplanted kidney responsive to noradrenaline which has overspilled from other areas and to circulating adrenaline released from the adrenal medula.

Renin and angiotensin (8)

On the present evidence angiotensin is the most important humoral regulator of sodium excretion, especially during sodium depletion when angiotensin levels are high. Converting enzyme inhibition, e.g. by captopril, then leads to marked increases in sodium excretion. The actions of angiotensin II increase reabsorption in the proximal tubule and it stimulates production of aldosterone which increases reabsorption in the distal tubule. In one view, the antinatriuretic action within the kidney is its major physiological role. The ways in which this peptide affects GFR and reabsorption have been discussed in Chapters 5 and 6. Factors affecting the release of renin and angiotensin are considered in Chapter 9.

Aldosterone (9)

This hormone, released from the zone glomerulosa (the outer region) of the adrenal cortex, has a vital role in the maintenence of sodium balance since its presence is required for normal reabsorption of sodium in the collecting system. In the absence of aldosterone the kidneys excrete an inappropriately large amount of sodium and in many species survival is then possible only with greatly elevated dietary input of salt. Similarly an excess of aldosterone enhances tubular reabsorption so that there is too little sodium excretion, causing sodium retention and some expansion of the extracellular fluid volume.

The decrease in sodium excretion is only transient, a phenomenon known as aldosterone escape. If an animal or a person is given excessive amounts of aldosterone the initial reduction in sodium excretion leads to sodium retention with increase in extracellular fluid volume. After a few days sodium excretion returns to match the level of the input and extracellular fluid volume levels off at a somewhat increased value. Now presumably changes in other factors such as suppression of renin release and angiotensin formation have exerted an influence on the nephron that counteracts the sodium retaining effect of aldosterone. It is important to note that 'escape' is a term coined to describe the return to normal sodium excretion rates. The kidney has certainly not escaped from the influence of aldosterone as evidenced by the maintained increase in the level of extracellular fluid volume. What has happened is that the renal function curve has been shifted to the right and made less steep by the elevated aldosterone levels as indicated by the dashed line in Fig. 14.5.

It is now thought likely that variations in the level of aldosterone cannot account for the hour to hour adjustments of renal sodium excretion. Modulation of the release of aldosterone and its effects on the kidney are too slow and too weak to explain the onset and magnitude of the changes in sodium excretion which can follow rapid changes in extracellular fluid volume. However, aldosterone levels do rise with sustained volume depletion and fall with volume overload. If these changes are prevented by infusing aldosterone into an adrenalectomized animal to hold levels steady near the normal value, the changes in extracellular fluid volume and arterial pressure which accompany salt loading are much larger. In sodium depletion elevated levels are critical to encourage the virtual removal of sodium from the fluid in the collecting ducts, and also from faeces in the colon. A further role for the regulation of aldosterone secretion may be to maintain potassium balance in the face of altered sodium excretion as considered in Chapter 12.

One reason that some workers attach great importance to aldosterone as a regulator of sodium excretion is that it is the only physiological agent known to affect sodium reabsorption late in the tubules. Although most of the sodium is reabsorbed by the time the fluid enters the collecting ducts, the few per cent of the filtered sodium remaining is highly significant in terms of excretion. Two per cent of the filtered load is about 400 mmol/day, an enormous sodium output; 0.1 per cent of the filtered load is about 10 mmol/day, an amount typical for a sodium depleted subject. Clearly therefore, the handling of sodium in the final stages of urine formation is critical. The reabsorption processes in the distal tubule and collecting system are not normally saturated and can reabsorb almost all the sodium delivered from the proximal tubule. The mechanisms that determine just how much sodium is allowed to get past the collecting duct are not understood. A varying level of aldosterone is presumably one factor, but there are almost certainly others that await discovery. Perhaps one of the natriuretic factors will turn out to have its main physiological influence on the collecting ducts.

Natriuretic hormones (10)

It has long been suggested that there are important hormonal influences on sodium excretion that cannot be attributed to aldosterone, circulating angiotensin, or ADH. The existence of plasma factors that enhance salt excretion was first inferred from experiments in which all known influences on renal sodium handling were held constant or actually altered so as to reduce sodium excretion. The circulating volume was then expanded from a blood reservoir so as not to alter plasma composition and the observed natriuresis was attributed to increased plasma levels of natriuretic factors. The plasma and urine of volume expanded animals and humans contains a heat-stable compound, MW about 500, not yet chemically characterized, that can cause natriuresis in experimental animals and inhibits the sodium pump. This inhibition would reduce sodium reabsorption by the tubules. The source of this putative natriuretic hormone is not known, but it can be extracted from the hypothalamus. Some suggest that it is secreted in response to stretch of 'volume receptors' in the atria and great veins; others that it is secreted in response to changes in CSF sodium concentration.

Recently another natriuretic factor has been found in secretory granules in granular cells of the atria in some species including man. This atrial natriuretic factor is a peptide. It does not inhibit the sodium pump but does appear to reduce sodium reabsorption in the distal nephron or collecting system. It is not yet established how secretion of the substance is controlled, but its location in the atrium suggests that its release could be directly responsive to atrial distension. Its amino acid sequence has now been worked out and its gene has been cloned so that it can be produced in reasonably large amounts. It should therefore prove possible to develop radio-immuno assays and specific monoclonal antibodies. These tools in turn should allow the role of this putative hormone in physiological regulation of body fluids and in pathological disturbances to be understood. Preliminary reports suggest that plasma levels of atrial natriuretic factor do indeed rise on expansion of the circulating volume. One other interesting point is that atrial natriuretic factor appears to be a potent vasodilator of the peripheral vasculature.

Many agents including various hormones can be shown to affect sodium excretion. The effects of parathyroid hormone were discussed in Chapter 6. However, there is no evidence at present that these hormones are involved in normal regulation. Unfortunately, our ignorance is still considerable and there may well turn out to be other control pathways which have not yet been elucidated.

Responses to varying salt intake

A normal person can stabilize their extracellular fluid volume over a wide range of sodium intake. Fig. 14.4 outlines the changes in sodium excretion, sodium content and body weight that typically go along with an abrupt switch from a low sodium to a high sodium diet. During the first day sodium excretion increases but not enough to match the extra intake; consequently there is an accumulation of sodium and, as a result of continuing efficient osmoregulation, an increase in extracellular fluid volume. This can be monitored by noting the increase in body weight. (Changes in weight over periods of hours to days fairly accurately reflect alterations in body water.) By the second day the sodium excretion is increased almost to match the intake and there is only a slight further increase in extracellular volume. By day three sodium input and output are back in balance. On return to a low salt diet the converse series of adjustments occurs. Presumably as indicated in Fig. 14.2 these changes in sodium excretion result largely from the consequences of the altered sodium content and volumes of the body fluids.

Changing sodium intake itself might have direct effects on sodium excretion. For instance saltier tasting food or increased sodium transport in the gut mucosa might influence sodium handling by the kidneys by nervous or hormonal routes. There is an analogy here with the proposed reflex effect of drinking on ADH secretion that was discussed in the previous chapter. Such effects are probably of only minor significance for sodium excretion because changes in extracellular fluid volume produced by routes that bypass altered intake of sodium through the gut, such as fluid loss in sweating or fluid excess provided by intravenous infusion, result in similar alterations in sodium excretion.

Normally of course, people do not change from one steady level of sodium intake to another but intake fluctuates according to the food being eaten. In virtually all work on the control of sodium excretion it has been assumed that the adjustments to these fluctuations occur by the same mechanisms as those seen in the more controlled conditions of experiments like those outlined in Fig. 14.4.

Increased or decreased extracellular fluid and blood volumes

Whether caused by changes in dietary intake, non renal losses, or experimental manipulation, decreases in extracellular fluid volume are normally met by avid sodium retention and increases by enhanced sodium excretion. These changes in excretion tend to restore the volume to its original value. Large changes in excretion can be produced with small alterations in extracellular volume and almost unvarying arterial blood pressure. There are two considerations which help to explain how these large changes in excretion come about. Firstly, there are many different influences on renal sodium handling. As discussed in the respective sections above and indicated in Fig. 14.2, each of these either directly or reflexly will contribute to increased sodium excretion. Secondly, it does not

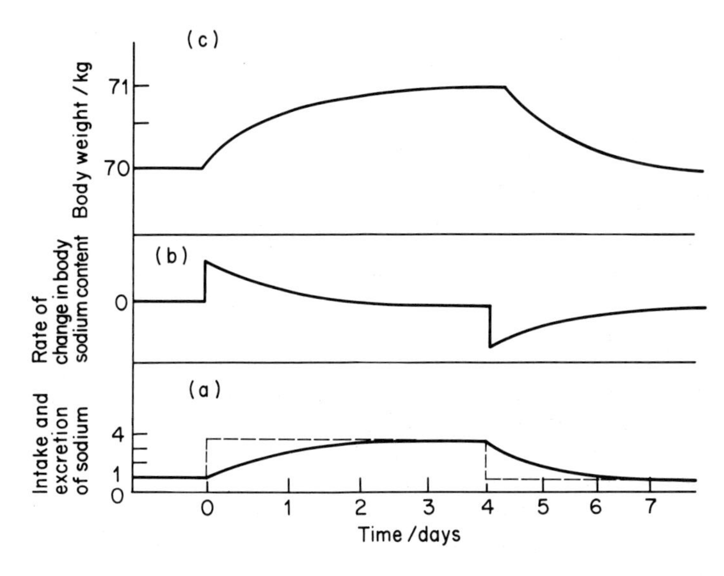

Fig. 14.4. The changes in sodium excretion and body weight following abrupt changes in sodium intake. Day to day changes in body weight occur primarily by changes in the amount of extracellular fluid in the body (*c* 1 kg/l). The amount of extracellular fluid in turn varies as a result of changes in the body content of sodium (about 1 litre for 140 mmoles of sodium). The dotted curve in (a) represents the rate of sodium intake, the solid curve the rate of excretion. When intake is increased, intake exceeds excretion and the body content of sodium, extracellular fluid volume, and body weight all increase. As a result of these changes, the rate of renal sodium excretion increases. In the new steady state intake again equals excretion.

take much alteration of the balance between filtration and reabsorption of sodium to achieve the necessary increases in excretion. The change from 99.5 per cent to 99 per cent reabsorption would double sodium excretion. Such small fractional changes in reabsorption (or filtration) cannot be measured in experiments on either isolated nephrons or whole animals.

It is not known which of the factors affecting the rate of sodium excretion is most important under which circumstances. If forced to guess at present, one might prefer altered colloid osmotic pressure for producing the initial changes whenever extracellular fluid is gained or lost without changes in the amount of plasma proteins. In the steady state, the most important control may be exerted by way of the renin-angiotensin-aldosterone system.

If blood is lost there is very little immediate change in colloid osmotic pressure (a small change occurs as interstitial fluid enters the blood in response to the decrease in capillary hydrostatic pressure) and the reduction in sodium excretion must result from other factors.

ADH and the interrelation between osmoregulation and volume regulation

ADH and thirst respond primarily to osmolality rather than to moderate changes in the volume of extracellular fluid. When the requirements of osmoregulation and regulation of extracellular fluid volume are in apparent conflict, osmoregulation generally takes precedence in the control of ADH and thus the excretion of water. This can be seen from the effects of either an excess or deficit of sodium salts. For example, if a person receives an infusion of hyperosmotic saline or drinks and absorbs seawater, their extracellular fluid expands while the osmolality increases and draws water from the cells. There is thus a decreased cell volume with substantially increased extracellular fluid volume. Osmoregulation demands stimulaton of ADH secretion and thirst; extracellular volume regulation might appear to be better served by suppression of ADH and thirst so as to excrete water and reduce fluid volume. In fact ADH secretion is stimulated and osmoregulation is achieved with restoration of cellular volume at the cost of further increase in the extracellular volume. The excessive extracellular fluid is then excreted over a longer period of time as a roughly isosmotic urine. It is worth emphasizing (see Chapter 8) that the kidneys can quickly excrete a large quantity of salt only when they are provided with ample water. Thus thirst is a highly appropriate response.

With sodium depletion, e.g. if one sweats and replaces the loss with water, osmoregulation is again primary at least in the initial stages of volume depletion. Under these conditions extracellular fluid volume falls, osmolality falls, and the cells swell. Osmoregulation demands water excretion in a dilute urine; regulation of extracellular fluid volume demands sodium retention, which it gets, and water retention which it does not get. The result is progressive loss of extracellular fluid volume and protection of cell volume. However, with the loss of 10–15 per cent of the extracellular fluid, at which stage cardiovascular function is threatened, osmoregulation is abandoned and ADH secretion is strongly stimulated, presumably due to reduced activity in atrial and arterial baroreceptors. The greatly increased ADH levels serve two functions: water is now retained which prevents further loss of volume, even though if water is drunk osmolality falls and the cells may swell; and the vasoconstrictor actions of ADH may help in maintaining blood pressure. Under these conditions the problems of hypo-osmolality are preferred to imminent death from circulatory collapse. The change from defence of osmolality to defence of volume as sodium depletion becomes severe was graphically illustrated in the 'heroic' experiments done by McCance on himself and other volunteers in the 1930s.

The interactions between osmoregulation and regulation of extracellular fluid volume have important consequences for the use of dilute salt solutions to restore extracellular fluid volume. Volume-depleted patients may be reluctant to drink enough fluid to obtain sufficient sodium to make good the deficit. As they absorb the hypo-osmotic fluid the extracellular sodium concentration will be reduced. This will tend to suppress ADH secretion and more importantly, suppress thirst so that they do not wish to drink. Most adult patients can be successfully instructed to drink what they need; small, sick children often cannot.

Sodium retention in congestive cardiac failure

Congestive heart failure is the clinical syndrome of progressive accumulation of extracellular fluid primarily caused by defective performance of the heart. The essential cardiovascular features are elevation of right atrial (central venous) pressure and often left atrial (pulmonary venous) pressure at each level of cardiac output and loss of 'cardiac reserve'. (Loss of reserve means there can be an adequate cardiac output at rest but the ability to elevate the output to meet the needs of increased metabolism, e.g. during exercise, is severely restricted). One effect of these changes is to reduce sodium excretion by the kidneys. Then, given a continued dietary intake of sodium, there is progressive accumulation. The consequent increase in blood volume may be beneficial up to a point if the heart can respond to extra distension (sometimes called preload) with an increased output. However, once the limit of operation of Starling's law of the heart has been reached, the fluid accumulation has only bad effects producing peripheral, and perhaps pulmonary, oedema.

What causes the sodium retention?

It cannot be the normal atrial receptor reflex because that works in the other direction. Furthermore changes in neither colloid osmotic pressure nor plasma sodium concentration can be implicated. However, arterial pressure maybe reduced and venous pressures are increased. Renal blood flow is greatly reduced, possibly as part of the systemic defence of arterial blood pressure, and renin levels are high as a result of stimulation via the fall in the pressure difference across the wall of the afferent arteriole, the decreased delivery of sodium chloride to the macula densa, and probably sympathetic nerve stimulation. Thus less sodium reaches the distal tubule, distal reabsorption is either intact or enhanced by raised aldosterone, and there is sodium retention. The increase in secretion of renin may be considerably greater than expected just from the drop in arterial pressure, perhaps as a result of the change in venous pressure. The important role of the high renin and angiotensin levels is indicated by the effectiveness of captopril (an angiotensin converting enzyme inhibitor) in increasing sodium excretion. Sodium retention in cardiac failure is discussed further in Chapter 15 of *Disorders of the Kidney and Urinary Tract*.

Diuretics

Diuretic drugs are usually administered for their natriuretic effects, i.e. to enhance the secretion of sodium along with osmotically entrained water. Most diuretics act by reducing tubular reabsorption at one or more sites in the nephron. An exception is dopamine whose renal effects are produced through increasing GFR.

Effects on sodium reabsorption

Sodium reabsorption could be reduced by

1. inhibition of uptake into the tubular cells;

2. inhibition of reabsorption through the tight junctions;
3. inhibition of extrusion across the basolateral membrane of the tubular cells.

Most of the diuretics in common use act on sodium transporters in the luminal membranes of cells in the distal tubule and/or the collecting system (see Chapter 7).

The potent loop diuretics, like frusemide and ethacrynic acid, inhibit Na, Cl-cotransport. There are two reasons why they act predominantly on the thick ascending limb. Firstly transport in that region depends almost exclusively on the function of these cotransporters while more proximal and distal portions can reabsorb salt by other mechanisms. Secondly these drugs are secreted into the lumen of the proximal convoluted tubule and are concentrated as fluid is removed. Thus they first reach higher and effective concentrations in the early diluting segment.

Amiloride and triamterene block the electrogenic sodium transporter of the late diluting segment and collecting system.

The thiazide diuretics probably act by inhibiting sodium uptake and possibly chloride uptake somewhere in the cortical part of the distal tubule. They are also thought to have some effect on the proximal tubule. The cellular mechanisms affected by these very widely used drugs are still unknown.

Acetazolamide blocks carbonic anhydrase which reduces H^+ secretion across the luminal membrane of the tubular cells. Reduced hydrogen secretion into the lumen inhibits the reabsorption of sodium bicarbonate. This process and the inhibition appears both proximally and distally. In the proximal tubule inhibition of sodium bicarbonate reabsorption reduces sodium chloride reabsorption through the tight junctions (see pp. 65–9).

Osmotic diuretics such as mannitol are substances which are freely filtered but not reabsorbed. When their plasma concentrations are low, <5 mM, they increase urine flow mainly by obligating water for their own excretion. This flow can be large since as flow rate increases the maximum osmolality of the urine falls (see Chapter 8). This action is put to use clinically to maintain urine flow rate and hence allow the excretion of toxic substances. At higher concentrations osmotic diuretics increase the excretion of sodium. The effect starts in the proximal tubule (see pp. 69–71) where the presence of mannitol in the lumen reduces or even reverses the concentration gradient for chloride which normally drives the passive component of sodium chloride reabsorption.

Because almost all solute and fluid reabsorption depends on sodium pumps, inhibiting this pump is severely diuretic and natriuretic. A pump inhibitor, the anion vanadate, is one of the most powerful diuretic agents yet discovered. A direct diuretic action may also be one effect of digitalis and similar pump inhibitors when they are used in the treatment of cardiac failure. The diuretic effect of metabolic poisoning or cooling of the kidneys is also attributable to reduced sodium pumping. It should be emphasized that it can be difficult to obtain a significant acute diuresis in vivo with pump inhibitors since effective doses produce severe adverse effects in the renal vasculature and the rest of the body.

Effects on potassium loss

As discussed on p. 84, any treatment which increases delivery of sodium to distal portions of the nephron will tend to increase distal potassium secretion and potassium excretion. Thus use of acetazolamide and/or frusemide leads to potassium loss. Amiloride blocks the actual sodium reabsorption in the late distal tubule and collecting system and thus indirectly inhibits potassium secretion. It is therefore often called a potassium sparing diuretic. The thiazides also appear to block sodium reabsorption somewhere in the distal tubule, but in contrast to amiloride, they increase the fraction of the remaining reabsorption which occurs as exchange for potassium and so potassium excretion goes up. This increase can be reversed by amiloride. Thus presumably the thiazides act at an earlier site in the tubule than do the potassium sparing diuretics.

Agents which produce water diuresis

Anything which blocks the action of ADH would cause a water diuresis. This is not a mechanism used by agents given for their natriuretic and diuretic properties but certain drugs, e.g. the antibiotic demeclocycline, and lithium may have such an effect. Inhibition of ADH release by, for example, alcohol, will also produce a water diuresis. Agents that directly reduce the water permeability of the nephron are not known.

Effects of diuretics on body fluids

Diuretic drugs shift the relation between renal excretion and extracellular fluid volume to the left as indicated in Fig. 14.5. The effect of the diuretic can be seen as either producing an increase in sodium excretion at a given extracellular fluid volume or reducing the extracellular fluid volume corresponding to any particular level of sodium excretion. Fig. 14.6 indicates the changes in sodium

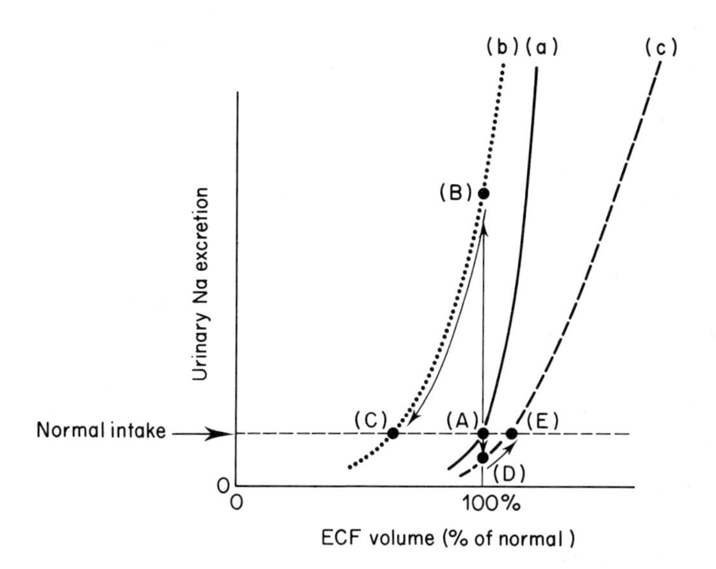

Fig. 14.5. The effects of diuretics (b) and excess aldosterone (c) on the renal function curve relating sodium excretion to extracellular fluid volume. The normal curve is shown as (a). If a diuretic is given the rate of sodium excretion increases from normal at (A) to the value at (B) and sodium excretion then exceeds intake. As a result body sodium content and extracellular fluid volume decrease and the consequences of these changes decrease the rate of excretion to (C). In the opposite direction if excess aldosterone is given, excretion decreases to (D) then increases to (E) as sodium is retained and the extracellular fluid expands.

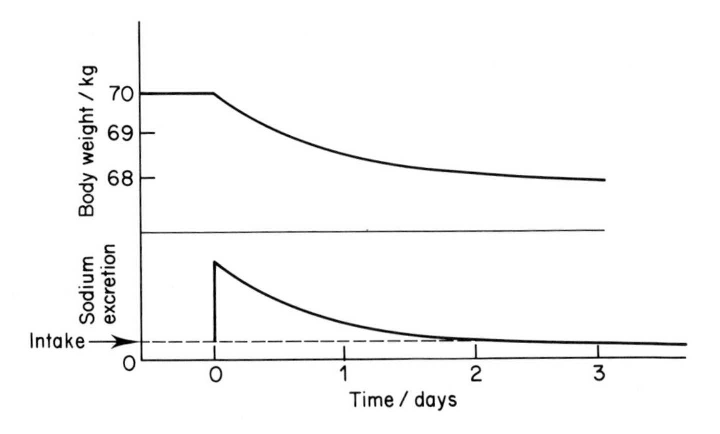

Fig. 14.6. Diagram to illustrate the changes in sodium excretion and body weight following administration of a natriuretic diuretic. When the diuretic is given sodium, excretion is increased and excretion exceeds intake. The body content of sodium, extracellular fluid volume, and body weight therefore all decrease. As a result of these changes, sodium excretion decreases. In the new steady state excretion again equals intake, but for a smaller extracellular fluid volume.

excretion, weight and extracellular fluid volume that typically occur when a person is started on a course of a diuretic drug. Note that the diuresis persists for only a few days. For constant sodium intake, the net effect of long term administration of a diuretic cannot be an increase in sodium excretion above the level of the input. Rather, it must be either a lowering of extracellular fluid volume or stimulation of some other changes in the body which bring the rate of excretion back down to equal intake. Such changes can include renin release (see pp. 193–4) or the development of a metabolic acidosis (see Chapter 6). Reduction in extracellular fluid volume is often the aim of giving the drugs, as in congestive cardiac failure. A similar argument applies to the use of diuretic drugs as antihypertensive agents as discussed in the next chapter. The use of diuretics is considered further in Chapters 3,4,8 and 15 in *Disorders of the Kidney and Urinary Tract*.

Further reading

Andersson, B. (1977). Regulation of body fluids. *Ann. Rev. Physiol.* **39**, 185–200. (A review of the effects of changes in intracerebral sodium concentration on renal function and thirst.)

Burg, M.B. (1981). Renal handling of sodium, chloride, water, amino-acids and glucose. in *The Kidney*, 2nd edn, Brenner, B.M. & Rector, F.C. Jr., eds, Saunders, Philadelphia. (On pp. 353–65 Burg discusses the factors which affect and control sodium excretion.)

De Wardener, H.E. (1973). The control of sodium excretion. Chapter 21, pp. 677–720 in *Handbook of Physiology, Section 8, Renal Physiology*, Orloff, J. & Berliner, R.W., eds, American Physiological Society, Washington, D.C.

Earley, L.E. (1972). Sodium metabolism. Chapter 3, pp. 95–119 in *Clinical Disorders of Fluid and Electrolyte Metabolism, 2nd Ed.,* Maxwell, M.H. & Kleeman, C.R., eds, McGraw-Hill, N.Y.

Gilmore, J.P. (1983). Neurol control of extracellular volume in the human and nonhuman primate. Chapter 2, pp. 885-915 in *Handbook of Physiology, Section 2, The Cardiovascular System, Vol. 3, Peripheral Circulation and Organ Blood Flow, Part 2*, Shepherd, J.T. & Abboud, F.M. eds, American Physiological Society, Bethesda.

Goetz, K.L., Bond, G.C. & Bloxham, D.D. (1975). Atrial receptors and renal function. *Physiol Rev.* **55**, 157–205. (A sceptical view of the importance of atrial receptors.)

Jacobson, H.R. & Kokko, J.P. (1976). Diuretics: sites and mechanisms of action. *Ann. Rev. Pharmacol.* **16**, 201–214.

McCance, R.A. (1936). Medical problems in mineral metabolism. III Experimental human salt deficiency. *Lancet* **230**, 823–830.

Manning, R.D. Jr. & Guyton, A.C. (1982). Control of blood volume. *Rev. Physiol. Biochem. Pharmacol.* **93**, 69–114. (The models analyzed by Guyton and his collaborators are based on arterial pressure as the critical long-term link between body sodium content and sodium excretion.)

Mudge, G.H. (1980). Diuretics and other agents employed in the mobilization of edema fluid. Chapter 36, pp. 892–915 in *The Pharmacological Basis of Therapeutics*, 6th edn. Gilman, A.G., Goodman, L.S. & Gilman, A., eds, Macmillan, N.Y.

O'Connor, W.J. (1977). Normal sodium balance in dogs and in man. *Cardiovascular Research* **11**, 375–408.

O'Connor, W.J. (1982). *Normal Renal Function*, Croom Helm, London. (Chapter 2, pp. 17–22, Glomerular filtration rate; Chapter 8, pp. 111–144, Excretion of sodium; Chapter 18, pp. 299–328 Sodium balance.) O'Connor claims that for small increases in body sodium content and extracellular fluid volume, excretion is increased by a fall in colloid osmotic pressure.

Reineck, H.J. & Stein, J.H. (1978). Renal regulation of extracellular fluid volume, pp. 24–50 in *Sodium and Water Homeostasis*. Brenner, B.M. & Stein, J.H. eds, Churchill, N.Y.

Reineck, H.J. & Stein, J.H. (1981). Mechanisms of action and clinical uses of diuretics. Chapter 22, pp. 1097–1134 in *The Kidney*, 2nd end, Brenner, B.M. & Rector, F.C. Jr., eds, Saunders, Philadelphia.

Seely, J.F. & Levy, M. (1978). Control of extracellular fluid volume. Chapter 8, pp. 371–407 in *The Kidney*, 2nd ed, Brenner, B.M. & Rector, F.C. Jr., eds, Saunders, Philadelphia.

Stein, J.H., Lameire, N.H. & Earley, L.E. (1978). Renal hemodynamic factors and the regulation of sodium excretion. Chapter 36, pp. 739–772 in *Physiology of Membrane Disorders.*, Andreoli, T.E., Hoffman, J.F. & Fanestil, D.D., eds, Plenum, N.Y.

Thompson, J.M.A. & Dickinson, C.J. (1976). The relation between the excretion of sodium and water and the perfusion pressure in the isolated, blood-perfused, rabbit kidney, with special reference to changes occurring in clip-hypertension. *Clin. Sci. Mol. Med.* **50**, 223–236.

Vander, A.J. (1980). *Renal Physiology,* 2nd edn. McGraw Hill, N.Y. (Chapter 7, Control of sodium and water excretion.)

Young, D.B., McCaa, R.E., Pan, Y. -J. & Guyton, A.C. (1976). Effectiveness of the aldosterone-sodium and -potassium feedback control system. *Am. J. Physiol* **231**, 945–953. (Sodium loading decreases plasma potassium concentration and increases arterial pressure markedly in adrenalectomized dogs maintained on constant infusions of aldosterone and hydrocortisone but hardly if at all in normal dogs.)

15

The role of the kidneys in the regulation of blood pressure

For healthy young adults normal arterial blood pressure is about 110/70 mmHg (systolic/diastolic) with a mean near 85 mmHg. Arterial pressure is lower in children and rises with increasing age. Hypertension, chronically and abnormally elevated blood pressure, is arbitrarily defined as occurring when diastolic pressure regularly exceeds 95 mmHg.

Before considering the role of the kidneys in the control of arterial pressure, it is first necessary to outline some basic properties of the circulation. The fundamental requirement is a correct cardiac output properly distributed, because each tissue needs a proper flow of blood. The various tissues and organs are perfused in parallel, so that the pressure drop, arterial minus venous, across each of them is nearly the same. Once arterial pressure is stabilized, the flow through any organ or tissue is governed by the resistance of its own vessels, i.e. the local state of vasodilatation or constriction. The requisite flows can be produced by any pressure gradient so long as the resistance of the blood vessels can be adjusted appropriately. So why should mean arterial pressure be somewhere between 80 and 100 mmHg rather than near 9 or 900 mmHg? There seem to be two main reasons for keeping arterial pressure as low as possible.

1. Since left ventricular work is determined (approximately) by cardiac output times arterial pressure, low pressure minimizes the work of the heart. One consequence of hypertension is ventricular overload with hypertrophy and eventual failure.
2. The higher the pressure the greater the stress on the walls of arteries and arterioles. Another consequence of hypertension is progressive structural damage to arteries and sometimes rupture at points of relative weakness.

Lower limits on the arterial pressure may be set by the following factors.

1. There is presumably some practical limit to the number and size of blood vessels which can exist in the tissues and this must set some lower limit to their resistances.
2. In large animals a sizeable pressure is needed to ensure continuous perfusion of the brain regardless of posture and movement. Interestingly, the giraffe with its brain up to 3 metres higher than its heart is the only mammal with a blood pressure very substantially greater than that in humans. The arterial pressure in an adult giraffe can average 300 mmHg,

and it has arterial walls thick and strong enough to cope with this large pressure.

3. A relatively high arterial pressure helps the flow of blood through exercising muscle in which the intramuscular pressure rises with each contraction. This may be important in heart muscle as well as in skeletal muscle.
4. Mammals operate a high pressure filtration system in the kidneys and they require a mean arterial pressure of more than 60 mmHg to obtain glomerular filtration.

The factors which determine arterial blood pressure

The arterial pressure is determined by cardiac output and total peripheral resistance.

$$AP = (CO)\,(TPR)$$

and it can be changed only by changing one or the other or both.

Total peripheral resistance (TPR)

The total peripheral resistance is the parallel combination of the resistances to blood flow of all the tissues except the lungs. The resistance to flow in each tissue depends primarily on the number and size of the arterioles.

1. Number of vessels

The growth or retraction of blood vessels in response to tissue needs, e.g. for oxygen, is well known even though the cellular basis for these changes is not understood. One example is seen in the growth of blood vessels to form a collateral circulation when a major artery is blocked. Vessel retraction is seen in these same collateral vessels if the blockage is removed. These changes take days to weeks to occur.

2. Structure of vessels

The walls of arteries and arterioles respond to raised transmural pressure by hypertrophy. This is, of course, appropriate to allow the vessels to withstand the increased pressure. However, it also increases resistance to flow since it decreases the size of the lumen. These changes progress over days and weeks. In their milder forms they are reversible, but the elaboration of connective tissue in response to grossly elevated pressures is not. It is unclear whether pressure induced changes occur in response to the mean pressure or to the maximum pressures encountered frequently.

3. Local control of vasoconstriction

The metabolic rate of a tissue such as a skeletal muscle affects blood flow primarily by local control of vasoconstrictor tone in the meta-arterioles and precapillary sphincters. There are many agents which can produce a local vasodilation including decreased pO_2, increased pCO_2, decreased pH, increased lactate, phosphate, adenosine, etc. These local changes can be large and can occur within seconds.

4. Neurohormonal control of vasoconstriction

Local control of blood flow through the tissues cannot achieve a proper distribution of cardiac output and maintenance of arterial pressure when the demands of the tissues are high. The necessary rationing is carried out by central control exerted both by the release of noradrenaline from sympathetic nerve endings and by changes in the plasma concentrations of circulating hormones, notably adrenaline and angiotensin II. For instance in exercise, blood flow to the intestines and kidneys is reduced by sympathetic nerve activity and by circulating adrenaline.

Given a stabilized arterial pressure, changes in the resistance vessels will produce changes in tissue blood flow. For example in active tissues local mechanisms and sometimes nervous or hormonal influences cause vasodilation to supply the requisite increased perfusion. If the arterial pressure increases, the immediate effect is greater flow, due to the altered pressure gradient. Within minutes however, there is in most tissues a vasoconstriction which increases the resistance and returns flow towards the resting value. This stabilization of blood flow in the face of changing pressure is called autoregulation. It is thought to be due to

(a) washout or accumulation of vasodilator metabolites and
(b) a direct response of the vascular smooth muscle to stretch.

The special case of autoregulation of renal blood flow was considered in Chapter 5; this is thought to be partly due to mechanism (b) above and partly to mechanisms special to the kidneys.

(c) In many tissues if the changes in arterial pressure are sustained over days and weeks blood flow regulation becomes at least partly a consequence of changes in the number and the structure of resistance vessels.

When severe, the pressure induced changes in the arteries can be irreversible and can act to prevent adequate blood flow to the tissues. Since these effects are clearly not a form of regulation, some experts prefer to reserve the term autoregulation for only the short-term local control of constriction. Whatever it is called, long-term reversible stabilization of flow occurs. For instance in almost all forms of hypertension the blood flows to all tissues except the kidneys are nearly normal.

Long-term autoregulation makes it more difficult to control arterial pressure in the face of imposed changes in cardiac output. If arterial pressure is increased by a sustained increase in cardiac output, long-term autoregulation will increase the total peripheral resistance which will increase the arterial pressure yet further. The effects when vasoconstriction or vasodilation is imposed by neural or hormonal means are less clear. The local control in 1. and 3. above would tend to oppose such changes in arteriolar constriction while that in 2. would augment them.

Blood volume and cardiac output

Under normal conditions a maintained increase in blood volume causes an increase in the long-term average cardiac output, and similarly a reduction in volume causes a decrease in output. There are two main ways of thinking about this relationship.

1. Increased filling of the heart stretches the cardiac muscle fibres in diastole. From Starling's law of the heart, this stretch, within physiological limits, increases the 'energy of contraction' and hence the cardiac output. Moreover, the heart is able to pass on any increased input regardless of changes in aortic pressure, again within physiological limits. Any increase in blood volume will be partly accommodated in the heart, and thus will cause more stretch on the fibres and increase output. Indeed, when increased filling of the heart causes a rise in atrial pressure without an increase in output, the heart is said to be in failure.

2. A semi-quantitative analysis has been worked out by Guyton and his colleagues. This uses the obvious equivalence of venous return and cardiac output to focus attention on the factors causing blood to flow from the periphery back to the right atrium. The return of the blood is regarded as being driven by the difference between the mean systemic filling pressure and the mean right atrial pressure. The mean systemic filling pressure is a measure of the extent to which the blood fills and stretches the blood vessels. Its value is determined largely by the volume of blood in the capacitance vessels (chiefly venules and veins) and the tension in their walls; the greater the volume distending these vessels, the greater the pressure within them. In healthy, alert individuals the mean right atrial pressure stays close to 0 mmHg (with respect to atmospheric). This occurs both because small increases in right atrial pressures can produce large changes in cardiac output by the Starling effect and because increases in venous return normally occur together with increased sympathetic discharge to the heart which make it a more effective pump. Thus the main factor determining the pressure gradient returning blood to the heart is the mean systemic blood pressure which is markedly dependent on blood volume.

Arterial pressure

From the preceding discussion it follows that arterial pressure is determined by blood volume, the relation between cardiac output (equal to venous return) and blood volume, and the resistances to flow in the tissues. The resistances to flow are determined by local regulation and by externally imposed changes, i.e. those via the sympathetic nerves, adrenaline, angiotensin, and possibly other factors. In the short term (seconds to days) changes in blood volume produce only small changes in cardiac output and arterial pressure as a result of the powerful 'buffer' mechanisms which stabilize arterial pressure against changes. In the long term the effect of a change in blood volume is to produce a change in cardiac output which is amplified by local control of resistance to a large change in arterial pressure.

Short term regulation of arterial pressure

Arterial baroreceptors

The many mechanisms involved in short-term regulation are discussed in textbooks on cardiovascular physiology. The best known and perhaps most important is the baroreceptor reflex. Receptors which respond to the stretch of the carotid sinus and aortic arch signal the arterial pressure to the medulla oblongata via the glossopharyngeal and vagus nerves. There is a normal periodic, resting discharge which increases with increasing pressure and decreases as pressure falls, ceasing at around 60 mmHg. Increased firing leads to reflex vasodilation and slowing of the heart. The vascular responses are usually the main factors tending to limit an increase in arterial pressure. Arteriolar vasodilatation acts to reduce the total peripheral resistance while reduction of venomotor tone lowers the pressure head in the capacitance vessels and so reduces venous return and cardiac output. A drop in firing rate in the baroreceptor nerves, in response to a fall in arterial pressure, causes reflex arterial vasoconstriction, increased venomotor tone, and speeding of the heart rate. The baroreceptor reflexes act within seconds and can reduce fluctuations of arterial pressure about its average level by 60 to 80 per cent. If the baroreceptors are denervated in an experimental animal, the average arterial pressure recorded on a 24 hour basis is hardly increased, but there is much greater fluctuation on either side of the average.

If the factors determining this average change, e.g. if blood volume changes, the baroreceptors reflexes initially oppose and minimize the change in pressure. However, the baroreceptors adapt, or reset, over hours and days. The reflexes now respond appropriately to damp down fluctuations about the new average value. The resetting may be partly a consequence of the pressure induced changes which occur in all arteries.

Short-term roles of the kidneys

About 25 per cent of the resting cardiac output normally goes to the kidneys. Vasoconstriction in the renal vessels therefore provides a useful way to increase total peripheral resistance, and in severe hypotension there may be no flow at all through the renal arteries.

The kidneys are directly involved in a second defence against falling blood pressure. They release renin (see Chapter 9) which leads to production of angiotensin, a potent vasoconstrictor for arterioles and venules. In cardiovascular emergencies the secretion of renin can be enormously increased and the resulting blood levels of angiotensin contribute significantly to limit the fall in arterial pressure. Similarly, with sodium depletion, levels of angiotensin can be high enough to contribute substantially to the resting vascular tone. In these conditions a marked fall in arterial pressure can be produced by administration of antagonists, such as saralasin, to block angiotensin's effects or of converting enzyme inhibitors, such as captopril, to block angiotensin formation. By contrast in normal subjects the administration of captopril produces little immediate change in the arterial blood pressure, indicating that angiotensin is only a minor contributor to normal vascular tone.

Long-term regulation of arterial pressure

The kidneys must play a critical role in the maintenance of normal arterial blood pressure by virtue of their regulation of blood volume as indicated in Fig. 15.1. The bold arrows between body sodium content, blood volume, and arterial pressure represent relations discussed in the preceding section; the remaining arrows were considered in the preceding chapter. There are three special features of this control system which should be noted.

1. The consequences of any change when followed round come back to counteract the initial change. For instance, an increase in blood volume will lead to increased sodium (and water) excretion which will tend to correct the increase in blood volume.
2. Body sodium content can be constant only if renal sodium excretion balances the net input by all other routes.
3. Because changes in body sodium produce changes in extracellular fluid

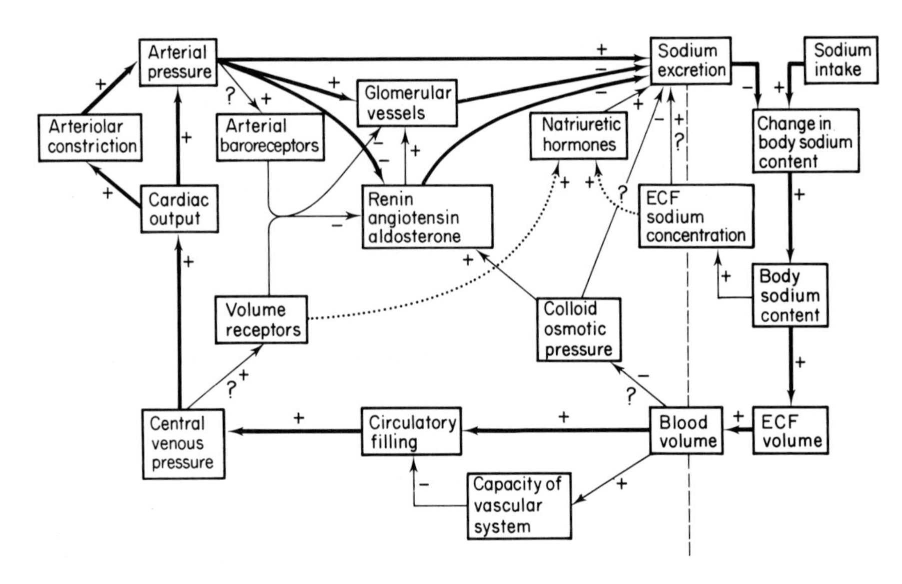

Fig. 15.1. The interrelation of the control of arterial blood pressure, blood volume, and sodium excretion. The arrows with plus signs denote that a change at the base of the arrow produces a change in the same direction at the head; that with a negative sign indicates a change in the opposite direction at the head. This figure is the same as Fig. 14.2 except that bold arrows are used to emphasize the elements of the control which are effective in long-term regulation. This principal control loop provides a powerful negative feedback control for body sodium content, extracellular fluid volume and arterial blood pressure. While the mechanisms for the short term buffering of arterial pressure prevent large changes in pressure even for quite large changes in blood volume, in the long-term the relation between arterial blood pressure and blood volume is normally steep, i.e. a small increase in blood volume produces a large increase in arterial pressure. Furthermore renal sodium excretion is strongly dependent on the prevailing arterial pressure by both direct and indirect mechanisms.

volume, blood volume, and arterial pressure, the arterial pressure can only be stable when sodium balance occurs.

It then follows that *a long term change in arterial pressure can occur only if either net sodium intake changes or something affects the kidneys so that the same sodium excretion can occur at a different arterial pressure.* Otherwise the changing body sodium content will eventually bring the arterial pressure back to its original value since it is still at this value that sodium intake will equal excretion.

A number of observations strongly support the conclusion that changes in renal function can change arterial pressure.

1. The blood pressure of patients who have had their kidneys removed and are maintained on periodic dialysis can be varied up and down by changing blood volume.
2. Diuretics which act on a number of different processes in the kidney reduce body sodium content and arterial pressure. They have little or no effect on pressure in anephric patients or animals.

3. The types of hypertension produced experimentally by renal artery clamps, desoxycorticosterone acetate plus salt loading, and reduction of renal mass plus salt loading (see below) provide clear examples where changes in some aspect of renal function produce maintained changes in arterial pressure. Also, hypertension is commonly seen in patients with chronic renal failure.
4. When kidneys are transplanted between genetically hypertensive and normotensive rats, the blood pressure 'follows the kidney'. Thus a kidney from a hypertensive rat produces hypertension in a normotensive rat and vice versa.

It is not known whether the long-term consequences of changes in the non-renal cardiovascular system can produce a maintained change in arterial pressure. In particular it is not yet established whether maintained increases in vascular resistance, outside the renal circulation can result in hypertension (see p. 191 below).

The endocrine role of the kidneys may also be important in the long-term control of blood pressure. While the available evidence suggests that renin and angiotensin are not necessary for maintenance of normal vascular tone, they do appear to be important in maintaining tone (in arteries and veins) during sodium depletion and in at least some cases of hypertension.

The kidneys may well produce other agents of importance which act on the rest of the body. There are two observations which suggest strongly that the renal medulla produces a factor which can lower blood pressure, at least when it has been abnormally raised. Firstly implants of medullary tissue can lower blood pressure in certain types of experimental hypertension. Secondly release of the clip in one kidney, one clip hypertension (see below) can bring blood pressure down to normal for hours and days even when the kidney is prevented from reducing extracellular fluid volume either by directing all urine back into the vena cava or by infusing isosmotic saline to replace all the sodium that is excreted.

Hypertension

Hypertension and its consequences are estimated to contribute to the deaths of more than 10 per cent of people in western societies. However, despite its undoubted importance and years of intensive study, only a small proportion of cases have known causes. These all involve obvious changes in the ability of the kidneys to excrete sodium. The remaining 80–90 per cent are still classed as essential hypertension; hypertension which is not obviously the consequence of any other disorder.

Experimentally produced hypertension

1. Salt loading hypertension

The arterial blood pressure of animals which have had all of one kidney and part of the other removed becomes markedly sensitive to the intake of salt. If isosmotic saline is substituted for drinking water, extracellular fluid volume expands, cardiac output increases, arterial pressure rises and after a few days sodium excretion increases to match intake. For the first several days there is little change in the total peripheral resistance. Any increase that one might have expected from tissue autoregulation is probably counteracted by vasodilatation dependent on the baroreceptor reflex. Furthermore renin and angiotensin levels are low since the surviving nephrons are all exposed to high pressures and a high rate of sodium excretion (see p. 164 and Chapter 9). Then, cardiac output begins to fall and total peripheral resistance rises, presumably via long-term autoregulation. At this stage the combination of increased cardiac output and increased resistance can lead to an extra rise in pressure. This in turn can cause some extra sodium excretion, thus lowering extracellular fluid volume and cardiac output most of the way back towards normal. The final stage is one of elevated pressure, elevated total peripheral resistance and nearly normal extracellular fluid volume and cardiac output.

Most results in hypertension research are disputed, these are no exception. While Guyton, Coleman, and their colleagues and others have repeatedly seen the results described above, others do not see a transient increase in cardiac output and argue that the increase in total peripheral resistance is caused by an effect on the smooth muscle in the blood vessels of raised plasma sodium concentration or of a natriuretic hormone (see p. 189). Regardless, the primary defect remains the inability to excrete the excessive salt load without an unusually large increase in either body sodium or arterial pressure. Autoregulation still presumably operates to adjust tissue resistances either up or down towards the correct flows.

2. Goldblatt hypertension, coarctation of the aorta and renal artery stenosis

In 1934 Goldblatt first convincingly produced hypertension in experimental animals. In the two variants of his procedure in modern use one renal artery is clipped or constricted, and the other kidney is either removed (one kidney, one clip hypertension) or left intact (two kidney, one clip hypertension). One kidney, one clip hypertension is investigated instead of the two kidney, two clip variety in order to avoid the complications of having different degrees of constriction in the two renal arteries.

The scheme shown by the bold arrows in Fig. 15.1 is thought to describe the essential features of one kidney, one clip hypertension. Renal artery constriction reduces the pressure in the kidney which reduces sodium excretion and increases levels of renin and angiotensin. As a consequence extracellular fluid volume, blood volume, cardiac output, and total peripheral resistance all tend to increase which increases systemic arterial pressure. Systemic pressure increases until within a few days the pressures within the clipped kidney are nearly normal and sodium excretion again matches input. In the steady state, which is reached in a few weeks, systemic pressure is elevated, total peripheral resistance is elevated further by long-term autoregulation and cardiac output has returned almost to normal. Renin levels are high when the clip is first applied but within a few days as the arterial pressure increases they fall to normal or below normal values. The return of cardiac output to normal values is associated with a fall in blood volume, presumably because excretion slightly exceeds intake as pressure and total peripheral resistance increase during the final approach to the steady state.

In some studies extracellular fluid volume initially increases as indicated above; in others there is apparently sufficient constriction of arterioles to elevate arterial pressure and bring sodium excretion back into balance without transient increases in blood volume and cardiac output. The primary defect in renal salt excretion (in this case the clip) prevents the excessive arterial pressure from producing extra salt excretion which would reduce blood volume and the pressure. Similarly autoregulation still presumably adjusts tissue blood flow. The reasons for the different behaviour observed in different laboratories is unknown.

Sympathectomy, renal denervation, and intravenous 6-hydroxydopamine which destroys noradrenergic nerve terminals, have little effect on the time course of one kidney, one clip hypertension. By contrast 6-hydroxydopamine injected into the cerebral ventricles is reported to prevent both fluid volume expansion and hypertension when a clip is applied. For this to be true, some consequence of this treatment must dramatically alter the renal response to changes in renal perfusion pressure.

Two kidney, one clip hypertension

When one kidney is removed leaving a healthy kidney behind, more sodium is excreted by the remaining kidney with little or no change in arterial pressure. By contrast when one renal artery is severely clipped and the other is untouched hypertension develops. Therefore some consequence of clipping the artery of one kidney reduces the excretion of sodium from the other. The nature of the message from the clipped kidney to the other is uncertain, but it is thought to be increased levels of renin and angiotensin. Pressure, blood flow and sodium excretion of the clipped kidney fall precipitously and do not recover unless the clip is removed. Thus within it both the pressure and macula densa mechanisms (see Chapter 9) stimulate renin release. The increased levels of angiotensin and also aldosterone reduce sodium excretion by the other kidney and angiotensin produces arteriolar constriction. Over days, total peripheral resistance continues to increase, presumably by pressure induced changes, pressure increases further and the levels of renin and angiotensin fall towards but do not reach normal. In the steady state the levels of angiotensin are not adequate to explain the maintained high total peripheral resistance which is therefore presumably kept high by the effects of the elevated pressure. However, the slightly elevated angiotensin and associated aldosterone may account for the high pressure needed for the unclipped kidney to excrete sodium chloride. Block of angiotensin II formation from angiotensin I by captopril or removal of the clipped kidney leads to a return of blood pressure and total peripheral resistance to normal.

Coarctation and stenosis

The hypertension which results in humans from coarctation of the aorta or stenosis of both renal arteries is thought to be similar in its development to one kidney, one clip Goldblatt hypertension. In the chronic state of both conditions, the pressure observed in the renal distributing arteries is normal while in renal artery stenosis the rest of the body, and in coarctation the upper half of the body, are severely hypertensive. In coarctation blood flow to the tissues is normal in both halves of the body which argues strongly for the importance of local autoregulation. Adequate pressure in the renal vessels to allow excretion of the net sodium input necessitates an elevated pressure upstream to compensate for the pressure drop across the arterial narrowing. These types of hypertension are often satisfactorily cured by surgical correction of the narrowing.

Essential hypertension

It is clear that the ability of the kidneys to excrete sodium at a given pressure is reduced and that total peripheral resistance is elevated in essential hypertension. But here agreement ends and we simply cannot say at present what causes essential hypertension. All we can do here is to outline some of the current proposals and point out that different cases may fall into different categories.

Proposal 1

Essential hypertension is caused by impaired excretion of salt. Peripheral resistance is elevated as a consequence of long-term autoregulation and/or the effects of renin and angiotensin.

Possible changes in renal function which might cause essential hypertension include a reduction in glomerular filtration coefficient, partial blocking of the small renal arteries, i.e. a sort of disseminated renal artery stenosis, a resetting of tubular-glomerular feedback, or excessive distal sodium reabsorption for a given level of aldosterone. The primary defect would lead to sodium retention and possibly to increased renin release much as in the variants of Goldblatt hypertension discussed above. If renin release is prominent the resulting blood pressure increase could be sufficient to lead to a net sodium depletion. Regardless, long-term autoregulation would ensure that steady state total peripheral resistance would lead to nearly normal tissue blood flow. Cardiac output would be slightly raised if the hypertension were driven primarily by sodium retention and slightly depressed if renin and angiotensin played the major role.

The proposal that some perturbation of renal function underlies essential hypertension has obvious attractions. However it is not clear that this mechanism can explain all types of essential hypertension and many workers have pointed out features which they find difficult to explain on this model.

1. Many cases are described without either an increase in blood volume or elevated renin secretion. Indeed some cases seem to have decreased blood volume with normal or low levels of renin.
2. Many patients cannot be successfully treated with diuretics which ought to be able to counter the renal tendency to retain sodium. However, as discussed below, this may sometimes reflect the stimulation of renin release by these drugs.

The argument that volume increase cannot be the cause of hypertension since excessive blood volume can be associated with low blood pressure in congestive heart failure is not sound. In congestive heart failure the pressure control loop in Fig. 15.1

is broken; the heart cannot maintain the proper cardiac output for any blood volume and thus pressure falls. The fall produces sodium retention and renin release which via angiotensin acts to maintain total peripheral resistance hence minimizing the fall in pressure. The angiotensin also acts as an antinatriuretic agent further enhancing the sodium retention. The importance of angiotensin in congestive cardiac failure is emphasized by the effectiveness of captopril in releasing the fluid overload.

Proposal 2

Impaired renal ability to excrete sodium in some way leads to increased production of natriuretic factors which as a side effect elevate total peripheral resistance.

Many experts have been reluctant to accept that long-term autoregulation and angiotensin can account for the increase in total peripheral resistance in essential hypertension. An alternative explanation, similar to that proposed by some for salt-loading hypertension, has gained some support. In this proposal the primary defect is still a reduced ability of the kidney to excrete the dietary load of salt, and body sodium content increases slightly. In some manner this stimulates the production of a natriuretic hormone (or hormones). The increase in blood volume is held to be too small to increase cardiac output measurably and difficult to detect because, according to these theories, the natriuretic hormone is very effective at increasing sodium excretion. Increased blood pressure is held to be an unfortunate side effect of arteriolar constriction produced by the increased levels of the natriuretic hormone. If, as some propose this natriuretic hormone acts like digitalis, its effect on vascular smooth muscle might be closely analogous to its effect on the heart and might reflect altered sodium–calcium exchange. This proposal has attractions, not least that it is actually testable by experiments, but there are also arguments against it.

1. It provides no explanation for the continued control of cardiac output at nearly the normal value.
2. Like proposal 1 above, it has difficulty accounting for hypertension with reduced blood volumes (though in one version the natriuretic hormone is released in response to an increase in sodium concentration which would avoid this difficulty).
3. To obtain plasma containing the natriuretic hormone, the extracellular fluid volume of experimental animals has been increased greatly. It is not clear that smaller, physiological challenges would release sufficient amounts to be effective.
4. This theory has considerable difficulty explaining the different pressures and resistances above and below the constriction in cases of coarctation of the aorta.

Proposal 3

Essential hypertension is caused by a change in total peripheral resistance.

Since total peripheral resistance is clearly elevated in hypertension, it has always seemed attractive to propose that some form of arteriolar constriction is the primary cause. The resistance could be raised in a number of ways, e.g.

through a reduction in the number of arterioles, through a primary change in the vascular smooth muscle (perhaps caused by chronically but slightly elevated plasma sodium concentration), or through a smooth muscle response to either excessive nerve stimulation or inappropriate circulating hormones. In this view the kidneys are thought to 'adapt' to the new pressure so that they excrete the normal sodium load at the elevated blood pressure.

There are arguments in favour of this proposal.

1. It provides an obvious means of explaining the observed importance of brain stem structures involved in short-term pressure regulation in the development and maintenance of hypertension.
2. It provides a ready explanation for the sometimes dramatic reductions in pressure which can be obtained by surgical or pharmacological sympathectomy.
3. It provides an obvious role for those antihypertensive drugs which are known to interfere with neural control of vasoconstriction.
4. It is also consistent with the popular prejudice that a stressful life in some way causes hypertension.

There are also arguments against.

1. Long-term infusions of noradrenaline do not produce maintained hypertension. Thus it is unlikely that simple overactivity of the sympathetic nerves produces the vasoconstriction.
2. The fall in pressure produced by sympathectomy or by pharmacological interference with neurally produced vasoconstriction is often only temporary. In these instances body sodium content increases and raises the blood pressure back to its hypertensive level. (This retention can often be prevented by the use of diuretics.)
3. There are many long-term increases in total peripheral resistance which do not produce hypertension, these include: treatment of patients with beriberi in which disease peripheral resistance is greatly reduced; treatment of thyrotoxicosis; removal of all four limbs; treatment of anaemia in which disorder the blood viscosity is initially reduced; delivery of a baby and the placenta; and hypothyroidism.
4. Following a primary increase in peripheral resistance the initial elevation of pressure will increase the rate of sodium excretion which reduces extracellular fluid volume and blood volume. As discussed above this reduction in blood volume should reduce cardiac output and at least partially restore the arterial pressure to normal. In the examples cited in 3 above, these changes have apparently restored the blood pressure all of the way to the original value. By contrast in essential hypertension cardiac output is usually normal or slightly elevated and by definition the blood pressure is still elevated. Thus if primary increases in peripheral resistance are the basis of essential hypertension they must be combined with mechanisms that prevent the kidneys from reducing blood volume sufficiently to decrease cardiac output and reverse the increase in pressure.

One mechanism whereby vascular resistances could be increased without a marked pressure natriuresis is for the resistance of the renal arterioles to be increased along with those in the rest of the circulation. The increase in renal vascular resistance would then prevent the increased blood pressure from causing increased sodium excretion. However, in this model there is a change in renal function (albeit vascular) which is necessary for the maintenance of the hypertension and this proposal is therefore a special case of proposal 1.

It is not known whether changes in arteriolar resistance which do not directly affect the kidneys can produce hypertension.

On the present evidence, discussed in the preceding chapter, changes in body sodium content can alter the rate of sodium excretion both by changing arterial pressure which changes excretion and also by mechanisms which do not require changes in arterial pressure. Guyton and his colleagues have analyzed models which implicitly assume that the pressure-independent effects represented by the thin arrows in Fig. 15.1 are negligible. If these are completely ignored, it then follows that primary changes outside the kidneys in the resistance of arterioles or the capacitance of the veins or changes in the contractility of the heart are all incapable of producing long-term changes in arterial blood pressure. This follows because any change in arterial pressure which is produced initially will change sodium excretion so that it no longer equals sodium intake. This imbalance between excretion and intake will continue to change the amount of sodium in the body and arterial pressure until excretion is changed all the way back to equality with intake. If control occurs only as indicated by the bold arrows, the pressure is then necessarily the same as the pressure before the change in resistance, capacitance, or cardiac contractility since nothing has occurred to change the relation between renal excretion and pressure. Thus with the assumption that body sodium content affects excretion only via changes in arterial pressure the renal system has the power eventually to bring arterial pressure all the way back to its original value despite the continued presence of changes in the circulation. This property of their model systems is called infinite gain feedback by Guyton and his colleagues.

The renal control system for arterial pressure does not have infinite gain if there are any mechanisms whereby changes in body sodium content can change sodium excretion independent of changes in arterial pressure. Consider an initial change in arterial blood pressure caused by a primary increase in arteriolar resistance other than in the kidneys. The raised pressure will still increase sodium excretion which will decrease the sodium content of the body and this will tend to lower arterial pressure. However, if the change in sodium content reduces sodium excretion by its effect on arterial pressure *and* by other mechanisms, excretion will again equal intake with the arterial pressure returned only part way towards its original value. Arterial pressure independent mechanisms for control of sodium excretion appear to exist and were discussed in Chapter 14. However their relative importance is not clear and will almost certainly vary with the circumstances. It is, therefore, not yet possible to decide, based on our knowledge of renal mechanisms, when the renal system will or will not have complete control over pressure.

Salt and hypertension

A reduced intake of sodium chloride is popularly supposed to lower the blood pressure and reduce the risk of developing essential hypertension. The present evidence is not conclusive.

For normal people on tolerable diets it is hard to measure any effect of salt intake on blood pressure over a period of weeks. This is also true for many

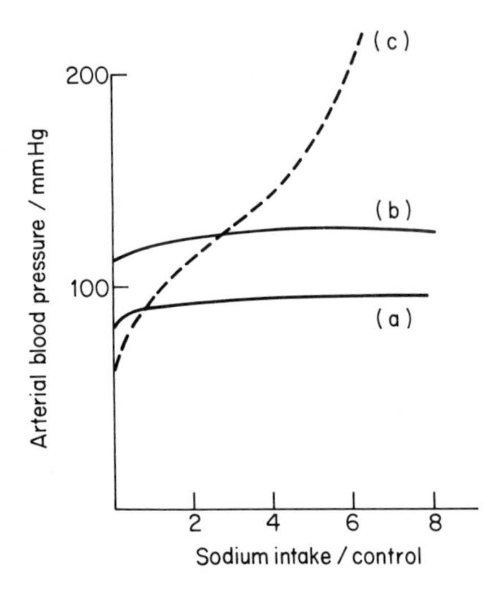

Fig. 15.2. The relations between arterial blood pressure and sodium intake seen normally (a), in salt insensitive hypertension (b), and in salt sensitive hypertension (c).

patients with hypertension. The relation for normal people is expressed as curve (a) in Fig. 15.2. In many hypertensives this relation is displaced upwards (b) sometimes by an obvious cause such as renal artery stenosis, but often for unknown reasons sometimes perhaps as a result of widespread narrowing of small arteries and arterioles in the kidneys. In other hypertensives, curve (c), blood pressure can indeed be usefully lowered by restricting the salt content of the diet, and an excessive salt intake makes their hypertension worse. One cause of this type of salt dependence is excessive aldosterone. Another is severe reduction of renal mass. For these patients avoidance of salt can obviously be beneficial.

When populations of people are compared, who over many years have either a high or low salt diet, there is significantly more hypertension in the high salt group. However, it is not certain that the differences in pressure are due to the differences in salt intake. Even if they are, the basis for this long term effect of high salt intake is not clear. It could be just that high salt intake exposes those people whose rate of sodium excretion becomes less sensitive to sodium content and arterial pressure as they grow older. Alternatively it may be that a life-long requirement for excreting lots of salt actually alters renal function so as to change this relation. Those who consider this latter possibility realistic may be persuaded to cut down on their salt intake even if they presently have normal blood pressure. If only the first possibility is true then only for those with elevated blood pressure is it worth trying salt restriction.

Antihypertensive drugs

Reductions in the sodium content of the body, extracellular fluid volume and blood volume reduce arterial blood pressure. Drugs which, other things being equal, increase sodium excretion should therefore be antihypertensive. Such an effect can obviously explain a large part of the antihypertensive effects of diuretic drugs. The immediate response to a diuretic is an increase in sodium excretion which returns to balance with intake over a few days as body sodium content, extracellular fluid volume (and body weight), blood volume, cardiac output and arterial pressure all fall. Subsequently over weeks total peripheral resistance falls, as a result of long-term autoregulation if nothing else. As resistance falls, blood volume and cardiac output return towards normal.

In many patients diuretics fail to produce an adequate reduction in arterial blood pressure. One of the possible explanations is that either the diuretic itself or the consequences of treatment with the diuretic stimulates the release of renin and the production of angiotensin II. The anti-natriuretic effect of the angiotensin II then counteracts the diuretic effects of the drug. This explanation is supported by the remarkable successes achieved in trials using combinations of a diuretic agent, which acts directly on the tubular cells, and captopril, which blocks the production of angiotensin II.

Renal effects are also likely to be an important part of the action of many other antihypertensive agents. Drugs which interfere with sympathetic nerve transmission or which directly vasodilate arterioles are often thought to reduce blood pressure by their effects on total peripheral resistance irrespective of their actions on the renal circulation. This view is correct for the initial, short term effects (and may be partly correct in the long-term, see small print p. 191). However, the renal response to such an initial decrease in blood pressure is to retain sodium and thus to return the blood pressure most if not all the way back to its original value. This response can be avoided and a large sustained fall in blood pressure achieved if the drug induced vasodilation also affects the renal vasculature or the renal response is effectively blocked by the simultaneous use of a diuretic.

Drugs such as clonidine and α-methyl dopa which lower blood pressure by actions in the central nervous system may also be able to produce sustained effects on blood pressure by virtue of sympathetic nerve fibres and centrally controlled hormones directed at the kidneys.

Drugs acting on β-adrenergic receptors, e.g. propranolol, are often thought to control arterial blood pressure by their negative inotropic action on the heart. However, such an effect is unlikely to produce a significant change in resting cardiac output from a healthy heart. Furthermore, the reduction in sodium excretion following any acute fall in pressure which did occur would return the pressure most if not all of the way back to its pretreatment value. An alternative suggestion is that these drugs act within the kidneys to decrease the release of renin, probably by blocking β-receptors on the juxtaglomerular apparatus. The consequent lowering of angiotensin levels produces a natriuresis which over several days should lower blood pressure. It is noteworthy that angiotensin converting enzyme inhibitors such as captopril, even given alone, are very potent antihypertensive agents in many though not all patients with essential hypertension.

Captopril appears to be effective in almost all patients with high renin and angiotensin levels and in most with normal levels. It is not effective when renin levels are low. It is important to realize that, at the elevated arterial pressures observed in hypertension, renin and angiotensin levels should be markedly lower than normal. The observation of the same renin level as in a normotensive person thus indicates that the response of the renin–angiotensin system is not appropriate and thus that this system is part of the disorder. The efficacy of captopril may suggest that many cases of essential hypertension result from inappropriate secretion of renin or of excessive renal sensitivity to angiotensin II.

Further reading

Barnes, R.J., Bower, E.A. & Rink, T.J. (1980). Haemodynamic responses to stimulation of the cardiac autonomic nerves in the anaesthetized cat with closed chest. *J. Physiol.* **299**, 55–73.

Bianchi, G., Fox. U., DiFrancesco, G.F., Giovanetti, A.M. & Pagetti, D. (1974). Blood pressure changes produced by kidney cross-transplantation between spontaneously hypertensive rats and normotensive rats. *Clin. Sci. Mol. Med.* **47**, 435–448.

Blaustein, M.P. (1977). Sodium ions, calcium ions, blood pressure regulation and hypertension: a reassessment and a hypothesis. *Am. J. Physiol.* **232**, *C*167–*C*173.

Borst, J.G.G. & Borst-DeGeus, A. (1963). Hypertension explained by Starling's theory of circulatory homeostasis. *Lancet* **1**, 677.

Buckalew, V.M. Jr. & Gruber, K.A. (1984). Natriuretic hormone. *Ann. Rev. Physiol.* **46**, 343–358.

Case, D.B., Sonnenblick, E.H. & Laragh, J.H. eds, (1980). *Captopril and Hypertension*, Plenum, N.Y.

Coleman, T.G. (1980). *Blood Pressure Control Volume 1*. Eden Press, Westmount, Quebec. (1013 references. An excellent but very dry survey of the experimental evidence.)

Coleman, T.G., Hall, J.E. & Norman, R.A. Jr. (1981). Regulation of arterial blood pressure, pp 1–20 in Brenner, B.M. & Stein, J.H. eds. *Hypertension*. Contemporary Issues in Nephrology Vol. 8. Churchill Livingstone, N.Y.

Conway, J. (1984). Hemodynamic aspects of essential hypertension in humans. *Physiol. Rev.* **64**, 617–660.

Dahl, L.K., Heine, M. & Thompson, K. (1974). Genetic influence of the kidneys on blood pressure. *Circulation Research* **34**, 94–101.

DeWardener, H.E. & Macgregor, G.A. (1980). Dahl's hypothesis that a saluretic substance may be responsible for a sustained rise in arterial pressure: its possible role in essential hypertension. *Kidney Int.* **18**, 1–9.

Dickinson, C.J. (1981). Neurogenic hypertension revisited. *Clin. Sci.* **60**, 471–477.

Ferrario, C.M. & Page, I.H. (1978). Current views concerning cardiac output in the genesis of experimental hypertension *Circulation Research* **43**, 821–831. (An authoritative review which gives quite a different impression from Guyton's writings about the role of blood volume and cardiac output in the observed increases in total peripheral resistance.)

Folkow, B. (1982). Physiological Aspects of Primary Hypertension. *Physiol. Rev.* **62**, 347–504. (This review contains a particularly full discussion of pressure induced changes in the cardiovascular system and in the kidneys.)

Freis, E.D. (1979), Salt in hypertension and the effects of diuretics. *Ann. Rev. Pharmacol. Toxicol* **19**, 13–23.

Genest, J., Koiw, E. & Kuchel, O. (1977). *Hypertension* McGraw Hill, N.Y. (A collection of articles representing the full spectrum of views.)

Golin, R., Stella, A. & Zanchetti, A. (1982). Reversible renal nerve denervation in the cat: Effects on haemodynamic and excretory functions of the ipsilateral and contralateral kidneys. *Clin. Sci.* **63**, 215s–217s.

Guyton, A.C., Jones, C.E. & Coleman, T.G. (1973). *Cardiac Output and Its Regulation*, 2nd edn, Saunders, Philadelphia. (The exposition of cardiovascular dynamics in terms of cardiac function curves, mean systemic filling pressure and resistance to venous return.)

Guyton, A.C., Coleman, T.G., Cowley, A.W. Jr., Manning, R.D. Jr., Norman, R.A., Jr. & Ferguson, J.D. (1974). A systems analysis approach to understanding long-range arterial blood pressure control and hypertension. *Circulation Res.* **35**, 159–176.

Guyton, A.C. (1980). *Textbook of Medical Physiology*, 6th edn. Saunders, Philadelphia. (A boiled down version of Guyton's monographs can be found in this well known textbook. While most experts disagree with some aspect or another of his analysis, it remains the most coherent account of cardiovascular control. Chapter 21, pp. 246–258 Short-term regulation of mean arterial pressure. Chapter 22, pp. 259–273 Long-term regulation of mean arterial pressure. Chapter 23, pp. 274–288 Cardiac output, venous return and their regulation.

Guyton, A.C. (1980). *Arterial Pressure and Hypertension. Circulatory Physiology III* Saunders, Philadelphia. (The analysis of blood pressure control embodied in the loop of bold arrows in Fig. 15.1 was developed in the early 1960s by a number of authors including Borst and Borst de Geus in Holland, Ledingham and his colleagues in London, and Guyton, Coleman and their colleagues in Mississippi. These last authors have developed the theory to provide quantitative simulation of both short and long term regulation of blood pressure. This book gives a full account.)

Guyton, A.C., Manning, R.D. Jr., Hall, J.E., Norman, R.A. Jr., Young, D.B. & Pan, Y. -J. (1984). The pathogenic role of the kidney. *J. Cardiovasc. Pharm.* **6**, S151–S161. (Restatement of their view.)

Hladky, S.B. (1985). Sodium excretion and arterial pressure. *J. Physiol.* **358**, 119P.

Korner, P.I. (1982). Causal and homeostatic factors in hypertension. *Clin. Sci.* **63**, 5s–26s.

Ledingham, J.M. (1971). Mechanisms in renal hypertension. *Proc. Roy. Soc. Med.* **64**, 409.

Murray, R.H., Luft, F.C., Bloch, R. & Weyman, A.E. (1978) Blood pressure responses to extremes of sodium intake in normal man. *Proc. Soc. Exp. Biol. Med.* **159**, 432–436.

Pickering, G. (1964). Systemic arterial hypertension, pp. 487–541 in *Circulation of the Blood. Men and Ideas*. Oxford University Press. Reissued in 1982 by American Physiological Society, Bethesda, Fishman, A.P. & Richards, D.W. eds.

Round Table Discussions (1979). *Clin. Sci.* **59**. (Very useful discussions of the roles of changes in cardiac output and extracellular fluid volume in hypertension and of the role (or non-role) of excessive salt intake in producing hypertension.)

Young, D.B., McCaa, R.E., Pan, Y. -J. & Guyton, A.C. (1976). Effectiveness of the aldosterone-sodium and -potassium feedback control system. *Am. J. Physiol.* **231**, 945–953. (Sodium loading decreases plasma potassium concentration and increases mean arterial pressure much more in adrenalectomized dogs maintained on constant infusions of aldosterone and hydrocortisone than in normal dogs.)

16

Regulation of pH

Arterial plasma pH is normally near 7.4, i.e. the hydrogen ion concentration is about 40 nanomolar. Interstitial fluid pH is slightly lower as a result of the continuous production of acid in the form of carbon dioxide by cell metabolism. Similarly venous plasma is also slightly more acid, about pH 7.36, since this carbon dioxide must be carried away by the blood. Intracellular pH, in those cells where it has been measured, is usually near 7.1.

If the pH inside cells with a normal resting potential of about 60 mV were at equilibrium with the extracellular pH, the intracellular pH would be about 6.4 rather than 7. It follows that these cells possess some means for expelling hydrogen ions or, equivalently, for acquiring hydroxyl ions. Mechanisms used in various cells include the ATP fuelled hydrogen pump and the sodium-hydrogen exchanger found in the luminal membranes of tubular cells in the kidneys.

In most cells intracellular pH is to some extent stabilized against fluctuations in extracellular pH, typically changing by only one-half to one-third as much.

Effects of disturbances of pH

Deviation from normal pH affects many different systems and usually occurs along with other serious disturbances in fluid homeostasis. It is therefore difficult to pin down the specific consequences of altered pH. Among the effects of increased extracellular hydrogen ion concentration, that is low pH, are:

1. hyperkalaemia due to the movement of potassium from cells into extracellular fluid and the depression of renal secretion;
2. with a fall in pH to less than *c*7, a widespread loss of smooth muscle tone which produces a severe drop in arterial pressure;
3. when persistent for weeks and months, leaching of minerals from bone to cause a condition known as *osteoporosis*.

One dramatic effect of decreased hydrogen ion concentration, i.e. raised pH, is tetany or spasm of muscles together with bizarre sensations and numbness. These symptoms are most typically seen when a subject hyperventilates thus blowing off carbon dioxide and raising plasma pH. They are due to spontaneous, spurious activity in peripheral nerve fibres. This activity arises because the reduced hydrogen ion concentration increases calcium binding to albumin, which decreases the *free* calcium concentration in the extracellular fluid. The fall in free calcium in turn makes the firing threshold for nerve axons nearer to the resting potential. Spontaneous fluctuations in potential now set up spurious action potentials.

The range of hydrogen ion concentration which is compatible with life is surprisingly wide, including at least a 5-fold range from 100 nM (pH 7) to 20 nM (pH 7.8). Fluctuations of hydrogen ion concentration of 20–30 per cent on either side of normal, i.e. within the range pH 7.3–7.5, are without serious effects.

Buffers

In order to understand the challenges to and the regulation of body pH, it is essential to have a grasp of the fundamentals of pH buffering. We shall not attempt a detailed explanation here but rather revise some of the main points as they apply to physiology. A more complete, introductory account is to be found in *Fundamentals of Acid-base Balance*, by J.R. Robinson.

1. In aqueous solutions the product of the hydrogen and hydroxyl ion concentrations is constant, approximately 10^{-14} M (depending on the temperature and ionic strength, etc.) Thus at pH 7, $[OH^-] = [H^+] = 10^{-7}$ M and the solution is said to be neutral. (Square brackets are used to indicate the concentration of the substance named between them.) As the hydrogen concentration rises above this value the hydroxyl ion concentration must fall and vice versa.
2. A *base* is conveniently defined as anything which when added tends to reduce the hydrogen ion concentration of a solution, e.g. sodium hydroxide or bicarbonate ions. An acid is similarly defined as anything which increases the hydrogen ion concentration, e.g. hydrochloric acid, hydrogen ions, and carbon dioxide.
3. A *pH buffer* is a substance that reversibly binds hydrogen ions. The pH change that follows the addition of hydrogen or hydroxyl ions can be greatly reduced by the presence of a buffer to take up or release hydrogen ions. Each buffer can exist in two forms; an acidic form which can release a hydrogen ion to produce the basic form and a basic form which can accept a hydrogen ion to produce the acidic form. For each buffer the concentrations of the two forms, [acid] and [base], and of hydrogen ions $[H^+]$ are related by the equation for a simple the chemical equilibrium so that for the reaction

$$\text{acid} \rightleftarrows \text{base} + H^+$$

$$K_A[\text{acid}] = [\text{base}] \times [H^+]$$

where K_A is the acid dissociation constant. Taking logs we can rewrite the equation for the equilibrium as

$$\log[H^+] = \log K_A + \log([\text{acid}]/[\text{base}])$$

and using the definitions of pH and pK_A, $pH = -\log[H^+]$ and $pK_A = -\log K_A$ we get the Henderson-Hasselbach relation.

$$pH = pK_A + \log([\text{base}]/[\text{acid}]).$$

From this equation the pH can be calculated for any given ratio of base to acid; equally this ratio can be calculated for each buffer present from the pH and its pK_A.

It may help to consider an example. For $H_2PO_4^+$ and HPO_4^{2-}, the pK_A is 6.8, i.e. at pH = 6.8, the two forms are at equal concentration (recall log(1) = 0). If the total concentration of buffer is 10 mM, then each form is present at 5 mM. (At pH 6.8, the concentrations of the uncharged and triply charged forms of the phosphate are negligible.) If now 1 mmole of HCl is added per litre of solution, almost all of the hydrogen ions combine with the basic form of the pair converting it to the acidic form, i.e. to an excellent approximation, the concentrations of the two forms become $[H_2PO_4^+]$ = 6 mM and $[HPO_4^{2-}]$ = 4 mM and the pH is

$$pH = pK_A + \log(4/6) = 6.8 - 0.18 = 6.6$$

Thus of the 1 mM HCl added about 0.1 μM of hydrogen ions remained free and decreased the pH from 6.8 to 6.6 and similarly a small quantity of hydrogen ions also combined with hydroxyl ions and reduced their concentration. The remainder, virtually all, combined with the basic form of the phosphate as stated above.

4. *Strength of buffering.* This can be defined in terms of how much acid or base must be added to produce a given change in pH. For a single buffer, the strength is determined by its concentration and how near or far its pK_A is from the initial pH. Buffers are most effective at pH values near the pK_A. For example the buffering strength, or capacity, of a simple buffer pair decreases 10 fold for each pH unit above or below its pK_A.
5. *Mixtures of buffers.* In any mixture of buffers the Henderson-Hasselbach equation applies to each pair. Furthermore, since there can be only one pH, alteration in the ratio of any one pair, to change the pH, necessarily alters all the others. Hence it is in principle necessary to regulate only one buffer pair to control the pH of the mixture. This is almost what the body does as it regulates the concentration ratio for carbon dioxide and bicarbonate.

Special considerations for carbon dioxide-bicarbonate buffers

The actual buffer pair is H_2CO_3 and HCO_3^-. However carbonic acid is the product of the reversible reaction $CO_2 + H_2O \rightleftharpoons H_2CO_3$. Under physiological conditions the equilibrium of this reaction is far to the left and the concentration of carbon dioxide is about 400 times that of carbonic acid. It is therefore usual to combine the equations for the equilibria of the reactions

$$CO_2 + H_2O \rightleftarrows H_2CO_3 \rightleftarrows HCO_3^- + H^+$$

into the form of a slightly modified Henderson-Hasselbach relation,

$$pH = 6.1 + \log([HCO_3^-]/[CO_2])$$

where $[CO_2]$ is the free concentration of physically dissolved carbon dioxide. The apparent pK_A in this equation, 6.1, is in fact a composite constant incorporating the true pK_A for the carbonic acid-bicarbonate buffer pair, which is approximately 4.4, and the log of the dissociation constant for carbonic acid to carbon dioxide and water which is approximately 1.7.

It is customary to measure and to express the free concentration of gases in blood as their partial pressures. The partial pressure is related to the free concentration by Henry's law so that $[CO_2] = K_p\, pCO_2$. For $[CO_2]$ in mM and pCO_2 in mmHg (millimetres of mercury), $K_p = 0.03$ at 37°C. A convenient form of the relation between carbon dioxide, bicarbonate, and hydrogen, is thus

$$pH = 6.1 + \log\{([HCO_3^-]/mM)/(0.03(pCO_2)/mmHg)\}.$$

The next complication is that the hydration, dehydration reaction $H_2CO_3 \rightleftarrows H_2O + CO_2$ is slow, taking tens of seconds at 37°C. However the reaction is enormously accelerated by the enzyme carbonic anhydrase which is present in those cells where rapid buffering or release of hydrogen ions by the bicarbonate system is required, e.g. in red blood cells and in renal tubular cells. For present purposes therefore we can take it that the carbon dioxide bicarbonate buffer system comes to an equilibrium fast enough for its physiological functions.

Why bicarbonate is a good buffer for hydrogen ions in the body

Although the apparent pK_A of this buffer seems far from the normal pH, 6.1 compared to 7.4, bicarbonate in fact provides considerable buffering capacity for two reasons. Firstly, the basic form, bicarbonate is present at high concentration, approximately 24 mM. Secondly the acidic form, carbon dioxide, is held at a steady concentration since the respiratory system stabilizes its partial pressure. The significance of this stabilization is best illustrated with numerial examples.

Consider a solution containing no buffers other than 24 mM sodium bicarbonate with $pCO_2 = 40$ mmHg. The pH is therefore $6.1 + \log(24/(0.03 \times 40)) = 7.4$. Addition of 12 mmoles of hydrochloric acid to each litre of solution will reduce the concentration of bicarbonate by 12 mM and increase the carbon dioxide concentration by the same amount. If the carbon dioxide cannot escape, the buffer ratio will become 12/13.2 and the pH will fall to 6.6. (The pCO_2 would be 440 mmHg.) If instead, the extra carbon dioxide is eliminated from the solution and the partial pressure stays at 40 mmHg, the buffer ratio becomes 12/1.2 and the pH falls to only 7.1.

The body in fact can do better than this by responding to the fall in pH by increased respiration which actually lowers the partial pressure, thus keeping the buffer ratio even nearer the normal level, as will be discussed below. Additionally there are other buffers present in the body fluids and thus even at constant pCO_2, the falls in pH and bicarbonate concentration are smaller than for the pure bicarbonate buffer.

Effects of changing pCO_2 on bicarbonate concentration in the presence or absence of other buffers

If pCO_2 is raised in a solution buffered only by carbon dioxide and bicarbonate, the bicarbonate concentration increases almost imperceptibly while the hydrogen concentration rises almost in proportion to the increase in pCO_2. For instance if pCO_2 is doubled, $[CO_2]$ increases from 1.2 to 2.4 mM, $[H_2CO_3]$ also doubles, and thus the product $[H^+][HCO_3^-]$ must double. This occurs as carbonic acid dissociates to form equal additional amounts of hydrogen and bicarbonate. Since $[HCO_3^-]$ is high while $[H^+]$ is very low, enough dissociation to restore equilibrium virtually doubles $[H^+]$ but hardly changes $[HCO_3^-]$. The total amount of carbon dioxide added to the solution is therefore only very slightly greater than the increase in the amount of physically dissolved carbon dioxide.

In the body fluids other buffers are present as well as the carbon dioxide bicarbonate pair. If the pCO_2 is increased, the increase in carbonic acid concentration now leads to more dissociation to hydrogen and bicarbonate since most of the hydrogen ions produced are taken up by the other buffers. The buffer ratio, $pCO_2/[HCO_3^-]$, does not increase as much as pCO_2 increases and $[H^+]$ increases by less than the increase in pCO_2. The size of this effect increases with the capacity of the other buffers present. Typically in the body an increase in pCO_2 causes the bicarbonate concentration in the extracellular fluid to increase by a factor about one-third to one-quarter as large (see Figure 16.1).

It is important to note that when pCO_2 is increased the amount of carbon dioxide added to the solution is the sum of the extra physically dissolved carbon dioxide and the extra bicarbonate. While the fractional increase in bicarbonate is smaller than that for carbon dioxide, in blood the absolute increase is much larger since the initial bicarbonate concentration is much higher than that of carbon dioxide. Thus the presence of other buffers greatly increases the amount of carbon dioxide which is added to the blood for a given increase in pCO_2 at the tissues (see below).

If the bicarbonate concentration is changed in any buffer mixture *at constant* pCO_2, the change in $[H^+]$ is inverse, e.g. a doubling of $[HCO_3^-]$ halves $[H^+]$ which is the same as an increase in pH of log2 = 0.3 units.

Any other buffers present must be titrated to the new pH. When the bicarbonate concentration is increased this is accomplished by changes such as

$$HCO_3^- + H_2PO_4^- \rightleftarrows HPO_4^{2-} + CO_2 + H_2O.$$

Thus in the presence of other buffers more bicarbonate must be added to change the bicarbonate concentration.

The special importance of the carbon dioxide, bicarbonate buffer system for pH regulation

The extracellular bicarbonate concentration and the partial pressure of carbon dioxide are under separate physiological control by the kidneys and lungs respectively. This means that normally their absolute concentrations and the buffer ratio can be kept within appropriate limits and the pH of the extracellular fluid set to the right level. Moreover acid or base challenges that alter the pH and hence the buffer ratio can be compensated by adjustment of one or both of the partial pressure of carbon dioxide and the bicarbonate concentration to bring the buffer ratio and the pH back towards normal.

It should be noted that the arterial partial pressure of carbon dioxide is determined by

1. the rate of production of carbon dioxide in the tissues and
2. the ventilation of the alveoli.

The rate of production is determined by the total rate at which metabolites are processed by oxidative phosphorylation. For a given rate of carbon dioxide production, if alveolar ventilation is doubled, pCO_2 is halved. Similarly if ventilation is halved, pCO_2 is doubled. Via these changes in pCO_2, changes in respiration will directly affect the pH of body fluids.

The buffers in the body

Extracellular

The carbon dioxide, bicarbonate buffer pair accounts for most of the buffering which occurs in the extracellular fluid. Extracellular fluid also contains low concentrations of phosphate and proteins which act as buffers.

Intracellular

Red blood cells

Red blood cells must be considered separately from other cells since they contain a high buffer capacity which is almost instantly available to buffer the extracellular fluid. The buffers are bicarbonate, organic phosphate compounds and, especially, haemoglobin. The immediate availability is a consequence of the rapid transport of both carbon dioxide and bicarbonate across the membrane, since the internal buffer ratio for bicarbonate and hence the internal pH can then change rapidly whenever the external pH changes.

Haemoglobin has a special role in buffering the acid challenge presented by addition of carbon dioxide in the tissues. Firstly it buffers the blood strongly. As noted above in the discussion of buffer mixtures, the presence of a buffer other than the carbon dioxide, bicarbonate pair greatly increases the carbon dioxide carrying capacity of the blood. Secondly removal of oxygen as the blood passes through the tissues increases the affinity of haemoglobin for hydrogen ions and causes the haemoglobin to take up most of the hydrogen ions produced from the added carbon dioxide with very little change in pH. (For a more complete discussion see *Respiratory Physiology* by Widdicombe & Davies).

Other cells

Other cells contain substantial buffering capacity in the forms of bicarbonate, which is typically 15–20 mM, proteins and organic phosphate compounds. For most cells external changes in pH take tens of minutes to hours to produce changes within the cells, but the amounts of acid or base which can be taken into the cells is large. The requirement for electroneutrality requires that uptake of hydrogen ions is accompanied by either uptake of anions or loss of cations. The main effect observed is a shift of cellular potassium into the extracellular fluid, so that acidosis often produces hyperkalaemia. Conversely alkalosis can cause an uptake of potassium into cells. The detailed mechanisms of these cation exchanges are not well understood.

Bone

The inorganic matrix of bone can bind large amounts of hydrogen ions, initially in exchange for sodium ions. The uptake of acid by bone over long periods as in chronic renal failure can be associated with extensive demineralization.

The physiological challenges to pH regulation

Carbon dioxide

Quantitatively the production of carbon dioxide is by far the most important challenge. Normal production amounts to about 12–15 mol/day which is the acid equivalent of 1 litre of concentrated HCl. Even though the body fluids are strongly buffered, the accumulation of carbon dioxide from only a few minutes of production would fatally lower pH. Fortunately the lungs eliminate carbon dioxide as rapidly as it is formed so that arterial pCO_2 is stabilized.

Non-volatile acids and bases

The amounts of non-volatile acids and bases which enter the extracellular fluid are small in comparison to the production of carbon dioxide. Nevertheless they pose a serious challenge. Unless they are eliminated their progressive accumulation over days can be fatal. Non-volatile acids and bases get into the extracellular fluid in the following ways:

1. As much as 25–50 mmoles of sulphuric acid per day comes from the metabolism of sulphur containing amino acids.
2. About 50 mmoles per day of acid phosphate can be derived from phospholipids and phosphorylated proteins.

   The oxidation of phosphatidyl choline and phosphatidyl ethanolamine yields the equivalent of dihydrogen phosphate, ammonium (which is removed by the synthesis of urea), carbon dioxide and water. Thus each mole oxidized produces one mole of phosphate (carrying 1.2 moles of hydrogen ions at pH 7.4) and 1.8 moles of non-volatile acid. 0.8 from the phosphate and 1 from the ammonium.

3. Organic cations such as ammonium or choline and the side chains of amino acids such as lysine are metabolized to urea (the end product of nitrogen metabolism), carbon dioxide, water, and hydrogen ions. Thus ingesting ammonium chloride as part of an artificial diet produces the same load of non-volatile acid in the body as an infusion of the same number of moles of hydrochloric acid.
4. Metabolizable anions such as citrate and the side chains of amino acids such as glutamate lead to production of bicarbonate and are thus a source of non-volatile base. Dietary potassium citrate thus has the same effect as potassium bicarbonate.

The primary carboxyl and α-amino groups of the aminoacids released in the catabolism of proteins are potential sources of equal amounts of ammonium and bicarbonate in the body. The quantities involved can be large, more than 1 mole/day of each. However, with the exception of that released in the kidneys, virtually all of the ammonium is immediately dispensed with by the synthesis of urea. The hydrogen ions released are then buffered by the bicarbonate ions, i.e. in effect

$$2NH_4^+ + 2HCO_3^- \longrightarrow H_2N{-}C({=}O){-}NH_2 + 3H_2O + CO_2$$

Since free ammonium concentrations in the body are very low, it is clear that this synthesis of urea is in someway closely linked to the rate of ammonium release (see also Chapter 11). The net effect of protein catabolism on acid-base balance is to add to the body an amount of bicarbonate equal to the excess of carboxyl over amino groups in the side chains, an amount of sulphuric acid equal to the amount of sulphur in the sulphur containing amino acids, and some phosphate primarily in the dihydrogen form.

A simple guide to the acid-base load for renal excretion imposed by the diet is that meat and cereals are a net source of non-volatile acid, and fruit, most vegetables, and milk are a net source of base. A typical mixed western diet might yield a final balance of 100 mmoles of non-volatile acid per day. Some vegetarian diets produce a small net load of base. The amount of acid excreted by the kidneys is consistently greater than the calculated dietary load. The difference is made up by the excretion of base in the faeces.

5. Organic acids are released from cells into the extracellular fluid under conditions where there is incomplete oxidation of either carbohydrates or fats. For example, lactic and pyruvic acids are produced and released by exercising muscle. Normally these acids are removed as they are subsequently metabolized, mostly in the liver, either back to glucose and glycogen or to carbon dioxide and water. Only when there is excessive production of organic acids or their complete metabolism is prevented does such acid formation constitute a pathological disturbance of body pH.

Disturbances of pH

It is often convenient to subdivide disturbances of body pH as follows: respiratory acidosis and alkalosis that result from primary alterations in pCO_2, and metabolic acidosis and alkalosis which result from an excess or deficit of any other acid or base in the body fluids. It will serve here to define acidosis as a significant lowering of plasma pH and alkalosis as a significant elevation of plasma pH.

Respiratory acidosis and alkalosis

Respiratory acidosis results from inadequate alveolar ventilation which can itself result from lung disease, mechanical impairment of breathing or central depression of the respiratory centres. Experimentally one can produce a picture of a respiratory acidosis by having an experimental animal or a subject breathe gases with increased concentrations of carbon dioxide. As discussed above some of the increased carbonic acid is buffered by the non-bicarbonate buffers in blood and converted to bicarbonate. Therefore in uncomplicated respiratory acidosis (see Fig. 16.1) there is a marked elevation of pCO_2, a smaller elevation

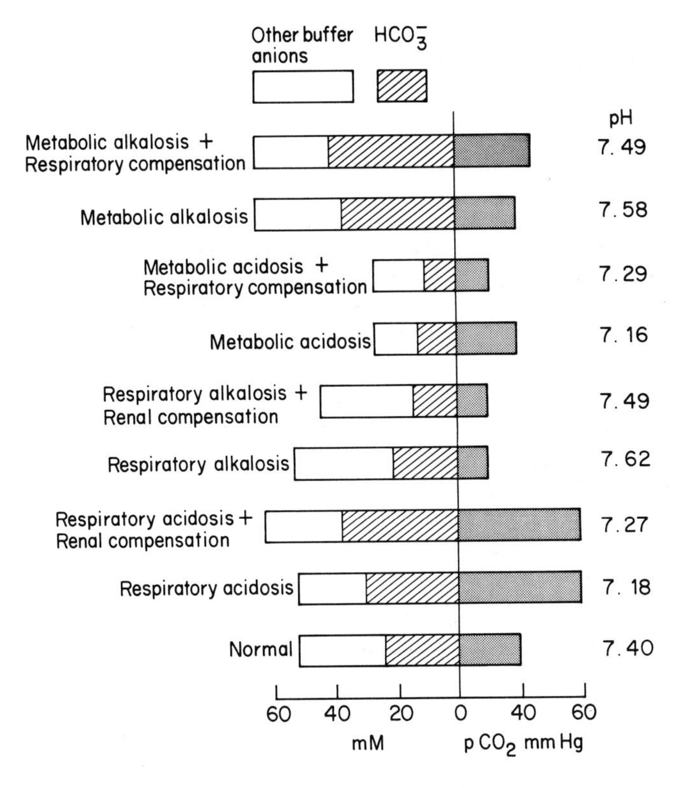

Fig. 16.1. Typical changes in bicarbonate, pCO_2, and other buffer anions in the different types of disturbances of pH. Also shown are the effects of renal compensation for respiratory disturbances and respiratory compensation for metabolic acidosis and alkalosis. The values indicated for $[HCO_3^-]$ and pCO_2 are those that might be found in arterial plasma. There are other buffers which are rapidly accessible, mainly buffer groups on haemoglobin and organic phosphates such as 2, 3-diphosphoglycerate in the red blood cells and also proteins and phosphate in the extracellular fluid. Each of these carries less negative (or more positive) charge when protonated and more negative (or less positive) charge when deprotonated. Their net negative charge is shown as 'other buffer anions' to emphasize that the changes in $[HCO_3^-]$ when either pH or pCO_2 changes depend upon the amount of these other buffers. (While the effects indicated are similar to those which would occur acutely in the intact animal, the actual numerical values used for the 'other buffer anions' are those for whole blood.)

of bicarbonate, a fall in the concentration of the deprotonated forms of the other buffers, and of course a fall to lower than normal levels of pH. As discussed in the next chapter, renal compensation for such an acidosis may somewhat further increase the bicarbonate levels.

Respiratory alkalosis is caused by hyperventilation of the alveoli. This can occur at high altitudes where the hyperventilation is a physiological response to hypoxia. It also can occur in hysterical overbreathing. The initial picture (see Fig. 16.1) is one of markedly reduced pCO_2, slightly reduced bicarbonate, an increase in the concentration of the deprotonated forms of the other buffers, and of course an elevated pH. After renal compensation the bicarbonate level will be further lowered and the pH returned partway towards the normal value. An account of these pH disturbances with more emphasis on respiratory aspects is to be found in *Respiratory Physiology* by Widdicombe & Davies.

Metabolic acidosis

This 'catch all' label can be used to cover acidosis arising from any cause other than a primary elevation of pCO_2. The picture of uncomplicated metabolic acidosis (see Fig. 16.1) is markedly reduced bicarbonate concentration, reduced concentration of the deprotonated forms of the other buffers, reduced plasma pH and either normal or reduced pCO_2 (as a result of the stimulation of respiration by the lowered pH). Metabolic acidosis can arise in a variety of ways including:

1. Excessive metabolic production of acid. Lactic acidosis results from a prolonged imbalance between glycolysis and oxidative metabolism so that lactic acid progressively accumulates in the body fluids. One cause can be severe and wide spread tissue hypoxia as in circulatory shock. Diabetic ketoacidosis results from the excessive production of β-hydroxybutyrate and acetoacetic acid during the incomplete oxidation of fatty acids.
2. Loss of alkaline secretions. The secretions into the small intestine are rich in bicarbonate. Excessive loss of these secretions as in various forms of diarrhoea leaves the remaining body fluids with a lower than normal bicarbonate concentration and therefore produces an acidosis.
3. Acidosis of renal origin. In severe renal failure excretion of all wastes including non-volatile acids is severely impaired. These acids accumulate in the body. Furthermore the kidneys no longer regenerate the bicarbonate that was used to buffer them, the $pCO_2/[HCO_3^-]$ buffer ratio rises, and a progressive acidosis ensues. The effects of this failure may be mitigated by providing a diet that minimizes production of non-volatile acids as metabolic end products. There are also more specific renal defects that impair excretion of acid and regeneration of bicarbonate without gravely affecting other aspects of renal function. The resulting acidosis is known as renal tubular acidosis. The effects can be largely compensated by providing dietary sources of non-volatile bases, e.g. sodium bicarbonate or sodium citrate.

   There appear to be at least two main forms of renal tubular acidosis. In the more severe type, proximal tubular hydrogen secretion is impaired leading to a continuous loss of sodium bicarbonate in the urine. In the less severe form the defect appears to be mainly in the distal tubule and thus most of the bicarbonate can be reabsorbed but the urine cannot be made acidic.

4. Experimentally induced acidosis. Acidosis can be produced by direct infusion of acid into the blood stream or by providing large amounts of the inorganic salts of metabolized organic cations. Ammonium chloride is used most often.

Metabolic alkalosis

Metabolic alkalosis arises in two main ways: excessive ingestion of base such as sodium bicarbonate, or loss of gastric acid due to the vomiting of the gastric contents. The features of metabolic alkalosis (see Fig. 16.1) are a markedly elevated bicarbonate concentration, increased concentration of the deprotonated forms of the other buffers, elevated pH, and a normal or perhaps slightly increased pCO_2. A temporary mild metabolic alkalosis can follow a meal as the secretion of large amounts of hydrochloric acid into the stomach leaves the extracellular fluid relatively alkaline. This 'alkaline tide' usually retreats as substantial amounts of sodium bicarbonate are secreted into the pancreatic juice shortly afterwards.

Disorders of potassium homeostasis and corticosteroid secretion

An increased plasma potassium concentration can cause an acidosis both by reducing hydrogen ion secretion in the renal tubules and by releasing hydrogen ions from the cells as they take up potassium. Converse effects may be seen with hypokalaemia. An excess of aldosterone can increase a tendency to alkalosis since it may enhance hydrogen secretion in the distal tubule and collecting system. Conversely an impairment of hydrogen ion secretion when aldosterone is deficient may cause an acidosis. The effects of excess or deficient aldosterone are not powerful in themselves but are significant when they enhance the pH disturbances produced by other factors.

Effects of extracellular fluid volume expansion and contraction

Extracellular fluid expansion leads to increased excretion of sodium which must be accompanied by chloride, bicarbonate or both. Thus expansion tends to increase bicarbonate excretion, or at least to decrease acid excretion, which can produce a metabolic acidosis. In the other direction extracellular fluid contraction can lead to almost total reabsorption of all sodium salts. In this state less bicarbonate enters the distal tubule (see Chapter 6), almost any level of distal hydrogen secretion reabsorbs the rest and the pH of the urine is low. On a mixed western diet for which an acid urine is appropriate, extracellular fluid contraction alone does not usually cause an alkalosis, but it is difficult or impossible to reverse an established alkalosis without re-expansion of the extracellular fluid and increased delivery of sodium bicarbonate to the distal tubules.

Defences against altered pH

Buffering

The initial defence of pH is provided by the various buffer systems. Hydrogen ions combine with or are released from the buffers in the extracellular fluid and red cells almost instantaneously. The additional buffers in other cells and on bone matrix are then more slowly available as discussed above.

The actual time course of the extracellular buffering when acid or base is injected into the blood is determined by the time taken for the acid or base to be mixed through the body fluids and by the time required either for the carbon dioxide produced in buffering the acid to be blown off by the lungs or for metabolism to produce the carbon dioxide required to buffer the base. At the end of this rapid phase of buffering, the pCO_2 is again determined by the balance between ventilation rate and metabolism.

Respiratory compensation for metabolic acidosis and alkalosis

Further defence of pH comes from respiratory adjustment of pCO_2. Decreased blood pH stimulates respiration which lowers pCO_2 and so partially returns the $pCO_2/[HCO_3^-]$ ratio towards normal and limits the disturbances of pH (see Fig. 16.1). The respiratory response to chronic metabolic acidosis develops slowly but it can lower pCO_2 to less than half the normal value. The stimulation of ventilation by acute renal failure or diabetic ketosis is sufficiently marked that it is an established clinical sign known as 'Kussmaul' breathing.

Respiratory compensation for metabolic alkalosis is often less prominent. The reduction in ventilation required to raise pCO_2 and so limit the increase in pH in this condition will also reduce pO_2 which is obviously undesirable.

Ventilation rate can be altered by changing either arterial pH or the pH of the CSF (the cerebrospinal fluid which bathes the surfaces of the brain). Carbon dioxide moves sufficiently rapidly across the blood-brain barrier that the pCO_2 of CSF will follow changes in the pCO_2 of blood within ten to fifteen minutes. By contrast the bicarbonate ion concentration of CSF changes much more slowly over a period of hours. Following addition of non-volatile acid to the blood and the removal of the extra carbon dioxide produced during the buffering, the arterial pH and bicarbonate concentrations are low. The decrease in arterial pH stimulates an increase in ventilation rate which lowers arterial pCO_2 thus partially returning the arterial pH towards normal. However, this increased ventilation is initially small since it is opposed by the effects of the increase in pH which it produces in the CSF. This increase occurs since the fall in pCO_2 in the blood lowers the pCO_2 in the CSF which increases the ratio $[HCO_3^-]/pCO_2$. Over the ensuing hours the bicarbonate concentration of the CSF falls, which lowers CSF pH (in most studies to very near normal) and allows the full increase in the ventilation rate and decrease in pCO_2.

The strength of buffering and respiratory compensation in illustrated by a classic experiment which was perfomed by Pitts and his colleagues on an anaesthetised dog. The kidneys were removed to prevent renal compensation and 156 mmoles of hydrochloric acid were slowly infused into a vein. Plasma pH fell from 7.4 to 7.1. It is noteworthy that this addition of acid to a volume of water equal to the total body water of the animal would have lowered pH to less than 2. Analysis of the composition of the body fluids of the dog after a few hours revealed the following patterns of buffering. About 40 per cent of the acid had been buffered in the extracellular fluid, mainly by reaction with bicarbonate which fell from 24 to 7 mM, 60 per cent of the acid was buffered inside cells or on the matrix of bone in exchange for sodium and potassium. The fall in plasma pH had also stimulated respiration so that pCO_2 fell from 40 to 23 mmHg. Without this respiratory response the pH reached would have been nearly as low as 6.8.

Elimination of added acid or base

In order to restore the normal composition of the body fluids, the added acid or base must eventually be eliminated from the body.

Acids

Elimination of acids can be accomplished in four main ways.

1. Carbonic acid is eliminated via the excretion of carbon dioxide in the lungs.
2. Many organic acids can be metabolized to carbon dioxide and water and the carbon dioxide excreted via the lungs.
3. Some organic acids can be converted to other neutral forms. For instance lactic acid which is produced by partial oxidation of glucose during anaerobic catabolism of glycogen can be recoverted to glucose in the liver. Furthermore this reconversion reforms the bicarbonate which was consumed in buffering the lactic acid when it was originally produced.
4. Those acids which cannot be metabolized to carbon dioxide or neutral compounds must be excreted in the urine.

Bases

Bases are eliminated from the body by renal excretion of the associated cation together with bicarbonate.

Further reading

Cogan, M.G., Rector, F.C. Jr. & Seldin, D.W. (1981). Acid-base disorders. Chapter 17, pp. 841–907 in *The Kidney*, 2nd edn. Brenner, B.M. & Rector, F.C. Jr., eds, Saunders, Philadelphia.

Hornbein, T.F. & Sørensen, S.C. (1974). The chemical regulation of ventilation. Chapter 23, pp. 378–392 in *Physiology and Biophysics, Vol. II,* 20th edn, Ruch, T.C. Patton, H.D. & Scher, A.M., eds. Saunders, Philadelphia.

Lambertson, C.J. (1980). Chemical control of respiration at rest. Chapter 71, pp. 1774–1827 in *Medical Physiology*, 14th edn. Mountcastle, V.B., ed, Mosby, St. Louis.

Pitts, R.F. (1974). *Physiology of the Kidney and Body Fluids* 3rd edn, Yearbook Medical Publishers, Chicago. (Chapter 10. Buffer mechanisms of tissues and body fluids.)

Rector, F.C. Jr. (1973). Acidification of the urine. Chapter 14, pp. 431–454 in *Handbook of Physiology, Section 8, Renal Physiology*, Orloff, J. & Berliner, R.W., eds. American Physiological Society, Washington, D.C.

Robinson, J.R. (1975). *Fundamentals of Acid-Base Regulation*, 5th edn. Blackwell, London.

17

The role of the kidneys in pH regulation

The kidneys are called upon to carry out several different functions which stabilize body pH. These can be divided into those required to excrete normal waste products, which the kidney does well, and those required to counter abnormal challenges.

The normal physiological role

The kidneys must excrete the load of non-volatile acid or base which arises from net absorption in the gastrointestinal tract and metabolism. Usually on a mixed western diet the final load for excretion is a variable amount of hydrogen ions together with sulphate and phosphate derived from metabolism of proteins and phospholipids. As these are excreted, the kidneys must regenerate the bicarbonate, and hence the other basic forms of buffers, which were consumed in buffering as the acid phosphate and sulphuric acid were produced in the body. On diets rich in salts of metabolizable anions such as citrate, the kidneys must excrete bicarbonate. The kidneys succeed in excreting the loads imposed by a wide range of diets without allowing significant changes in either plasma pH or plasma bicarbonate concentration.

The response to abnormal challenges

1. The kidneys can be called upon to excrete organic acids derived from incomplete metabolism of carbon compounds as in diabetic ketosis.
2. The kidneys are called upon to eliminate hydrochloric acid from the body when the diet is, artificially, rich in metabolizable cations or when bicarbonate is being regenerated in the body during recovery from metabolic acidosis.
3. The kidneys can be required to excrete large quantities of sodium or potassium bicarbonate when gastric secretions, which contain a high concentration of hydrochloric acid, are lost from the body by vomiting, or when large quantities of sodium-bicarbonate-like antacids are ingested.
4. The kidneys partially compensate respiratory acidosis and alkalosis by respectively increasing or decreasing the plasma bicarbonate concentratión.

The manner and extent to which the kidneys meet the normal and abnormal challenges are discussed below. There are no known nervous or hormonal mechanisms for controlling the renal response.

Excretion of hydrogen ions accompanied by sulphate or phosphate

Increased production of acid phosphate or sulphuric acid is met by a rapid and appropriate increase in the renal excretion of these anions together with elimination of the associated hydrogen ions and replacement of the bicarbonate used when the acids were buffered in the body fluids. As a result of this highly effective homeostatic response, changes in the input of these anions over a range far exceeding normal variation do not seriously disturb pH or bicarbonate concentrations in the body. This regulation is a direct consequence of the way these ions are handled by the kidneys.

Whenever plasma levels of sulphate or phosphate are increased the filtered load will further exceed the reabsorptive capacity of the proximal tubules and more of these anions will be present in the fluid delivered to the distal tubule and collecting system as discussed on pp. 120ff, 140–2. These increases in luminal concentration of sulphate or phosphate will lead to increased secretion of hydrogen ions into the tubule as discussed on p. 87ff and hence to excretion of the acid and regeneration of plasma bicarbonate without much change in plasma pH.

Excretion of organic acids

Large amounts of acid accompanied by organic anions (more than a hundred mmoles of acid per day) can be excreted efficiently partly by titration of the anions to more acidic forms and partly in association with ammonia in much the same way as for phosphate (see above and p. 87ff). However, in metabolic disorders such as severe diabetes mellitus the loads are much larger still and exceed the ability of the kidneys to excrete acid. Then even though plasma pH and bicarbonate concentrations are low most of the organic anions are excreted with sodium and potassium rather than with hydrogen ions or ammonium. The result is extracellular fluid contraction (as a result of the sodium excretion), potassium depletion, and severe metabolic acidosis. The volume contraction promotes sodium chloride retention while the organic anions continue to be excreted partly with the maximum amount of ammonium and the rest accompanied by sodium or potassium. So long as the abnormal input of organic acids continues more acid is retained in the body each day, i.e. the effect is equivalent to a continual input of hydrochloric acid.

Excretion of hydrochloric acid: chronic failure of excretion to match large loads

Large loads of hydrochloric acid for excretion arise clinically as described just above. They are produced experimentally without the complications of ketosis by infusing hydrochloric acid slowly into a vein of an animal or by adding ammonium chloride to the diet of animals or volunteers. Pitts and co workers have reported the results for loads of about 150 mmoles per day. The kidneys attempt to excrete the acid as ammonium chloride. The excess chloride reaches the distal tubule. However, since chloride is permeant, unlike phosphate or sulphate, its presence in the tubule does not directly promote acid secretion (see p. 87ff). In fact, the excretion of acid now depends on reductions in plasma pH and bicarbonate concentration. The fall in pH tends to increase hydrogen secretion and the fall in bicarbonate decreases delivery of bicarbonate to be reabsorbed which together lead to acid excretion. If the daily acid load is sustained, ammonia production and the amount of acid excreted as ammonium ions increases over a period of days to as much as 4 or 5 times the rate seen acutely. However, the higher rate of acid excretion persists only while the pH and bicarbonate concentration remain far below normal. So long as the large input of hydrochloric acid remains, the excretion rate must be high and the severe acidosis will persist. Unfortunately the lowered extracellular pH leads to gradual progressive uptake of hydrogen ions by bone and the amount of acid retained in the body increases each day. This process can continue for years, but eventually it must be fatal (patients with persistent severe metabolic acidosis are usually dead sooner from other causes). The excretion of acid in chronic renal failure is considered in Chapters 3, 4, & 14 of *Disorders of the Kidney and Urinary Tract*.

Animals or subjects made acidotic by ingestion of ammonium chloride become volume depleted. The probable explanation is that the fall in plasma and luminal bicarbonate concentration reduces the fractional proximal reabsorption of both sodium bicarbonate and sodium chloride as described in Chapter 6. The bicarbonate delivered to the distal tubule is reabsorbed, but some of the extra sodium chloride is excreted. The extra excretion of chloride is appropriate since extra chloride is being ingested, but that of sodium is not. Excretion of sodium falls back into balance with intake (at a reduced extracellular fluid volume) over a period of days as two processes occur. Firstly volume depletion stimulates proximal reabsorption and secondly increased ammonia production allows sodium to be replaced by ammonium in the collecting system.

Excretion of hydrochloric acid: recovery from metabolic acidosis

If the cause of a metabolic acidosis can be removed, the kidneys can restore plasma pH and bicarbonate concentration to normal by continued excretion of ammonium chloride over many days. As explained in Chapter 7 for each ammonium ion excreted a bicarbonate ion is added to plasma.

Excretion of base

How the kidneys handle the excretion of excess base is intimately connected with the handling of sodium (see Chapter 6 and 7). Three possibilities must be considered:

1. with extracellular fluid expansion, increased sodium chloride and sodium bicarbonate are delivered to the distal tubule and there is a copious urine. Since distal hydrogen secretion is not stimulated adequately to reabsorb the extra bicarbonate the urine contains sodium bicarbonate;

2. with normal extracellular fluid volume, distal hydrogen secretion is reduced by the high plasma pH and bicarbonate is excreted mainly with potassium;
3. with an extracellular fluid deficit as after extensive vomiting less sodium chloride and sodium bicarbonate reaches the distal tubule and there is reduced, often no, excretion of bicarbonate. Metabolic alkalosis with accompanying extracellular fluid contraction can only be corrected following reexpansion of extracellular fluids, sometimes both can be achieved simply by supplying salt and water.

Renal compensation for respiratory acidosis and alkalosis

Respiratory disturbances of pH can be corrected only by restoring normal respiratory control of pCO_2. However, the changes in pH that are produced by the altered pCO_2 can be partially offset by renal adjustment of the bicarbonate concentration. At the onset of respiratory acidosis the pCO_2 increases, the bicarbonate concentration of blood increases somewhat less and the pH falls. The increased bicarbonate concentration does not lead to renal bicarbonate excretion, which would lower the pH further, since hydrogen secretion in the tubules is stimulated by both the increase in luminal bicarbonate concentration and the fall in plasma pH. Over days if the respiratory acidosis persists the kidneys in fact do even better. By some means (see Chapter 8) ammonia production is stimulated which increases the rate of acid excretion as ammonium chloride and generates new bicarbonate to be added to plasma. Thus the plasma bicarbonate concentration rises and with it the pH rises partway back to normal. As this compensation occurs, the rate of acid excretion falls back to the level of the net input of non-volatile acid and the bicarbonate levels in the body become stable. The normal state, the state in acute respiratory acidosis, and that in compensated respiratory acidosis are indicated in Fig. 17.1. In respiratory alkalosis, e.g. that associated with hyperventilation at high altitudes, pCO_2 and the bicarbonate concentration are initially low and the pH is raised. The kidneys respond by excreting less acid for a period of days which lowers the bicarbonate concentration further and lowers the pH more than half way back towards normal. These changes are also shown in Fig. 17.1. It should be noted that the changes in plasma bicarbonate concentration are slow.

Traditionally it has been taught that the changes in pCO_2 act directly on the kidney tubules to change the rate of acid secretion. However, as explained in Chapter 6 direct evidence for an effect of pCO_2 rather than pH and bicarbonate on tubular processes is lacking. To keep the description given above as simple as possible it has been assumed that the agents acting are the pH and bicarbonate concentration of plasma.

Chloride

The regulation of chloride excretion must be considered last since it is related to the excretion of all other ions. In the standard view of the control of renal function, once the concentrations of renal wastes, phosphate, sulphate, bicarbonate, calcium, magnesium, sodium, potassium, and ammonium are determined by their respective control mechanisms, the chloride concentration has

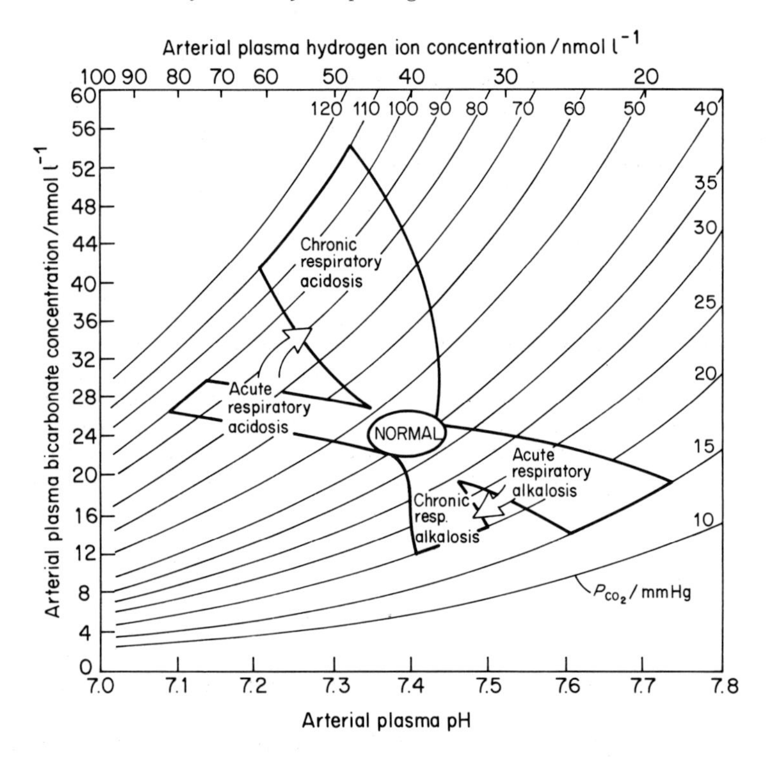

Fig. 17.1. The observed relations between arterial plasma pCO_2, pH, and bicarbonate concentration in the normal state and during respiratory disturbances. When pCO_2 is increased, the extra carbonic acid formed tends to dissociate which lowers the pH and increases the bicarbonate concentration as described in Chapter 16. The range of observed values for the pH and bicarbonate concentration for each value of pCO_2 are those whose lines intersect the pCO_2 curve within the area labelled 'acute respiratory acidosis'. Normally the raised pCO_2 and lowered pH would stimulate a hyperventilation which would remove the excess carbon dioxide within minutes. Maintained respiratory acidosis occurs when for some reason this elimination cannot occur. The kidneys respond to the maintained disturbance by excreting extra ammonium chloride for several days, thereby adding bicarbonate ions to the plasma. As a result the bicarbonate concentration and pH both increase, while pCO_2 remains constant or increases as suggested by the open arrow. The range of values observed after these changes are those which fall within the area labelled 'chronic respiratory acidosis'. The interpretation of the regions which describe respiratory alkalosis is similar. (Reproduced with permission from Cogan *et al*, 1981.)

also been determined; its concentration must bring the total charge of the urine to zero.

In the orthodox view there is no separate control of chloride, there are no renal mechanisms which respond specifically to the concentration of chloride, and the concentration of chloride in the urine is determined by the difference between the rates of excretion for all other cations and anions. The weak link in this argument is that plasma pH and plasma bicarbonate concentration are not themselves well controlled under all circumstances and thus it is not obvious that urinary bicarbonate and ammonium levels are any more controlled than that of chloride. Thus when experimental animals or volunteers are given large daily doses of ammonium chloride, plasma pH and bicarbonate concentration both fall markedly and plasma chloride increases. Acid excretion does increase, but only modestly such that even after five days, the excretion still does not match input. By contrast chloride excretion increases rapidly to match (and even transiently to exceed) the extra chloride input. Results such as these have lead some investigators (who concentrate primarily on whole animal data) to the extreme opposite view that plasma pH has little or no effect on renal excretion, that chloride excretion is controlled, and that it is the net excretion of acid (as ammonium) or base (as bicarbonate) which is determined by difference.

The unorthodox view is remarkably successful in explaining the responses of the kidneys to different types of acid–base challenge. For this reason some of its more successful features have been included in the compromise view presented here. However, the evidence now available about tubular mechanisms still suggests that plasma pH and bicarbonate concentration act more directly on the tubular processes than does the chloride concentration. The dramatic increase in chloride excretion seen with ammonium chloride loading is then explained as a decrease in proximal tubular reabsorption of all sodium salts caused by the lower luminal concentration of bicarbonate.

Further reading

Cogan, M.G., Rector, F.C. Jr. & Seldin, D.W. (1981). Acid-base disorders. Chapter 17, pp. 841–907 in *The Kidneys*, 2nd edn, Brenner, B.M. & Rector, F.C. Jr., eds. Saunders, Philadelphia. (Best read in conjunction with Warnock & Rector below.)

DeSousa, R.C., Harrington, J.T., Ricanati, E.S., Shelkrot, J.W. & Schwartz, W.B. (1974). Renal regulation of acid-base equilibrium during chronic administration of mineral acid. *J. Clin. Invest.* **53**, 465–476. (Sulphuric acid is handled differently from hydrochloric acid.)

O'Connor, W.J. (1982). *Normal Renal Function*, Croom Helm, London, (Chapter 20, pp. 335–348. Anion-cation excretion: acid-base balance. An interesting, but unorthodox account: Read the last small print section here before consulting this reference.)

Sartorius, O.W., Roemmelt, J.C. & Pitts, R.F. (1949). The renal regulation of acid base balance in man. IV The nature of the renal compensations in ammonium chloride acidosis. *J. Clin. Invest.* **28**, 423–439. (This is the classic paper reporting the results of daily ingestion of large quantities of ammonium chloride. Different subsequent authors give very different summaries of the data presented in this paper. Eventually, if you are interested, you will have to read it yourself.)

Schwartz, W.B. & Cohen, J.J. (1978). The nature of the renal response to chronic disorders of acid-base equilibrium. *Am. J. Med.* **64**, 417–428. (Schwartz and his colleagues take the view that the rate of distal hydrogen secretion is determined overwhelmingly by the rate of delivery of sodium to the distal tubule and the avidity with which it is reabsorbed.)

Warnock, D.G. & Rector, F.C. Jr. (1981). Renal acidification mechanisms. Chapter 10, pp. 440–494 in *The Kidney*, 2nd edn, Brenner, B.M. & Rector, F.C. Jr., eds, Saunders, Philadelphia.

Index